As ever, for my family:

Mum

Duncan, Jana & Emma

Chris, Katka & Elena

A New Start for the Wrens

Vicki Beeby writes historical fiction about the friendships and loves of service women brought together by the Second World War. Her first job was as a civil engineer on a sewage treatment project, so things could only improve from there. Since then, she has worked as a maths teacher and education consultant before turning freelance to give herself more time to write. In her free time, when she can drag herself away from reading, she enjoys walking and travelling to far-off places by train. She lives in Shropshire in a house that doesn't contain nearly enough bookshelves.

Also by Vicki Beeby

The Women's Auxiliary Air Force

The Ops Room Girls
Christmas with the Ops Room Girls
Victory for the Ops Room Girls

The Wrens

A New Start for the Wrens

VICKI BEEBY

A New Start for the Wrens

CANELO

First published in the United Kingdom in 2022 by

Canelo
Unit 9, 5th Floor
Cargo Works, 1–2 Hatfields
London, SE1 9PG
United Kingdom

A CIP catalogue record for this book is available from the British Library.

Print ISBN 978 1 80032 425 1
Ebook ISBN 978 1 80032 424 4

Look for more great books at www.canelo.co

Printed and bound in Great Britain by Clays Ltd, Elcograf S.p.A.

I

Chapter One

June 1941

'You're not going out in those, are you?'

Iris's heart sank at her mother's scathing tones. She paused, dropping her hand from her coat, which she had been about to pull on. Letitia Tredwick had emerged from the drawing room before Iris was able to make her escape, and now pointed at the high-waisted, wide-legged trousers Iris had slaved over for hours, modelling them on a pair she'd seen in *Vogue*.

'What's wrong with them?' In her opinion, they were the height of elegance, and would ensure George only had eyes for her. 'Katharine Hepburn wears slacks just like these.'

'Darling, they might be suitable for Americans, but they're not at all the done thing for nice young girls in England. I'm sure George would be shocked if he could see you. Why don't you put on your navy polka dot dress? Far more suitable.'

While it was framed as a question, Iris had no doubt her mother meant it as a command. She had looked forward to seeing George's admiration when he saw her in her latest creation, though, so she tried again. 'I don't really have time to change.'

Letitia waved away her objection. 'He'll expect you to be a few minutes late. You don't want to look too keen. He should be the one doing the chasing.'

Iris gave up and raced back upstairs to her bedroom. At least when she was married, she would no longer be under her mother's thumb, and she was determined that today was the day she persuaded George to propose. She took off the trousers and pale blue ribbed sweater and stowed them carefully in the wardrobe, giving the trousers a regretful stroke before pulling out her polka dot dress. They had displayed her elegant, willowy figure to perfection, and the blue of the sweater had matched her eyes. Wearing a dress also meant wearing stockings. Thankfully, last week's announcement introducing clothes rationing hadn't caught Iris as unprepared as it seemed to have caught most women. She had a good supply of silk stockings, and as long as she treated them with care, she was confident she could make them last. A keen dressmaker, she had lavished her generous allowance on fabrics that caught her eye on her regular shopping trips, and the large antique chest where she stored them was now so full the lid didn't close. While other women might be lamenting the impossibility of making their clothes coupons stretch, Iris would have no trouble making new outfits even if the war lasted a decade.

When she dashed downstairs a few minutes later, she found Letitia still there. Her mother looked her up and down and gave an approving nod. 'That's better. Much more suitable for the future mistress of Sherbrook Manor. George comes from an old family, remember. He won't want a wife who dresses like she's from new money.'

'But we're not new money, Mummy. George knows that.' Their family had lived in Tredwick Place in this leafy valley in the Chiltern Hills for four hundred years. Iris had dropped that into conversation soon after they had met, ensuring her suitability as his wife was clear from the start.

'Even so. You want to show him you will make the perfect wife and will uphold the standards expected of a member of the Silverwood family.'

Her mother was right, Iris reflected as she set out on the mile-long walk to West Wycombe. George was in the RAF, attached to Bomber Command at RAF High Wycombe, and didn't get much time off, poor dear. Iris was forever suggesting times when they could meet, but he wasn't often free. George was clearly smitten with her, yet had frustratingly remained oblivious to all her hints that she was open to a proposal of marriage. Today, she was determined to get him to utter the question he was obviously too shy to ask.

Iris was all too aware that time was running out.

She strode down Tredwick Place's tree-lined drive, glancing at her watch after every few paces; George was terribly busy and not to be kept waiting. Through the gates, she turned onto the West Wycombe lane only to bump into an old classmate from Wycombe Abbey School coming around the corner. Felicity lived only a few miles away and they were the only two girls in the area that had attended the prestigious girls' boarding school. Therefore, they had often been placed together in village functions, as people assumed they must be friends. In fact, although they didn't dislike each other, they had never been close. For some reason, Felicity had never laughed along with Iris's jokes or shown any desire to be friends, so Iris had eventually given up. It had been something of a relief to take her Higher School Certificate and leave school the summer before the war had broken out, for she hadn't seemed to have the knack of making friends.

Felicity gave a visible start when she glanced in Iris's direction, and her expression froze. Trying not to let her discouragement show, Iris gave Felicity a pleasant smile.

'I'm surprised to see you here. You weren't coming to see me, were you?'

'Iris. Lovely to see you.' Felicity's fixed smile didn't altogether support this statement. 'No, actually I've just been into Wycombe and got off the bus a stop early. It's such a pleasant walk from here.' Her cheeks were a little pink. However, it was a sunny day, so maybe she was just warm from her walk.

'What were you doing in Wycombe?'

'I just applied to join the ATS.'

'The ATS? My goodness. What did you do that for? You'll look a fright in khaki.' Iris couldn't imagine giving up her life of comfort to spend her days in an ill-fitting uniform, and certainly not one that would make her look sallow.

'They say all young unmarried women will be made to do war work soon. I heard that if you volunteered, you were more likely to get your choice of job, and I want to be a driver.'

Iris had heard this too, but had paid it little heed. 'That doesn't really apply to me. Do you remember George?'

Iris had first met George at a dance in High Wycombe that Felicity had also attended. They had both been sitting at the same table when George had approached them. George was a rather shy, serious young man. To be honest, he wasn't the dashing, heroic type she had always dreamed of, but, as Letitia had told her at the time, she couldn't expect a man to be like the heroes she saw in the pictures.

4

In real life, men didn't know their own minds and needed encouraging. But she had known he liked her by the way he ignored her and spoke to Felicity. A shy man like George couldn't approach her directly and taking an interest in her friend was his way of making it known that he was interested in Iris. When George had stammered out that there was a good film on at the Majestic cinema in Wycombe, Iris had taken his arm and exclaimed that she would love to go with him. Felicity had said that she couldn't make that night, and Iris had felt embarrassed on her behalf for not understanding that George wanted to go on a date with Iris.

Now Felicity nodded, seeming absorbed in picking a loose thread from her sleeve. 'George Silverwood?' Her cheeks turned pinker. Poor girl. It looked like she still carried a torch for him.

'That's right. I've been seeing rather a lot of him. Isn't it wonderful he's based at Naphill? So many young couples are separated by hundreds of miles these days.' A nagging feeling prodded the back of her mind that she was being unkind to elaborate on how much she and George were seeing of each other. However, she was too excited to keep it in. 'In fact' – she lowered her voice, even though there was no one else around – 'I think he's working himself up to propose.'

'Propose?' Felicity's head snapped up and she regarded Iris with narrowed eyes. 'Are you sure?'

Her tone of disbelief nettled Iris, making her forget she felt sorry for Felicity having no beau. 'Well, I suppose I could be mistaken, but he's so fond of me, the dear.' In fact, Iris had no doubt. Last time they had met, he had tried several times to say something, but when Iris had fixed her gaze upon him, smiling to show she was ready to give a favourable reply, he had changed the subject and talked of the weather or the rationed food he missed most. It had been all very frustrating. She was confident, though, that today she would be able to coax him into a proposal.

'Anyway,' she said, hoisting her gas mask over her shoulder, 'I mustn't keep him waiting.'

Iris spared only a few moments feeling sorry for Felicity after they'd parted. She was a pretty girl, even if she wasn't blessed with the same fashionably willowy figure as Iris and had mousy brown hair instead of Iris's golden waves. Felicity would soon get over her disappointment and, if she joined the ATS as a driver, was bound to meet plenty of army officers. Maybe they would be prepared to look past the unfortunate colour of her uniform. If Iris wasn't going to marry George, and would therefore be forced to do war work, she wouldn't be seen dead in khaki. The blue WAAF uniform would suit her better.

Thankfully, it wasn't something she had to give serious consideration to, as she would in all likelihood soon be married and mistress of Sherbrook Manor.

George was waiting for her in a tea room in West Wycombe. She knew he was there because his car, a shiny green Morris Eight, was parked on the street outside the pretty row of half-timbered buildings. Although it was an easy walk from Tredwick Place to West Wycombe, Iris was a little annoyed that he hadn't come to pick her up. Still, she fixed a smile on her face as she walked into the tea room. There was George, looking very smart in his uniform, the three rings on his sleeve denoting the rank of Squadron Leader clearly on display. No doubt about it, he was the perfect match for Iris.

His face wore a strained expression when he rose to greet her, and Iris's heart melted. Any uncertainty she might have had about his feelings disappeared. This was exactly how she had imagined he would look as he mentally rehearsed his proposal, worrying about her response. When he went to shake her hand, she daringly leaned forward and kissed him on the cheek, to show him he had nothing to fear. He had chosen a table in the window, and Iris mentally commended his choice, happy that this important moment in her life would be set against the backdrop of this pretty street, accompanied by the scent of roses drifting through the open casement. They were the only couple in the shop – the other tables were occupied by housewives, their shopping bundled under the tables while they sipped their tea. Iris was acutely aware of eyes on herself and George as they ordered tea and fruitcake. Clearly, they were the most interesting thing in the village.

'Isn't this the perfect day?' Iris said when their food and drinks arrived. She indicated the blue sky and quaint village scene. 'So romantic,' she added, in case George still needed encouragement.

The furrows on George's brow deepened, and he raked his fingers through his hair. 'Actually, Iris, I've got something serious I really need to say.'

Iris leaned forward, her heart pounding. This was it. This was the moment. She wanted to remember every detail, so that in years to come, when their children asked them how George had proposed, she would be able to tell them all about it. 'Go on,' she said.

'Well, it's about us. Or…' Then his face screwed up in a prelude to a sneeze. 'Dash it… hay fever,' he muttered. He pulled his handkerchief from his pocket, and a small jeweller's box rolled onto the table. He was too busy sneezing to notice, but Iris picked it up with trembling hands and eased the lid open. Inside was a gold ring with a large oval rose-cut diamond, flanked with a ruby on either side.

'Oh, George, it's beautiful.' Around the room she was aware of the other women falling silent and making no attempt to conceal their interest. 'Of course I'll marry you.' While he hadn't exactly asked, it was obvious he had been working up to it.

She slipped the ring onto her finger, and heard soft sighs around the room. George, bless him, was staring at her as though he had been struck by lightning, clearly too overcome with joy to say anything.

She leaned across the table and kissed him on the cheek. George remained frozen, his expression of shock making her laugh. 'Oh, there's so much we need to discuss. I can't wait to tell Mother. Do you think you'll be able to get leave in September? That would be the best month for the wedding, I think.'

A woman approached the table. 'Can I see the ring?' she asked.

Iris, beaming, held out her left hand. If she was honest, the ring was a little heavy and old-fashioned for her taste but the main thing was that he had finally got his act together and popped the question. Well, he hadn't asked exactly, but the story of the sneeze and the ring falling out of his pocket pre-empting the question would make an entertaining story in years to come.

'Oh, isn't that gorgeous,' the woman said. 'You two make a lovely couple. I was just saying so to my friend. Congratulations to you both.'

George bestirred himself enough to give a rather strained smile and thank her.

Once the woman had returned to her table, Iris said, 'Mother will be so thrilled. Such a pity Daddy is away.' For her father, who had been in the Royal Naval Reserve before the war, had been called up on the commencement of war. 'Still, he'll be so pleased when he hears. I must write to him tonight. Will you come up to the house? There's so much to organise.'

George glanced at his watch. 'I must get back to base. I'll… be in touch soon.'

'Oh.' Iris felt a twinge of disappointment. She had been looking forward to parading George in front of her mother. Then she brightened. 'Never mind. I dare say you won't have time for wedding plans, but leave it to my mother and me. Such a pity Sherbrook Manor has been requisitioned, or we could have held the reception there. Still, there's plenty of space at Tredwick Place.' She laughed. 'Oh, that rhymes!' She was still talking while George paid for their food and hadn't finished when he made a dash for his car.

—

Iris was still ecstatic the next day as she sat in the morning room with her mother, pencil and notebook in front of her as they discussed plans.

'I'm so pleased you won't have to do any war work,' Letitia said, ringing the bell for tea. 'I wouldn't want to see you mixing with girls of inferior upbringing.' Then she smiled. 'Sherbrook Manor. Your father will be so proud. And it's a weight off my mind. There's no danger of you ending up like your Aunt Sybil.'

Aunt Sybil's fate had loomed heavily over Iris's life. Letitia's younger sister had married beneath her. 'To a completely unsuitable man,' Letitia would always say when speaking of her sister's marriage, pulling a face as though there were a bad smell under her nose. Sybil's husband had then promptly got himself killed in the Great War, leaving Sybil with nothing more than a meagre widow's pension. Iris had never met Aunt Sybil; from what Letitia let slip, Iris had an impression of a slatternly woman drinking herself into oblivion. She didn't sound like someone Iris would want to meet, and certainly not someone whose fate she wanted to share.

Of course, she no longer had to worry about that. George came from one of the wealthiest families in the land. Not only did he own Sherbrook Manor in neighbouring Oxfordshire, but he had a large house in Mayfair and several other properties around the country. It was a pity that Sherbrook Manor had been requisitioned as a girls' school for the duration of the war, but Iris was sure she had heard George mention a house in Cornwall with its own private cove. Yes, that would make the ideal place to live until the war was over.

Mrs Webb, their housekeeper, entered the room, teacups rattling on the tray she carried. 'The post's arrived.' She handed three envelopes to Letitia and one to Iris. 'And Mrs Hill from the WI just phoned,' she said to Letitia. 'She would like to know if her ladies can pick strawberries from your garden for jam.'

Letitia rose. 'I'd better get back to her. We must be seen to be doing our bit.' She followed Mrs Webb out of the room.

Iris looked at her letter and recognised George's handwriting. With a flutter of excitement, she thought he must have already spoken to his commanding officer and got permission to marry. Perhaps he even knew the dates he would be available. She picked up her mother's silver letter opener and slit open the envelope.

> *Dear Iris,*
>
> *This is not an easy letter to write, and I hope you will excuse me for writing what I should have told you in person yesterday. However, with all those women watching, I found it impossible to tell you the truth. Before this sham continues any longer, I must put an end to this unfortunate misunderstanding.*

Iris's heart gave a lurch. Sham? Misunderstanding? What did he mean? She had always made it perfectly clear that she wanted to be his wife. She hoped he wasn't getting cold feet over the amount of time they would be forced to spend apart while the war lasted. It would be just like him to get all chivalrous and have reservations over leaving her alone, but she would be perfectly happy. Already, she was composing a reassuring reply in her head as she read on.

> *I have tried not to hurt your feelings and so have let our relationship continue far longer than my conscience should have allowed. Yet in recent weeks it has become clear that while I regarded our pleasant meetings as nothing more than friendship, you viewed them in an altogether different light. If I have ever given you reason to believe I felt anything deeper then I can only apologise.*

In growing bewilderment, Iris read and reread this paragraph. No matter how she tried, she couldn't make sense of it. Nothing more than friendship? How could he say that when he had presented her with a diamond engagement ring? He was talking nonsense. Maybe the rest of the letter would explain. But when her eyes fell on the next line she felt the blood drain from her face.

> *I am still not being perfectly honest. I must tell the whole truth so there are no further misunderstandings. On the same day I met you, I also met your friend, Felicity Fleetwood. We have been seeing each other ever since, and last week she consented to be my wife. I only had the ring in my pocket when I saw you because I was taking it to the jeweller's to get it resized. It was pure accident that it fell out, and when I tried to explain, all those women were cooing over what a lovely couple we made, and I didn't want to embarrass you in front of them. I couldn't explain to them that you had jumped to a conclusion that I'd never led you to believe could be possible. In fact, I had agreed to meet you with the sole purpose of making it clear that there was nothing more than friendship between us. Felicity had told me you viewed our relationship in a different light, but I hadn't believed her. It took this afternoon's events, and a phone call from a very upset Felicity shortly after I returned, to convince me that Felicity was right.*
>
> *I am truly sorry about the confusion. I can only hope this letter reaches you before you tell too many people. Felicity and I will not be getting married until the war is over, so you need not fear any announcements in the newspapers.*

No. This couldn't be real. Iris jumped up from her chair, painfully aware that her mother would return at any moment. She couldn't face her. Not yet. Crumpling George's letter in her fist, she dashed from the room. Her mother was putting down the phone as Iris tore into the entrance hall.

'Good gracious, Iris, whatever is the matter?'

'I've just remembered something.' Iris pulled on her shoes and yanked a silk scarf from the coat hooks with a force that nearly ripped it.

'But the wedding plans—'

'Later.' Iris snatched up her gas mask case and ran out of the door. The words of George's letter hammered at her brain. She couldn't think. The only thing she was fully aware of was a crushing weight of humiliation. How would she ever explain to Letitia that her engagement was nothing but a hideous misunderstanding?

Chapter Two

She hurried up the lane and struck out on a path that would take her into the woods. One thing was for sure: she wasn't going back until she had worked out how to resolve this awful mess, because if Felicity thought she was going to be mistress of Sherbrook Manor, she had another think coming.

As she marched, kicking stones and twigs out of her way, she composed an angry letter to George in her head. This was all his fault. His and Felicity's. Why should she be the one humiliated? Wasn't there such a thing as breach of promise that meant she could force George to honour their engagement? After all, it had been witnessed by all the women in the tea room.

Eventually, she came to her favourite tree. It had a long, low branch that she had always liked to bounce on as a child, pretending it was a horse. She hadn't sat on it for years, but she perched there now, her back to the trunk, and gazed out across the valley. From here she could see the Church of St Lawrence amidst the trees on top of West Wycombe Hill, the golden ball atop the tower gleaming in the sunshine. Thankfully, she couldn't see West Wycombe itself; she didn't think she could ever face going there again.

The letter was still crumpled in her hand. After a while she smoothed it out and read it through again. As she read, her anger leached away, replaced by acute embarrassment. George had said he wanted a serious talk, and she had taken it to mean he was going to propose. This assumption had led her to believe that the ring was for her, and that George had just been too tongue-tied to pop the question. Now she could see he had been trying to explain that he wasn't in love with her. The more she thought about it, the deeper her humiliation became.

There was no question of forcing George to honour the engagement. There had never been an engagement except in her own head. She would have to return the ring and, worst of all, explain to her mother that there would be no wedding.

Her mind shied from this as soon as the thought occurred. For once in her life she had earned her mother's approval. Confessing that she had made a terrible blunder would cast her lower than ever.

She gazed moodily at the view while she ran possibilities through her mind. The sight of West Wycombe Hill was an uncomfortable reminder that other people besides her mother knew she had considered herself engaged. While she didn't know the women in the tea room well, she knew they recognised her. The Tredwicks were one of the most important families in the area. For all she knew, the leafy valleys of the Chilterns were now all abuzz with the news that the Tredwick girl was getting married. If the truth came out, she would never live down the disgrace.

Then, through the haze of misery, one memory came to the fore as though summoned by a power outside herself. She saw Felicity saying she was volunteering for the ATS because she was more likely to get the job she wanted if she volunteered. With a horrible lurch, it struck Iris that soon all unmarried young women would be required to do war work, and she would no longer be exempt. She, Iris Tredwick of Tredwick Place, would be conscripted and either forced to wear an ill-fitting uniform or work as a Land Girl or in a munitions factory.

But in amongst the dismay came a tiny kernel of hope. It would get her away from home. Away from George and the gossipmongers and far from her mother's disapproval.

She jumped down from the branch and brushed the dried moss from her skirt. As there was no other way out, she needed to act fast before things got out of hand.

–

When she got back to the house, instead of going into one of the family rooms, Iris descended the narrow servants' stairs and went into the kitchen. Before the war, Tredwick Place had housed four servants: a housekeeper, two maids and a gardener. The gardener had joined the RAF on the outbreak of war, and the maids had been lured into joining the forces by advertisements urging them to serve their country. This left only the housekeeper.

She found Mrs Webb washing the breakfast dishes at the sink. Now that the housekeeper had no maids to assist her, Iris and her mother pitched in where they could, although Iris was aware that her mother's idea of helping was confined to telling Iris she needed to do more. Still, drying dishes was one of the less objectionable tasks, so Iris picked up a tea towel from where it hung above the range and set to work.

'Mrs Webb,' she said as she picked up a Royal Worcester teacup and dried it carefully, 'I seem to remember Polly collecting leaflets on volunteering for the women's services. Do we still have them?' Polly was their former maid. She had left last year to join the ATS when she turned eighteen.

'Let me think.' Mrs Webb placed a sudsy plate upon the rack and then started on the cutlery. 'I'm sure I wouldn't have thrown them away,' she said as she scrubbed at a lump of dried porridge upon a spoon. 'I might have put them with the Ministry of Food recipe leaflets. If you need them, I can dig them out once I've finished here.'

'Thank you.'

Mrs Webb had a way about her that always induced Iris to reveal more than she intended. She never asked questions outright. Instead, she would give Iris a look with her keen brown eyes, eyebrows slightly raised as though waiting for the whole truth. Iris could never hold out for long. Mrs Webb practised that look on her now.

'I'm thinking of volunteering,' Iris said after a brief pause.

Mrs Webb placed the now clean silver spoon in the cutlery rack then plunged her reddened hands back into the water. She said nothing but kept her eyes fixed upon Iris's face.

'I've decided to postpone the wedding,' Iris said in the end. She couldn't bring herself to say the wedding was cancelled. There was no way she could tell anyone that George didn't want to marry her because he was in love with someone else. Let them find out once she was gone. 'I thought I should contribute more towards the war effort.'

'Very commendable,' Mrs Webb said. 'Marry in haste, repent at leisure, that's what I've always said. It wasn't my place to say anything before, but I do think young people are rushing into marriage these days. I understand why, but I worry they're storing up trouble for themselves in the days to come. If you and Mr Silverwood are right for each other, it won't hurt to wait, and you're saving yourself a lifetime of grief if it turns out you're not.'

'That's what we thought,' Iris said, crossing her fingers behind her back. It was a relief to have told one person and not have her decision derided, and now she had a good idea how to pitch it to her mother. Once she was safely away from home, she would write to say the engagement was over. That way she wouldn't have to face her mother's inevitable outburst.

A little later, Iris sat at the desk in her bedroom, the various leaflets scattered around her. While she still didn't have any clue what role she could take on, she knew what service she wanted to join. It wasn't for any reason she could give during an interview, though: she doubted an interviewer would be sympathetic with her desire for a uniform that suited her colouring. She would have to come up with something better before visiting the recruitment office.

Now for the most difficult task of all: she would have to tell her mother.

—

'I don't understand.' Letitia tossed aside the WAAF recruitment pamphlet and brushed her hands as though afraid it might be harbouring deadly germs. 'You don't have to join up at all. Why not get married?'

Because Felicity Fleetwood had got her claws into George and made sure it was no longer an option. Iris bit her lip, imagining the outburst if she told the truth. Letitia would consider it all her own fault for not holding onto George tightly enough and would never forgive her. Instead, Iris tried the approach she had decided upon when telling Mrs Webb.

'I decided it was too much of a rush. We hardly know one another. Not really.'

'Nonsense. You'll have all the time in the world to get to know one another when you're married. The important thing is to get his ring on your finger.'

Iris bit her lip, uncomfortably aware of the diamond ring weighing on her left hand. A ring she had no right to wear. She would have to send it back to George and pray her mother didn't notice it was missing. She tried to push thoughts of the ring from her mind as she struggled for an adequate reason for joining the WAAF. She should have known Letitia would never accept her needing more time as a reasonable excuse. What else could she say? 'George can't get leave.'

Letitia's frown deepened. 'Not even to get married?'

Iris shrugged. 'Obviously not.' Then inspiration struck. 'It looks like he's about to be posted overseas. He couldn't say anything in his letters, of course.'

Her mother's face cleared. 'That would explain it. Sadly, even the gentry are unable to escape duty.'

Iris nodded. 'There won't be time to marry before the National Services Act comes into force, meaning I'll *have* to do war work. And everyone says the best jobs go to volunteers.'

Letitia indicated the pamphlet with her perfectly manicured index finger. 'I suppose you have no choice.' She picked it up between thumb and forefinger and tossed it into the wastepaper basket. 'However, you don't want to join the WAAF. They let in all the riff-raff. You don't want to find yourself mixing with maids and shop girls.'

'But—' Iris broke off when her mother raised a finger for silence.

'You must join the Wrens, darling. It's the Senior Service. You'll be with the right sort. Anyway, your father is in the RNVR; you really can't go anywhere else. With your family background, you'll have to be an officer, of course.'

Iris twisted the engagement ring around her finger then saw what she was doing and thrust her hands behind her back. She struggled to come up with a counterargument, but once her mother had made up her mind there was no changing it. It was only now that she could admit to herself that she had hoped joining the WAAF would bring her back into contact with George. Maybe if he saw she was a responsible adult, willing to serve her country, he would realise she was the one for her.

Still, by the time Iris was standing in the queue in the High Wycombe recruitment office, she had come round to her mother's way of thinking. She could picture herself living in a bustling naval base such as the ones in Portsmouth or Plymouth, attending dances with the officers. Her mother was right: she didn't want to mix with the shop girls and servants who would be joining the WAAF. She was expected to uphold certain standards, and someone of her class was best placed in the Wrens. As for meeting George, well, she probably wouldn't have been posted anywhere near him even if she had joined the WAAF.

While she waited, shuffling forward every couple of minutes, she couldn't help overhearing the conversation between a group of young women standing behind.

'What job are you going for?' one girl asked.

'Writer. I did a typing and shorthand course.'

'Lucky you. You'll get to sit in an office all day. Wish I'd done something like that. I'll probably end up as a cook.'

Iris gave a little shudder. Good thing she was going to be an officer. In her opinion, spending the days chopping vegetables was only slightly better than working on a farm.

Then another voice joined in. 'I'm going to try for visual signaller.'

'What's one of those?' the typist asked.

'There's a picture over there.'

Iris glanced at the posters while doing her best not to make it obvious she was eavesdropping. They all showed photographs of cheerful young women in uniform. One sat at a typewriter, another held a mail bag while another showed a woman dressed in bell-bottoms, standing beside a large signal lamp. This must be the visual signaller. Iris couldn't help admiring how she looked in her bell-bottoms, which looked very much like the wide-legged trousers her mother had scorned.

When she reached the front of the queue, she took her place at a trestle table, facing a middle-aged woman in dark blue uniform. Iris gave her best society smile. 'Good morning. I would like to be an officer in the Wrens.'

The woman's eyes narrowed and swept Iris with a gaze that left her feeling like a naughty schoolgirl hauled in front of the headmistress. 'And I'd like to be the Queen of Sheba. You'll join as a rating like everyone else.'

'Oh. I thought—'

'You might want to think more carefully before you join up. You clearly haven't done nearly enough thinking so far.' The woman pushed a form towards her. 'If you do decide you're not too high and mighty, fill in this form and post it to the address given.'

Iris was too shocked to speak. In all her life she had never been spoken to like that by a stranger. She was volunteering, for goodness' sake. She had expected to be welcomed, not told to think more about her decision. It was only the knowledge that her options at this point were limited that made her reach for the form.

The woman stopped her. 'If you decide to apply, you'll need to say what position you'd like to apply for.'

'Oh.' Iris thought of the conversation she'd overheard. 'What jobs are available?'

'Depends. Can you type?'

Iris shook her head.

'They need dispatch riders. Can you handle a motor-bike?'

Iris hesitated. Her father had a motorbike, and she had ridden it a few times. Only for short distances, though, as controlling the throttle had made her hand ache. 'Not really.'

'They'd give you training.'

Dispatch riders were sent out in all weathers. What if she was expected to ride through a storm? She hated storms. 'Well, maybe,' she said. 'What else is there?'

'They always need cooks.'

Absolutely not. Iris shuddered, picturing herself with a reddened face and hair frizzy from working all day in a steamy kitchen. 'What about visual signaller?' She pointed to the poster of the Wren wearing bell-bottoms.

'Not many places available. Certainly not for young women who are just joining to meet men.'

Iris felt a flush creep up her neck. This was unfair, considering she was only joining because a man had let her down.

'Plenty of young women want to be visual signallers. What skills have you got that would persuade the powers that be to invest in putting you on the sixteen-week course in place of someone else?'

'I can do Morse and semaphore. I learnt them in the Guides.' This was true, although it had been some years ago now, and she couldn't remember anything other than the Morse for SOS. Iris prayed she wouldn't be required to demonstrate her knowledge here and now.

The woman's eyebrows rose fractionally. 'That might help. Well, just be sure to put cook or dispatch rider as your second choice and don't be too disappointed if you don't get on the course.'

Much later, Iris spread the form out on her desk at home with a regretful glance at her now ringless finger. That had been sent back to George at Bomber Command together with a curt note. Seeing the empty space where it had been for a whole glorious day seemed to release the last shreds of doubt. She could either volunteer or wait here to be called up while fielding questions about the postponement of her wedding. Dipping her fountain pen into her ink bottle, she filled in her name and address.

When she came to the 'Category' section, she paused. She had to indicate two choices. In the space for first choice she wrote, 'Visual Signaller.' But what should she put for second choice? There was no way she could face potentially years of working in a kitchen, yet the fear of carrying dispatches through a storm was very real. In the end she put down visual signaller as her second choice as well. If they rejected her application, she would join the WAAF and make sure she did her research more thoroughly before applying. She would enter the Wrens as a visual signaller or not at all. As she walked to the post box, she indulged in daydreams of striding around a harbour in a pair of navy-blue bell-bottoms, collecting admiring glances from every naval officer she passed.

There followed an agonising wait, in which she was forced to endure her mother's incessant questions about George. It was getting more and more difficult to persuade her that all was well. Several times she nearly crumbled and admitted there was no engagement; the prospect of Letitia's all-too-vocal disappointment was the only thing that enabled Iris to hold her tongue.

Finally, after three long weeks, a brown envelope arrived through the post, addressed to Iris. She opened it with trembling fingers, scarcely daring to read the contents. She had to read it through twice before she could take it in, and the weeks of tension drained away. The letter instructed her to present herself at HMS *Mercury* in Hampshire at the beginning of September. HMS *Mercury* was the new location for the visual signaller training. She would soon be free from her mother, and the dream of being the Wren in the poster would become reality.

Chapter Three

So this was the Senior Service. Iris's feet throbbed and her back ached. Her initial relief at being selected for the visual signalling course was short-lived. She would only progress to that training if she survived the two-week probationary period, and right now, only two days into the first week, she didn't think she could endure much more of this torture.

At her first sight of HMS *Mercury*, she had been delighted. It was what was known in the navy as a stone frigate – a naval establishment on land. It was situated at Leydene House in the Meon Valley, some fifteen miles from Portsmouth. The main house, which Iris soon learned to call Peel House after the family it had been requisitioned from, was an elegant stately home set in large grounds. It had only been opened two weeks earlier in August, and as Iris had walked up the drive clutching her case on her first day, she had rejoiced in the good luck that had brought her here. Her mother had been right to insist she joined the Wrens. She envisaged idle afternoons, enjoying the September sunshine after her classes, exploring the grounds with handsome naval officers.

The reality had been a rude awakening. Iris winced as a large blister rubbed against the heel of her shoe. Her pleasant daydreams hadn't involved endless marching up and down the parade ground. To add to her misery, her arm still throbbed from the inoculations she'd been given the day before, and her hands were chapped and reddened from scrubbing floors.

'Keep in step, Tredwick,' the Wren sergeant who was putting them through their paces that morning shouted, jerking Iris back from her reverie. Iris cursed her lapse of concentration. In trying to get back in step she caught the heel of the girl in front, earning a hissed, 'Watch it, you clot!'

Face burning, she managed to get back in step, only to trip again when she missed the order to turn.

Much later, when they were released from the seemingly endless drill, chores and lectures, Iris climbed the stairs up to the top floor of the main house. She could hardly keep her eyes open long enough to stumble into her cabin where she slumped onto her bunk. This was something else she had to get used to: the whole new language associated with being in the Wrens. They didn't sleep in dorms or bedrooms but 'cabins', even though they weren't on board ship but very much on land. All naval establishments were HMS this or that, and treated as though they were ships, with different areas being 'decks'. The kitchen was the 'galley'.

'I don't see the point of all this square-bashing.' Iris took off her shoes and let them drop to the floor. She massaged her abused feet with a groan. 'How's it supposed to teach me to be a signaller?'

'You could always leave.' This was from the girl who occupied the bunk above Iris's, a petite young woman with dark wavy hair pinned into a severe bun. She spoke with a Welsh accent. Iris tried to remember her name. Mary; that was it. Iris didn't like the note of hope in her voice. 'As you never tire of pointing out,' she continued, hopping down from her bunk, 'we're volunteers. Nothing stopping you from walking out the door.'

True, she hadn't signed up to anything yet. They were all still on probation and could leave at any time. Part of her longed to go home. She missed her comfortable bed, having a room to herself and deciding how she spent each day. Most of all she missed being someone of consequence instead of someone to be shouted at and ordered about. The only thing keeping her here was the thought of facing everyone at home once they discovered that George didn't want to marry her. Anyway, if she went home she would be required to do some form of national service before long. She might as well see this through and hope things improved. Mary's implication that she was frequently complaining needled, though. She had heard the other girls complain about the hard work. She didn't understand what made her comment any worse than theirs. 'I don't want to leave,' she said. 'I was just letting off steam. I'm sure I'll cope.'

'Well you can start by tidying away your shoes. If we end up on punishment fatigues because you're too spoiled to tidy up after yourself, I'll never forgive you.' Mary's lips curled in a contemptuous expression. 'I suppose you're used to your mummy picking up after you.'

'Actually we've got a housekeeper.'

In the silence that followed, Mary simply gave a slow shake of the head, her hands on her hips. Iris's face burned so hot she could probably fry an egg on it. Why, oh why couldn't she stop herself from blurting out the first thing that came into her head? This was like being at school all over again, when Celia Hillyard had shown her a photo of her younger sister. All the other girls had cooed over it and said how pretty she looked, and then Iris had said it was a shame about her unfortunate snub nose. How was she supposed to know Celia was worried because the poor girl was being bullied about her looks? She had been sent to Coventry for a week for that blunder.

'I mean—' Iris swallowed and gave up. No doubt the other girls had already decided she felt she was above performing menial tasks, and there was nothing she could say to change that.

She scrambled off her bunk and picked up her shoes and arranged them in her assigned space in the wardrobe. A spot between her shoulder blades itched as she imagined all eyes boring into her back. She had never felt so small and insignificant in her life.

Picking up her diary, she retreated to her bunk and leafed through the pages. She didn't have the heart to write anything; today's experiences weren't ones she wished to remember. Pretending to write gave her an excuse not to join in the merry chatter among the other girls, though, so she uncapped her pen and jotted down a few words. Then she began a letter to her father. At least there was someone who would enjoy hearing what she had to say. If only she could be with him now, strolling through the woods above West Wycombe. Instead, he was who knew where with his ship, and she was earning the scorn of her sister Wrens. This was going to be a long two weeks.

–

A few days in, Iris had improved her marching skills and was getting used to the new vocabulary. She now spoke of sleeping in her cabin and used the twenty-four-hour clock with confidence. She knew that they ate in the 'mess deck' instead of a dining room, and if anyone was ill they were sent to the 'sick bay'. She also knew to call the lavatories 'the heads'.

No matter how used she was getting to the vocabulary, however, she doubted she would ever get used to the life of a Wren. Or, rather, Pro Wren. For she and her fellow trainees were probationers and not officially signed up to the service. This meant doing all the duties that only the lowliest of servants were supposed to do. When they weren't attending lectures on life in the WRNS, Iris had expected to have time to herself, and maybe visit Portsmouth or Winchester, which were both about fifteen miles away. How wrong she was. For they were assigned to various appalling duties. There was Long Watch. This meant getting onto her hands and knees and scrubbing one of the seemingly endless corridors. Another hateful task was Mess Duty. This involved clearing up after one meal, setting up for the next and doing the washing up. Much to Iris's distress, after four days of this cruel and unusual punishment, her hands were cracked and reddened and her nails were ragged. The worst of it was that she didn't get to wear a smart uniform like the ones in the posters. Not a jaunty cap or pair of bell-bottoms in sight. No. She would only get her uniform if she survived the hell of being a Pro Wren. Pro Wrens wore vile blue overall dresses called 'bluettes', over thick lisle stockings. When they walked the dresses clung to their stockings, causing them to ride up. Hardly the stylish uniform she had envisaged.

Actually, the worst thing wasn't the clothes. She could put up with them as long as she didn't allow herself to imagine the sneers of her school classmates if they could see her now. The worst thing was seeing the others form friendships and supporting each other through their trials. Iris had tried being approachable but she always seemed to say and do the wrong thing. While the others didn't exactly avoid her, nor did anyone offer to lend her their hand cream when she returned from an agonising Long Watch that left her with bleeding knuckles, or offer to darn a hole in her stockings when she was faint from hunger and exhaustion after her turn on Mess Duty. Yet she had seen them offer the same services to others. What would it take to get them to change their attitude towards her?

In the end she decided to give up trying and wait until she was assigned the group with whom she would do her signalling training.

She hoped she would finally meet some like-minded girls when she started the visual signallers' course. Despite her mother assuring her she would meet the right kind of people in the Wrens, she had been surprised to discover most of the girls doing basic training were not at all the kind of girls her mother would want her to mix with. For instance, Mary, the girl who had told her to pick up her shoes, had turned out to be a fisherman's daughter from a remote part of Wales. She probably lived in a squalid slum. No wonder she had not been amused by Iris's housekeeper comment.

Iris really hoped Mary would be on a different course once their probationary fortnight was over.

–

The fortnight dragged. By the end of it, Iris thought the cracked and bleeding skin on her knuckles would never fully heal. It was unreasonable to expect her to do such menial work. If only she had stood up to her mother and joined the WAAF instead. The WAAFs she had seen around High Wycombe had seemed happy with their lot, so surely they couldn't be made to work like servants.

However, her probationary period finally came to a close, and Iris had to decide whether she should sign up. If she did, she would be in the Wrens for the duration of the war, however long that might be. Two things stopped her from packing her bags: her unwillingness to confess to her mother that she was no longer engaged to George and the knowledge that she would have to do some form of national service. Feeling that things could only improve once she started the visual signaller training, she opted to stick with the Wrens.

At the end of basic training, the group of girls she had joined with at the start of September were separated into their different groups. In addition to visual signalling there were also courses for those destined to become coders or wireless telegraphers – roles Iris hadn't been aware of when she'd applied, having been swept away by the glamorous image of the visual signaller Wren on the poster. From what she had learned, though, coders and wireless telegraphers were based in offices, and wouldn't get to wear the coveted bell-bottoms, so she was still glad she was to be a visual signaller, or V/S Wren. As she packed her belongings to move them to her new cabin, which she would share with two other trainee visual signallers, she hoped that she would now get in with the right set. Maybe then she would start to enjoy life in the Wrens.

Whether the right kind of girls were on her course remained to be seen, but they certainly weren't in her new cabin. The first girl she saw as she walked into cabin twenty-four was a quiet young woman that Iris had been only vaguely aware of until now. She had light brown wavy hair cut in a chin-length bob and dreamy brown eyes. She couldn't see the other girl she was to share the cabin with, as the wardrobe door was open and she was standing behind it, hidden from view as she tidied away her belongings.

'Isn't this exciting?' the brown-haired girl said as she tacked a creased and rather faded photograph onto the wall beside her bunk. It showed a man and a woman, who Iris assumed must be the girl's parents, standing outside a small stone cottage. 'I'm Sally, by the way. Sally Hartley.' She spoke in what Iris guessed was a Yorkshire accent.

'Iris Tredwick.'

'What did you do before you joined up?' Sally asked. 'I worked in a fishmonger's after...' She glanced at the photograph, her smile fading a little before she carried on with forced brightness: 'Anyway, being a visual signaller has to beat going home every day stinking of fish.'

'You're wasting your time, asking what *she* did.' This was spoken in a lilting Welsh accent, coming from behind the wardrobe door. Iris's heart sank. She didn't have to see behind the door to know who stood there. 'That one never did a day's work in her life before she came here.' The wardrobe door closed, and Mary Griffiths stepped into view. 'She had a housekeeper.'

Great. Her visions of strolling through the streets of Portsmouth with like-minded friends faded. The next fourteen weeks were going to be a nightmare.

-

Despite her disappointment with her cabin mates, Iris couldn't fail to feel a thrill of anticipation as the trainee visual signallers filed into their assigned classroom and sat at their desks. At last, she was going to start learning the mysteries of signalling. A Wren stood at the front beside the blackboard. She had a round, cheerful face and red curly hair pinned into neat rolls, falling to the regulation height just above the collar. Iris decided she must be an assistant to their teacher and looked around for the man she assumed would be taking the course.

Once everyone was seated, the Wren spoke. 'I'm Petty Officer Wren Deidre Dickson,' she said, 'and I'm to be your signals instructor.'

Deidre Dickson looked barely any older than her. How could she know enough to teach them anything? Iris listened in disbelief while Dickson explained what the course would entail.

'After ten weeks,' she said, having listed the different signalling methods she would be covering, 'you will be required to take a series of tests. If you fail, you will not be allowed to continue with the final weeks of the course but will be transferred to another part of the service.'

Iris went cold. The possibility of failure hadn't crossed her mind. What would she do if she didn't make the grade? She couldn't bear the thought of being sent to work in the galley instead. Although she had learned some Morse and semaphore in the Guides, she had forgotten most of it, and had never learned to signal at the speeds she needed to achieve to pass.

Dickson went on, and now there was a hint of steel in her voice. 'If you wish to pass, you will need to study hard. I expect you to practise at every opportunity. When you have breakfast, you must think of the Morse for cornflakes and milk. If you're not dreaming in Morse by the end of the first month, you haven't been working hard enough.'

The brief introduction over, Dickson wasted no time in starting them on Morse code. 'The secret is to learn the rhythm of each letter,' she explained.

Before she knew it, Iris found herself chanting along with the others, 'A-*lone*, dit-dah: A. Hippety-hop, dit-dit-dit-dit: H. Victory *Vee*, dit-dit-dit-dah: V.' Feeling a little silly, Iris caught the eye of the girl at the next desk and grinned before she saw it was Mary. To her surprise, Mary grinned back. It proved to be a brief truce, however, for when Dickson divided the class into pairs to flash single letters at each other using hand-held Aldis lamps, she paired Iris with Mary.

Mary was quick to roll her eyes when Iris mistook a U for an S. 'I thought you would find U easy to remember,' she said. She imitated Iris's accent. 'Upper *Class*, dit-dit-dah.'

A few of the girls who were nearby giggled. Iris's cheeks burned, and to her dismay she heard the buzzing in her ears that always heralded tears. This couldn't be happening. If she started crying, she would never live it down. It took all her self-control to smile at Mary and say, 'Actually that's a good way of remembering it. Thanks.'

All hopes of making friends had faded by the time lessons had ended for the day and the Wrens piled into the mess deck. While no one else had teased her, neither had anyone said or done anything to make her feel included. As she approached the table occupied by the other girls on her course she hovered for a moment, hoping one of them would look up and invite her to join them. No one did. She didn't think they were deliberately ignoring her. At least, she hoped not. It was just that they were all so absorbed in their own conversations that they hadn't noticed her. Finally, she sat at the corner nearest the door.

The buzzing in her ears had started up again. She looked down at her plate, and her throat closed up at the sight of the watery stew that seemed to consist mostly of cabbage and potatoes. She had been starving on her way here. Now she wasn't sure if she could manage it. She thought wistfully of the flavoursome stews and pies Mrs Webb always managed to make, even with the limitations of food rationing.

On the edge of her consciousness she was aware of Mary approaching the table. The conversation further down ceased, and someone invited her to sit with them. Feeling lonelier than ever, Iris made a huge effort to swallow a soggy piece of cabbage to clear the lump in her throat. She grimaced as the slimy leaf clung to the roof of her mouth.

'Dreaming of caviar and champagne?' Mary had sat next to her without Iris noticing.

Sunk in melancholy, Iris couldn't think of a clever retort. Without thinking, she responded from the heart. 'I was thinking of the pies Mrs Webb, our housekeeper, makes.' As soon as the words were out of her mouth she wished she could take them back. She braced herself for Mary's next dig about posh girls whose families kept housekeepers.

'My mam makes the best pies.'

Iris stared at Mary in surprise. Rather than looking at Iris as she usually did, eyes narrowed as though calculating the best way to needle her, she was gazing into the distance while absently pushing a piece of potato around her plate with her fork. She sighed. 'What I wouldn't give for one of her oggies right now.'

It was on the tip of Iris's tongue to laugh and say what a ridiculous word 'oggie' was. Remembering how much it had hurt to be on the receiving end, she bit it back. 'What's an oggie?' She took care to keep any ridicule from her voice.

'Like Cornish pasties, only better. Made with lamb, leeks and potato.'

Much to Iris's embarrassment, her stomach rumbled. 'Sounds good,' she said. 'I'd take oggies over this.' She wrinkled her nose at her plate.

Mary raised her eyebrows. 'But you'd rather have the caviar and champagne.'

'Can't stand caviar.' Iris took another mouthful. While it didn't taste any better, she found she could swallow with ease now. 'Although I've got to admit, this is worse. I wouldn't mind a glass of champagne. It would help wash it all down.'

Mary grinned then tucked into her own stew. Although Iris still didn't feel part of the group, she didn't feel quite so alone. She and Mary ate in companionable silence and by the time they returned to their cabin, Iris was starting to think she might survive the course.

Mary went straight to the chest that stood between the bunks and opened her drawer. Iris didn't mean to pry but a glint caught her eye. Despite her better intentions, she looked over and saw a ring. It had a thin gold band and was set with a single tiny diamond.

'Oh, is that an engagement ring? Are you engaged?'

Mary slammed the drawer shut and turned to face Iris. She had taken out her notebook which she now clutched to her chest. Gone was the more open expression she had shown at supper. 'I was. He died.'

'I'm sorry.'

Mary didn't reply. She climbed into her bunk, opened her notebook and turned her back upon Iris.

With a heavy heart, Iris picked up her own notebook and started to study, muttering the Morse for each letter under her breath. So much for trying to show an interest in Mary. Well, if she couldn't make any friends, she would have to make up for it by making sure she passed all her exams with flying colours.

Chapter Four

The next two days were copies of the first one. Soon Iris's head was full of Morse, flag signals and semaphore. She always seemed to be paired with Mary when it came to practical work. Mary was invariably polite but withdrawn. There was no return to the brief camaraderie they'd enjoyed at that first supper. Sometimes she was paired with her other cabin mate, Sally. While Sally was always pleasant to Iris, she seemed rather wary. No doubt she had witnessed some of the exchanges between herself and Mary and had wanted to distance herself from any potential conflict. Sally was a gentle soul. Not timid, exactly, but dreamy and something of a romantic. Sally was the third occupant of their cabin, so conversation at night was rather limited. At least they didn't get into trouble for riotous behaviour like some of the other Wrens did.

On the fourth day there was a buzz of excitement at lunch. Iris had taken to bringing her notes to meals to avoid the discomfort of eating in silence. While she was still lonely, it did at least mean that she was improving rapidly. This morning she was trying to consign flags to memory. *Black to the hoist*, she chanted in her head as she ate, *blue to the fly, red to the deck and yellow on high*.

'I heard we get our uniforms today,' one girl said as she took her seat.

Iris looked up from her notebook with interest. She had longed for the day they would get rid of the hated bluettes. They made her feel like a workhouse inmate. Wearing a uniform might finally make her feel like she belonged.

Sure enough, after breakfast she and her classmates were summoned to a hut where a long counter was piled high with clothing. Leading Wrens stood behind the counter at intervals, handing out pieces of clothing to the Wrens as they filed past.

'Wait. Don't we get measured?' Iris asked the Leading Wren who handed her two skirts.

'You'll get what you're given,' came the reply. 'Move on. You're holding up the line.'

Iris was staggering under the weight of a mound of clothing by the time she reached the other end. Her arms aching, she climbed the stairs to her cabin, scarcely able to see over the top of the cap that was perched upon her greatcoat. She dumped the lot onto her bunk with a groan and sorted through it, looking at the garments she would be wearing for who knew how long. She heard Mary and Sally arrive but didn't look round. She was too busy rummaging through the pile for the items of clothing she had most longed to wear. She pulled them out: a pair of navy bell-bottoms. Although tempted to try them on right away, she decided to wait until she had the cabin to herself so she could enjoy the moment in peace. They were issued two pairs of bell-bottoms for outdoor wear, along with a seaman's jersey, gloves and thick socks. Also...

'Look at these under-kegs! Did you ever see such a thing?'

Iris turned to see Sally holding up an enormous pair of navy woollen knickers. The legs were so long they would reach to the knee. They had also been issued two pairs of knickers in navy artificial silk. The Leading Wren who had supplied them had told Iris they were 'blackouts'. 'Oh my word.' Iris dug through her pile and saw she, too, had been issued two pairs of the woollen knickers. 'I can't imagine wearing the artificial silk ones, let alone these.'

'Trust me, you'll be grateful for them if you find yourselves on duty on a cliff top at midnight.' It was Mary who spoke. Apart from necessary talk during lessons, they were the first words she had spoken to Iris since she had asked about the engagement ring.

'How do you know?' Iris asked.

'I live in a fishing village,' Mary replied, her Welsh accent seeming more pronounced as she spoke of her home. 'Trust me, if you'd ever had to unload a haul of fish from your da's boat in January, with your arse freezing off, you wouldn't turn your nose up at them.'

Iris managed to bite back a shocked gasp at such coarse language, knowing it would only provoke Mary. It occurred to Iris then that she knew little of Mary and Sally's backgrounds. She had shared a cabin with them for four days and knew nothing more than their names and that, judging by their accents, Mary was the daughter of a Welsh fisherman and Sally was from somewhere in Yorkshire. No wonder no one was interested in becoming her friend if she didn't even take any interest in her own cabin mates.

Perhaps, she reflected, as she stowed most of the clothes in the wardrobe and her drawer, she should make more of an effort to be friendly to the other girls on the course rather than wait for them to make an approach. She pulled off the bluette with a sigh of relief and started to dress in one of the shirts and skirts. The blackouts, however, she left in the back of the drawer. She refused to wear anything other than her silk cami knickers unless she was either standing on a cliff top in a gale or climbing aboard a boat.

'Oh, will you look at this!'

Sally, who had just slipped on one of her navy uniform skirts, was looking down at it in dismay. It was so long, it reached to her ankles.

About to simply sympathise and turn her attention back to her own clothes, it suddenly occurred to Iris that she could help.

'I'm good at sewing,' she said. 'I could alter it for you this evening.'

'That's very kind of you,' Sally said. 'I never really got the hang of sewing. It always drove my mother to distraction, the botched job I made of the darning.'

'It's no trouble,' Iris replied with a smile, almost breathless with gratitude at receiving a kind word. The feeling gave her the courage to turn to Mary. 'What about you? Would you like help with any alterations?'

Mary looked somewhat taken aback. 'No, thank you. I can manage myself.'

Mary was swamped by her uniform, looking like a toddler dressed in her mother's clothes. If anyone looked like they could use help, it was Mary. However, Iris held her tongue, unwilling to risk a put-down.

Presently Mary, back in her bluettes, grabbed one of her skirts and her sewing kit and muttered something about going to the common room for better light. Once the door had shut behind her, the atmosphere seemed to lighten.

'What's wrong with her?' Iris said, rummaging through her sewing kit for her pincushion.

'Don't be too hard on her. She lost her fiancé, remember.'

'I suppose so.' Iris did her best to shake off the unhappiness caused by Mary's obvious dislike. 'Anyway, we've got work to do if we're going to have wearable uniforms tomorrow.'

Sally smiled. 'You sound like you're almost looking forward to it.'

'I love sewing. My mother always tries to make me use a dressmaker, but I enjoy it too much to let someone else make my clothes.' Iris stepped back. 'Right. Stand on a chair so I can pin your hem.'

Iris couldn't remember a time when she'd had so much fun. It didn't take long to raise Sally's skirt to a more fashionable knee-length. Then the pair tried on all their clothes apart from the underwear. They roared with laughter when they put on the bell-bottoms. The waists were far too wide and were so high they rose nearly to the armpits.

'Oh my goodness,' Iris said when she could speak. 'Whatever possessed the Leading Wren to think these would fit?'

By the end of the evening their cabin was scattered with the clothes they had tried on. Iris had made a note of all the necessary alterations, which she promised to get through before they received their postings. 'We'll be the most stylish Wrens in the Service.' Then she paused. 'As long as we're not wearing our woollen blackouts.'

Maybe it was the euphoria of finally feeling like she was making friends, but a sudden urge struck her. She fished the hideous blackouts from her drawer and pulled them on then took off her skirt so she was dressed in just her pyjama top and blackouts. 'Naval officers beware,' she cried. 'No man can resist the allure of the blackouts.' She struck a pose.

The door banged open. A Wren petty officer stood in the doorway, scowling. 'I'm surprised at you,' she said. 'I'll be back in ten minutes. If you've not cleared up this… this pigsty by then, you'll be doing fatigues for the next week.'

She shut the door and the girls hurried to obey. Iris didn't mind her first reprimand, however. For the first time since she had joined, she finally felt she had a friend.

—

Iris squinted across the parade ground at Sally who was using semaphore flags to send signals to her. She read the message slowly as she jotted each letter into her notebook. 'Where are you going next weep? Dash it, week! I'm always getting P and K mixed.'

Iris rose from the low wall she was perched upon and picked up her flags. She had felt horribly self-conscious the first few times she had used flags for semaphore or Morse, but she was starting to get used to it.

They were now nearly halfway through the course and would be going on leave next week. Before that, however, they had a set of important tests on everything they had learned so far. A pass would earn them their Signals branch badges. Iris hadn't asked what would happen if they failed. She didn't want to know. While she had spent the early part of the course wishing she could go home, she was now happier than she had been since the end of her non-engagement. Determined to do well, she and Sally were helping each other revise and practised at every opportunity. Today being Sunday, they had no lessons, so once they had returned from church parade, they had turned their back upon the comforts of the common room and gone out into the damp late October air to improve their semaphore.

Iris signalled her reply: 'Home. Maybe. You?' If she could, she would have preferred to spend her week's leave at HMS *Mercury*. She still hadn't summoned up the courage to write to her mother to say George was never going to marry her. Iris knew the moment she arrived home, her mother would be bound to bring up the subject of her marriage and pester her until Iris had confessed the truth. While she missed home and longed to see the beech woods in their full autumnal glory, she couldn't face having to explain her embarrassing misunderstanding. Her dread was so severe, she would rather spend the whole week being subjected to Mary's scorn.

Not that Mary had been so bad since Iris had helped Sally alter her uniform. Although she still made digs about Iris's wealthy background, the sting was no longer there. Or perhaps Iris had just grown used to it. Mary didn't mix much with the other girls on the course either. Instead, she spent every night hunched over her books, her frown discouraging any interruptions.

A chill wind made Iris shiver as she concentrated on Sally's reply. She guessed the answer from the first letter, although she waited until the end. 'Left hand high, right hand down: E,' she muttered. 'Yorkshire,' she called. It would have saved a lot of time if Sally had said 'home' instead of 'Yorkshire'. She jogged over to Sally's side of the parade ground. 'I'm cold. Let's go and warm up in the common room.'

Sally nodded and was gathering up the flags when a magpie swooped past and landed in a tree a few yards away, its black and white feathers clearly visible against the yellowing leaves. 'No, hold on. We can't leave yet.'

'Why not? My feet are about to drop off.'

Sally pointed at the magpie. 'One for sorrow. We have to wait for another, or summat... *something* bad will happen.'

'Worse than getting frostbite? Don't tell me you actually believe that superstitious nonsense.'

But Sally twisted the red and yellow fabric of one of the semaphore flags until Iris feared she would tear it. 'Please, can we not stay?'

Her distress was clear, and made sense of her rare slip into Yorkshire dialect. Iris had noticed Sally do things like touching wood or throwing salt over her shoulder after spilling some, although only now did it dawn on her that it must come from a deeply ingrained belief rather than automatic gestures. Now she regretted dismissing Sally's worry as superstitious nonsense. Not that Iris believed it herself, but it obviously meant a great deal to Sally.

She nodded, and returned to her perch on the wall, Sally going with her.

Her eyes fixed on the annoyingly single magpie, Sally said, 'You must think me daft as a brush.'

'No. Not at all.' Iris's tone wouldn't have convinced a child; she had never been much of an actress.

Sally gave a crooked smile. 'It's all right. I dare say I'd feel the same way were I in your shoes. It's just... well, I saw a lone magpie the day my uncle had his accident.'

'I'm sorry. He's not...?' Iris hesitated, not wanting to say 'dead'. 'I hope he's all right now.'

Rubbing her eyes, Sally said, 'Not really. He got thrown by his horse and hurt his back. He couldn't work the farm any more, so we lost it – we were only tenants – and had to move to Whitby.'

'What about your father?'

'He died when I was a bairn. I don't remember him. My mother and I moved to Uncle Ted's farm when I was only two.'

'How awful. I'm sorry.' Iris couldn't imagine not knowing her father. Her happiest memories were of tramping through the woods with him.

'It's hard to miss someone I never knew, although my mother's told me so many wonderful stories about him, I'm proud to be his daughter. I do miss the moors, though. It's so beautiful up there.' After a brief pause, Sally brightened. 'Whitby is lovely too, so I mustn't complain, and at least my uncle is still with us. Things could have been so much worse.'

As Sally spoke, a second magpie flew by in a blur of black and white and settled on the branch beside the first. 'There you are. All will be well. Let's go in.'

'Thank goodness,' Iris muttered, stamping her feet to restore circulation.

It was only after they had carried their notebooks into the common room and were warming their hands on steaming mugs of Horlicks that Iris recalled the conversation they had started during their semaphore practice. Now she knew about Sally's family losing their farm, she understood why Sally hadn't said she was going home for the holidays. 'Don't you want to go home on leave? I thought it was a bit odd when you said you were going to Yorkshire instead of going home.' The inkling of an idea was forming, and Iris was feeling her way towards proposing it.

'It's silly, I know,' Sally replied. 'We've lived in Whitby for five years now. It's just that the thought of going there brings back all the painful memories of Uncle Ted's accident.'

'Why don't we go somewhere else together?' Iris said, feeling excited about the holiday for the first time. 'I can't face going home, and we could get train tickets to wherever we want.' Although the idea had only just occurred to her, suddenly she knew exactly where she wanted to go: Bath. She had wanted to go ever since reading her first Jane Austen book. She could afford a hotel room on her generous allowance, and it would be even more fun to go with a friend.

'Oh, I'd love to, but my mother would be so upset. Her letters have been full of my visit for the past month.'

Iris felt a lurch of disappointment. She tried to hide it beneath a bright smile. 'Never mind. It was just an idea.'

She obviously hadn't managed to disguise her feelings very well, for Sally gave her a look of concern, her head tilted. 'You could always come with me to Whitby.'

But she sounded doubtful, and Iris shook her head, guessing there wouldn't be much room for her. 'I wouldn't want to impose, and you'll want to be with your family without me getting in the way.' When Sally looked like she was about to protest, Iris hurried on. 'Anyway, I've decided I'd like to go to Bath, and there's no reason I can't go alone. Now I've thought of it, I'm rather looking forward to it.'

Sally was still regarding her as though she were an object of pity. 'Why don't you want to go home?'

Suddenly Iris was overcome with the urge to unburden herself to someone. Telling Sally would be good practice for telling her mother when she finally couldn't avoid the meeting. 'I can't face anyone at home just yet,' she said. 'I feel such an idiot.' And she poured out her tale. It was still painful to speak about it, even now, and when she finished she braced herself for laughter.

Sally patted Iris on the arm. 'How awful. But if George fell in love with that other girl, it means he wasn't the right one for you.' She gazed dreamily over the rim of her mug for a moment. 'I think there's someone out there for all of us, and when we meet him, we'll just know he's the one. That's what my mother always says.'

'You don't believe that rub—' Iris broke off with a cough and went on, picking her words more carefully, not wanting to offend. 'Maybe George wasn't the right one for me. I don't know. I don't think I believe in true love. I just wanted a husband and a nice home. Isn't that what we're all supposed to want?'

'Oh, I couldn't live with someone I didn't love,' Sally said. 'Imagine sharing the same house for the rest of your life with someone you didn't love!'

Behind them came the sound of a snort. Iris twisted around in her seat to see Mary, regarding them with an odd, crooked smile. 'You're forgetting this is Iris. She and her husband will probably live in different wings of their manor house.'

Iris felt her cheeks flood with heat. How long had Mary been there? She must have heard the whole hideous tale about George. She braced herself for another scathing remark then noticed how strained Mary's smile looked, as though it was an effort to hold it in place. With a lurch of horror, Iris remembered about Mary's fiancé.

She heard Sally suck in a breath that hissed between her teeth; evidently she regretted her comment about finding 'the one'. 'I'm sorry, Mary. I didn't mean you would never find anyone else.'

'Who says I want to?' Mary replied.

There was an awkward pause while Mary picked up her mug and took a sip. Iris shifted in her seat and exchanged glances with Sally.

After a moment Mary spoke again, although she almost sounded as though she were talking to herself and had forgotten Iris and Sally. 'Maybe that's why I'm reluctant to go home. Everyone treats me like I'm this fragile thing that might shatter if they say anything that might remind me of Owen. The truth is, I think of him all the time.'

Iris studied Mary covertly across the rim of her mug. Mary seemed mesmerised by the spiral of steam rising from her drink. Iris was longing to know what had happened to Mary's fiancé but had put her foot in it too many times to speak now.

Sally came to her rescue. 'What happened to him, if you don't mind our asking?'

A silence stretched out for so long that Iris thought Mary wasn't going to answer. Finally Mary seemed to rouse herself from her contemplation and replied. 'He was in the navy. His ship was torpedoed by a U-boat.'

Iris found her voice. 'I'm sorry.'

Mary shrugged. 'It wasn't your fault. Anyway. That's why I joined the Wrens. Felt I owed it to Owen to take his place.' She shot a crooked smile at Sally. 'Now you know my sad story and Iris's. What about yours?'

Now it was Sally's turn to look away. She brushed an invisible blemish on her skirt, a lock of light brown hair falling across her face. Eventually she said, 'Promise you won't laugh?'

Iris guessed this was aimed at her. She said, 'It can't be worse than my story, can it?'

'I suppose not.'

'Ouch.'

That seemed to break the tension, and they all giggled.

'Come on, Sally. You've heard our stories. You owe us,' Mary said.

'It's not much of a story, to be honest. There's this young man.'

Mary shook her head. 'Of course there is.'

'Well, he joined the navy as soon as war broke out.' Sally gave a wistful smile. 'He's so brave. He didn't wait for the call-up.'

'And so you joined the Wrens in the hope you'll be posted somewhere near him,' Mary finished for her.

'Wouldn't it be wonderful if that happened? I've been counting down the days until I was old enough to volunteer. We're meant to be together, I'm sure.'

'You mean you're not already?' Mary shot Sally a sharp glance.

'Oh, we're just friends at the moment.' Sally's cheeks turned pink. 'But I know he's the one for me. One day he'll realise that too.'

Iris gave a sad shake of her head. 'We're a sorry bunch.' She picked up her notebook and waved it at the others. 'I, for one, am not going to think of men until I've got through this course.' She opened the book at random and stared at the page without seeing what was written. After a while, though, it hit her that the crushing weight of humiliation had eased a little. For the first time since getting George's letter, she felt more optimistic about her future.

The Badge Test passed by in a blur, and just before they went on leave, the girls were given their results. Much to Iris's delight, she found all her hard work with Sally had paid off: they had both achieved top marks. The evening before they went on leave, Iris sewed their new badges – a pair of crossed flags – onto their right jacket sleeves. It was the last change that needed making to their clothes, and Iris took quiet pride in the fact that she and Sally now had the best-fitting uniforms in the class.

Mary also passed with high marks. Much to Iris's disappointment, their sharing of confidences before the Badge Test had not resulted in more friendly behaviour on Mary's part. When Iris had asked if Mary would like her to sew on her badge for her, Mary had replied that she could manage perfectly well herself and passed the rest of the evening in silence. Iris concluded that Mary was embarrassed at revealing her feelings and was now counting down the days until they went their separate ways. Well, that made two of them. She got the train to Bath the next day consoling herself that in another two months, she need never see Mary again.

A week later, she returned, half sorry to leave the beautiful city and half relieved to be back in the ordered world of HMS *Mercury*. She had never been alone in a strange place before, and she found it exhilarating to decide for herself how to spend each day. She had walked in the footsteps of Catherine Morland and Anne Elliot and daydreamed of the same streets bustling with women in Regency gowns and dashing men in tall hats and tailcoats. Never once had those pleasant strolls been interrupted by comments from her mother telling her to: 'Stand straight, darling. You look like you're auditioning for Richard III. No wonder you're still single.' Or: 'Surely you don't want to eat in there. Look at the state of the woman they just let in.' Best of all, she could decide what to wear without fear of her mother's disapproval. A fortnight earlier, she had sent home for more clothes, without revealing she was due for some leave, and on two occasions had sallied forth in her beloved bell-bottoms, revelling in the admiring glances they earned.

On the other hand, she had been lonely, especially at mealtimes, and much as she had enjoyed visiting the Abbey and ambling over Pulteney Bridge, she had found herself wishing she could share her impressions with a companion. Still, she had enjoyed her first taste of independence and was eager to see more of the world. She returned to HMS *Mercury* looking forward to finishing the course and exploring a new town or city. Next time, though, she hoped to be with a friend. Now that she no longer had to spend her evenings sewing, she and Sally spent even more time studying while the autumn wind and rain lashed the window panes. The weeks flew by, and before she knew it, it was December. Her final week of the course was overshadowed by news of the Japanese attack on Pearl Harbor and the United States' entry into the war. With a growing sense of the whole world being sucked into a whirlpool, Iris applied herself to her studies with fresh determination.

The trainee visual signallers sat their exams and waited with dread for the results. There was much jubilation when they were posted, with everyone on the course passing. To Iris's delight, she and Sally were again at the top of the class, although they had to share the honour with Mary this time. They were given forms to fill in with their preferred posting. Iris requested Portsmouth. Already, she could picture life in the bustling naval port, enjoying parties with the officers of the Royal Navy. Who knew – she might soon find a man even wealthier than George to marry.

Much to her dismay, however, the Wrens were told they were to be sent on leave and would be sent their postings while on leave. With Christmas nearly upon them, Iris knew she would have to go home. The guilt of missing Christmas with her mother would have been too much to bear. The evening before they were to leave, Iris packed her belongings with a heavy heart. Once home, there would be no further putting off the dreaded confession about her engagement. It promised to be a particularly *un*-merry Christmas.

She was just packing her shirt collars when there was a sharp rap on the cabin door, and Petty Officer Wren Deidre Dickson strode in bearing buff envelopes. She addressed Iris, Sally and Mary. 'The three of you must defer your leave, I'm afraid. You're needed right away.'

'Thank goodness. I didn't fancy Christmas at home.' Iris took her envelope, grateful for her reprieve. Instead of a gloomy Christmas at home, she would be enjoying the social scene of one of the busiest naval bases in the country. She could almost see herself strolling along the sea front, arm in arm with a handsome captain. She had already decided that she would only be seen with an officer who outranked George. Then she could go home and tell her mother.

She tore open the envelope and read the contents. That couldn't be right. She turned the paper over but it was blank. She read her instructions through again.

'There's been a mistake,' she said to Dickson. 'I requested Portsmouth.'

'But they don't need anyone in Portsmouth. They do need three visual signallers in Scapa Flow.'

Scapa Flow. The Orkney Islands. She visualised the colourful atlas she'd had as a child. If you went as far north as you could, all the way to the top of Scotland, then took a boat and carried on going north, you would eventually arrive at the isles of Orkney.

Mary folded up her letter and put it in her pocket. 'Good thing we didn't get rid of those woollen blackouts.'

'Are you going to Orkney too?'

Mary nodded.

Wonderful. Not only would she be spending Christmas in the middle of nowhere, she would be forced to endure her exile with Mary.

'Sally?'

Sally's eyes were shining. 'Isn't this wonderful? We're staying together.'

Iris clung to this crumb of comfort. And faced with Sally's enthusiasm, she couldn't help smiling. 'You do realise we're going there at the darkest time of the year? Just about every watch will be a night watch.'

'But Orkney! So mysterious and romantic. I've always wondered what it would be like to live on an island.'

'You can ponder the romance while you're packing,' Dickson said. 'You'll all need an early night – you leave tomorrow at 0500.'

Chapter Five

Once she got to Stromness, assuming she survived that long, she was never leaving. Not even if she was offered a commission and a transfer to Portsmouth. Nothing would induce her to board this boat ever again. It was over two hours since she had boarded the *Earl of Zetland*, and it felt like two years.

The boat lurched sideways, and Iris clamped a hand to her mouth. Not for the first time, she wished she had stayed on deck with Sally and Mary. Despite Mary's advice that she would be less likely to get sick if she stayed outside, Iris hadn't liked the look of the waves lashing against the vessel's hull and had headed for the safety of the saloon. Besides, Mary's assumption that she knew best when it came to sailing had rankled. However, once the *Earl of Zetland* had left the harbour and was being tossed around the Pentland Firth like a cork, Iris realised her mistake. All she could do was wedge herself in the angle between the bench and the wall, squeeze her eyes shut and pray she wouldn't disgrace herself. What terrible crime had she committed to deserve this hideous ordeal? To think she had considered the train a nightmare.

The journey up to Thurso had gone on for hour after hour. It had been crowded with servicemen and a few women. Everywhere Iris looked she could see nothing but khaki, navy or slate-blue uniforms. Iris, Mary and Sally had managed to bag seats in a compartment, where it was impossible to carry on much conversation over the din made by the troops. At times the train would stop for ages in the middle of nowhere with no explanation. Sometimes when it pulled into a station, there would be volunteers manning tables set with vast vats of soup. Then the girls would take it in turns to get off the train to use the lavatory and buy soup, dreading to hear the train's warning whistle before they were ready to board again.

At the end of the train journey they had been herded onto trucks to take them the few miles to Scrabster harbour. Once off the truck, stiff with cold, they had shuffled up the gangway onto the *Earl of Zetland*. It was by now early morning. In the civilised world, the sun would be coming up; here, in the far north, there was no sign of dawn. Or, at least, there hadn't been when she had entered the saloon. For all she knew, the sun had risen and set a hundred times since the start of the voyage. It certainly felt that long.

'Drink, love? A tot of whisky'll put you right.'

Iris risked opening her eyes to see a wiry sailor offering her his hip flask. Pungent fumes emanated from it, making her eyes water. At that moment the ship rolled again. From somewhere behind her came the sound of retching followed by a horrible splashing sound.

It was no good; she couldn't stay here. Rising, she clutched the bench to get her balance. The door to the deck rose and fell. She fixed her eyes on it. It couldn't be more than ten feet away. She released her grip on the bench and took one tottering step. Then the floor disappeared from beneath her feet, leaving her momentarily weightless. An instant later, it heaved up against the soles of her feet so hard she feared the force of the rising floor would slam her knees into her chin. Toppling backwards, she landed on something soft.

'Well, if you insist, love.' The sailor's face filled her field of vision; the alcoholic fumes on his breath made her senses reel.

With a squawk of protest, Iris ducked under his arm, slithered off his lap and back onto her seat to the accompaniment of laughter.

'They do say all the nice girls love a sailor.' One of the other men slapped the whisky drinker on the back.

Iris's face burned. She wanted nothing more than to escape to the deck, but didn't trust her legs to get her there without further mishap. She turned her face away and closed her eyes, willing away the nausea. She lost all track of time. Perhaps she even dozed off, for the next thing she knew, someone was prodding her arm.

'Iris? Iris! You've got to come and see.'

Iris opened her eyes to see Sally.

Sally frowned. 'You look pale. Are you feeling sick?'

Iris nodded.

Sally held out her hand. 'You'll feel better on deck. I'll help you.'

With Sally's support, she found she was able to cope with the floor rising and falling beneath her feet and made it out onto the deck. As soon as a blast of fresh air met her face she breathed deeply. 'That does feel better. Thanks.' She released Sally's arm. 'I think I can manage from here.'

She set out towards the rail, only to be sent scampering sideways when the deck dipped violently. Strong arms caught her and set her right.

'Woah there, lass. First time at sea?'

She looked up into a pair of twinkling eyes, the same grey-green shade as the sea. She nodded, feeling flustered. 'Thank you.'

'Dinnae mention it. I'll help you to your friends.'

'Really, there's no need.' Now she wasn't plastered to the man's chest she could see more of him. He was tall and looked to be in his mid-twenties. Her heart skipped as she took in a pair of deep-set eyes creased with laughter lines, a strong jaw and cropped auburn hair showing beneath his cap. He wore naval uniform with an insignia showing he was a petty officer. Feeling somewhat unsettled to be this close to a strange man, she started to walk to the rail where she could see Mary and Sally watching her. A moment later the boat heeled again, and the man caught her arm.

'If you let me help you, you won't end up in the sea.'

Iris had no choice but to allow him to guide her across the deck. She had to admit it was easier when supported by a man clearly at home on the waves. She reached the rail beside Sally and clutched it.

'Here you go,' he said to Sally and Mary. 'One errant Wren, present and correct.'

'Thanks,' she said to him again.

Sally was eyeing him with interest. 'How gallant,' she said. 'Are you a crew member on this boat?'

He shook his head. 'Returning from leave. Petty Officer Rob Sinclair at your service. I'm a Tiffy on the *Kelpie* – a minesweeper working out of Scapa Flow.'

'A Tiffy? What on earth is that?' Iris had thought she knew all the naval terms, but this was new to her.

'Engine room artificer.'

He might have said more; Iris had no idea. Her stomach gave a nasty lurch at that point, forcing her to whip round and lean over the rail, gulping air.

By the time she was able to face the group again, Sally was speaking. 'It's nice to meet you, Rob. The Wren you just rescued is Iris. I'm Sally and this is Mary. We're just arriving so it's lovely to meet you. Hopefully we'll see you again.' She shot Iris a sly look. 'I'm sure Iris will like that.'

'I look forward to it.' Rob gave a mock salute then went to stand with a group of men, all in naval uniform.

Sally grinned at Iris. 'He's lovely. Maybe there's a reason he was there to catch you.'

Iris shook her head, although carefully, to avoid triggering further queasiness. 'Don't go pairing me off with anyone. Especially when we haven't even set foot in Orkney yet.'

'Talking of which…' Sally gestured ahead. 'Isn't it beautiful?'

The sun was up by this time, and Iris now saw they were sailing alongside red sandstone cliffs so high that craning her neck to see the top made her almost as giddy as the heaving deck. Here and there, waterfalls cascaded from the cliff tops, bowing in the wind like ribbons of the sheerest white chiffon. 'Where are we?' she asked.

'I heard someone say this was Hoy,' Sally said.

Mary didn't seem to be paying any attention to the conversation, but gazed ahead, her expression set in a scowl that kept everyone at arm's length.

'How far from Stromness?'

'About another hour, love.' This was from a sailor on Sally's other side. Although the whole deck was crowded with men, they seemed to be packed tightest around the three Wrens.

Iris gritted her teeth. If the boat continued to pitch this wildly, the men standing downwind from her were going to regret it. 'An hour?' She gripped the icy rail as another wave threatened to throw her against Sally. 'I'll never make it.' She forced a laugh. 'Even my ears feel sick. I never knew that was possible.'

—

'What in blazes are you doing here, Sinclair?' One of Rob's shipmates, a stoker returning from leave, took a drag from his cigarette and eyed Rob through narrowed eyes. 'You're supposed to be on leave.'

Rob had rehearsed his answer, knowing he would be unable to return unseen. 'I got to Scrabster then couldnae face spending the best part of a day in that cattle truck of a train.' Nightmarish as the journey was, what he really couldn't face was ten days of listening to his mother's litany of complaints about his father. 'I spent a couple of nights in Thurso then thought I might as well return early to Orkney.'

'Don't tell me you're spending your leave on *Kelpie*?'

Rob shook his head. 'I'll go to the Heddles'. Help out on their croft.' He had first met the Heddles shortly after the sinking of the *Royal Oak*. Suffering from the shock and horror of that night, he had been in no state to be posted to active duty on a new ship. The Heddles had welcomed him into their home, treating him like a son. The peace of their cliff-top croft and the Heddles' wholehearted acceptance had worked wonders on him, and when he had been well enough to return to duty, he'd been delighted to have a posting in Scapa Flow. Now he spent what time he could with the couple, doing odd jobs in return for their hospitality.

'Not what I'd call a holiday.' The stoker ground his cigarette butt under his heel then turned back to the group.

Rob, however, found he couldn't concentrate on the conversation. His gaze kept returning to the Wren he had helped. Even with her pallor of seasickness, she was a looker. With her blonde hair and blue eyes, she was a point of brightness against the dark uniforms and grey sky.

His shipmate's laugh drew his attention back to the conversation. 'A sight for sore eyes, isn't she? What do you say, lads, is this why Sinclair's so keen to return to this hellhole?'

'Nah,' said a crewman from another minesweeper, 'she's too posh for the likes of him. He wouldn't stand a chance.'

'You think?' A minute ago, Rob would have agreed that Iris was out of his league. Her crisp, BBC accent marked her as someone from an altogether different world from his, and anyone who had spent five minutes with his parents would know that those worlds should never mix. Now, though, he wanted nothing more than to prove the jeering sailors wrong. 'Just you wait and see.'

He strode across the heaving deck to where Iris stood with her two friends. Well, the one with light brown hair seemed to be her friend; the dark-haired girl stood with her back to the others, with a curiously intent expression as she gazed up at the cliffs of St John's Head. He reached them in time to hear Iris complain about how seasick she felt. He abandoned any thought of flirtation in favour of simply helping another human being through her suffering.

'Dinnae look at the boat, lass.' He gave her an encouraging smile. 'Pick a point on the horizon and keep your eyes on it.' The western edge of the Mainland had now come into view. He pointed it out. 'Fix your eyes over there. That's where we're going.'

'Thank goodness the end's in sight.' She clamped her mouth closed, clearly still fighting nausea. The brown-haired girl rubbed her back.

Knowing he would have to carry the conversation, Rob pointed out the places of interest as they came into view. 'See that flat island between Hoy and Mainland? That's Graemsay. And the high hills behind us are the Hoy hills. Mainland's much flatter, although there are plenty of rolling hills. You'll get used to seeing the Hoy hills, though. You can see them from just about anywhere on Mainland. If you ever get lost, just look for these hills, and they'll put you right.'

'And if I can't see them?' Iris shot a sideways glance at him before snapping her head round to face front again. Rob was pleased to see the colour returning to her cheeks.

'Then the haar must have descended.'

'Haar?'

'Sea fog.'

'Sounds delightful.' Her sarcasm sounded all the more pronounced when spoken in her upper-class accent. It made Rob grin. 'What other joys lie in wait for us?'

'I won't hear a word against Orkney. It's a beautiful part of the world. Where are you going to be based?'

'Kyeness Signal Station.'

At this, Rob perked up. The Heddles' croft was not far from Kyeness, so there was every chance he would meet Iris again. 'That's near Stromness. I expect you'll be billeted there. It's a bonny town.' He went on to describe the places he knew, including the NAAFI and St Peter's church hall, which often hosted events for the servicemen and women of Stromness.

Iris listened in silence for some time until eventually, when they rounded a headland and were sailing through

Hoy Sound, she tore her gaze from the horizon long enough to shoot a smile at her helpers. 'Thanks. I feel a bit better now.'

'Aye, you're not looking quite so green,' Rob said.

As if on cue, the sun peeked through a gap in the clouds, lighting the scene with a golden glow.

Sally gasped. 'Isn't it beautiful?'

'It is indeed,' Rob said. 'You certainly picked a fine time for your first view of Orkney. Nowhere like it in the world.'

'I'll take your word for it,' Iris said.

Usually his first view of Stromness was a sight to raise his spirits. Now, however, he couldn't deny a slight twinge of regret. The end of the voyage meant saying goodbye to Iris. Quite aside from her knockout looks, he'd enjoyed her slightly abrasive observations, and she'd managed to keep up her good humour despite her seasickness. He was intrigued and hoped to see more of her.

When the *Earl of Zetland* made its approach to the pier at Stromness, Rob took his leave. 'I'm sure you girls will be busy, but I hope we'll see one another again.' He looked at Iris as he spoke. 'If you like, I could show you around, try and persuade you Orkney's not so bad after all.'

'Perhaps,' was all Iris said.

The brown-haired girl, Sally, elbowed Iris. 'She'd love to, I'm sure.'

Rob went to rejoin his friends feeling rather flat. It was pointless trying to arrange a time to meet the girls when they didn't know where they were staying or when they would be free. As he endured the sailors' jibes, he hoped it wouldn't be long before they met again.

Now Iris thought she might live long enough to reach dry land, she studied the island she knew to be Mainland with a sinking heart. Apart from the barrage balloons that seemed to lift the island from the waters, it looked bleak and empty. Not a tree in sight. A flattish small island – Graemsay, Rob had called it – stood between Hoy and Mainland, dividing the channel into two and obscuring her view of the bay beyond. She had never pictured somewhere as barren and gloomy.

And cold. Now she was no longer fighting nausea, it dawned on her that she was shivering. An icy wind managed to cut right through her many layers of clothes and seemed to flay her skin from her body. This was a far cry from Portsmouth or Plymouth. Who would have thought that such a wilderness could exist in Britain?

They had rounded a point, and now Iris saw a huddle of grey buildings clustered near the water's edge, a low, rounded hill rising behind them. As they drew nearer, she saw that some houses – high-gabled buildings of grey stone – stood right down beside the water, while others were grouped a little way up the hillside. A church with a stone spire dominated the skyline. It looked little more than a village to Iris's eyes.

While the *Earl of Zetland* sailed to the pier, Iris looked back and for the first time saw part of Scapa Flow, the anchorage of the Home Fleet. It was a huge natural harbour, formed by Mainland at her back, Hoy to the west and, although she couldn't see that far, she knew there was a string of islands marking the eastern side of the harbour. Stromness was in an inlet, and the curve of Mainland obscured the eastern side of Scapa Flow. Nevertheless, the sight made the breath catch in her throat. Several ships were anchored far out, near Hoy, looking no more than toy boats from this distance. Small boats chugged between them and the islands, casting wakes that sparkled in the low sun.

A great rattle of chains drew her attention back to Stromness, and she saw they had arrived at the pier. She still clung to the rail with a tight grip, and when she let go and tried to shoulder her bag, her legs tottered beneath her. 'I wish there was someone to carry our bags.'

'Shall I call for a porter?' Mary hoisted her bags with ease and followed the crowds towards the steep gangway.

'There are porters? Thank goodness.' Then Iris saw Mary's eyebrows arched in ironic amusement. She tried to pass off her embarrassment with a laugh. 'Oh, of course not. I didn't really...' Thankfully, at this point she got separated from Mary as the crowd funnelled down the gangway. Glancing back, she got one last glimpse of Rob before the crowd closed up again and she lost sight of him. She wondered if she would ever see him again.

As she stepped ashore the wind cut through her, just as vicious as it had been on board the boat.

'By heck, it's cold.' Sally muttered, standing on the pier beside Iris. Her accent sounded more Yorkshire than ever.

'I'm really glad Mary persuaded us not to get rid of the woollen blackouts,' Iris said, although quietly so Mary, who was approaching, didn't overhear. She didn't want to give Mary the satisfaction of hearing Iris admit she had been right.

'As soon as we find our lodgings, I'm putting on my bell-bottoms and seaman's jumper, and you'll never get me out of it again,' said Sally, rubbing her chapped hands together.

Iris noticed a Wren petty officer holding a clipboard, standing beside a car. Now she walked up to the girls. 'Griffiths, Hartley and Tredwick?'

The girls chorused their replies.

'I'm to take you to your quarters.'

They piled their bags into the transport and the Wren petty officer climbed into the driving seat. 'You'll be working at Kyeness Signal Station,' she said, shouting to be heard above the growl of the engine. 'You're the first Wrens to be sent there, to free up three of the lads there for duty on ships. You'll be billeted in Stromness, so that will mean a fair old walk to the signal station every day.'

Iris didn't mind. She preferred a long walk to and from each watch rather than being billeted in the middle of nowhere with no one but Sally and Mary for company.

The car pulled up outside a large, high-gabled house, up the hill from the main town. 'Wait inside,' the driver told them. 'The duty orderly will show you where to go.'

Hefting their bags, they walked into a large hall, their shoes ringing on the black and white floor tiles. It was a relief to shut the door against the wind.

The duty orderly appeared – a Wren in her early twenties. 'You'll be sleeping up in the attic,' she said. 'It's a bit basic but better than being billeted separately.' She pointed out the mess and the common room as they passed, then led them up a rickety flight of stairs. From the upper-floor landing, she went to what looked like a cupboard door. Inside was an even narrower flight of stairs, each one creaking beneath their weight. At the top, Iris saw that they were, indeed, in the attic. Low rafters criss-crossed the space, meaning they had to duck their heads as they filed inside. Three camp beds were set up on unpolished floorboards, each with a low locker beside it. On one side of the door stood a wardrobe, and a matching chest of drawers stood on the other. At opposite sides of the attic, the room narrowed into a gable end, with a window set into each. Iris dumped her bag onto one of the beds then ducked beneath the rafters and peered out of the window. She could see the little town of Stromness clustered below and beyond, the sea and the islands of Graemsay and Hoy.

'I'll leave you to unpack,' the duty orderly said. 'Someone will take you up to the signal station at 1400.'

Iris looked out of the window again, at the grey, choppy sea, at the flags on the boats standing out stiff in the wind, and the barrage balloons encircling the bay. All the while, the window panes rattled as the wind howled around the house. Her breath formed a mist in the air. Suddenly the prospect of the return journey didn't seem so bad. At the first opportunity, she would try to get a transfer out of here.

Chapter Six

At 1400 prompt, a cheerful naval rating called Joe Pallant came to collect them and give them a tour of the signal station that would be their base of operations for who knew how long. By this time, Iris, Sally and Mary had unpacked their possessions, tidied them away and changed into their warmest clothes. Despite her gloom, it had given Iris a thrill to don her bell-bottoms and feel she was finally starting to look like the Wren in the poster. She also took satisfaction in seeing that Mary hadn't done as good a job on the alterations to her bell-bottoms as Iris had on hers and Sally's. The material around the waist was rucked, spoiling the line.

'Bring torches,' Joe told them. 'The sun sets in a couple of hours so it will be dark before you get back.'

Iris gazed at him in disbelief. It felt like they had only just seen the sun rise. She could hardly believe such a wilderness existed in the British Isles. With her torch in her greatcoat pocket, banging against her thigh with every step, she followed Joe down the lane that led away from Stromness.

'Where's the signal station?' she asked. She couldn't see any sign of any buildings, let alone one that could serve as a naval signal station.

'There's still a way to go yet,' Joe replied. 'It's out on Kyeness, about two miles away.'

'Two miles? Don't we get transport?'

'Afraid not. You might get a motorbike down the track, but not a car.' He paused by a line of barbed wire that seemed to serve as a fence, strung between wooden posts. He pulled up one of the posts and folded back the length of barbed wire, and now Iris could see it marked the start of a rough track. The girls walked through, and Joe closed the rudimentary gate behind them. Realising they would have to find their way alone after today, Iris made a note of the location to be sure she could find the entrance again.

The rocky track wound up a hill.

'This cuts through to the cliffs facing Hoy Sound,' Joe said. 'That's where the signal station is. The walk'll keep you all fit.'

They trooped after Joe. Iris had her collar turned up against the wind but even so, it seemed to find its way down her neck. She had never been more grateful for her blackouts and warm clothes. She tried to imagine what the walk would be like in the rain or, heaven forbid, snow, but couldn't imagine feeling any more miserable than she did at this moment. She had never felt farther from home. Thankfully, her frequent walks in the Chiltern Hills had kept her fit, and she had no trouble keeping up. Both Sally and Mary also walked with easy strides. Iris guessed that this hill was nothing to Sally, who came from the moors, or Mary, who must be used to the steep coastal paths in her Welsh fishing village.

It took about three-quarters of an hour to follow the path over the hill. Once they reached the top, they could see a headland, with the sea raging far below. At the highest point of the cliffs was the boxy outline of the concrete signal station. Iris eyed it with a mixture of interest and foreboding as they approached. This was the place she would be spending most of her time until she got her transfer. It was a two-storied building with a balcony around three sides of the upper level. One ladder led up to the balcony and another from the balcony up to the flat roof. Iris could see a ten-inch signal lantern mounted on the balcony. Outside the building was a mast flying the White Ensign.

'Welcome to Kyeness War Signal Station,' Joe said.

Iris couldn't think of a place that looked less welcoming.

He led them to a door around the back where there were two outbuildings. Before going in, he indicated these one at a time. 'Coal hole, head.'

'You mean we have to go outside to the lavatory?' The words burst out before Iris could stop herself.

'Course not,' said Mary, speaking for the first time since leaving the Wrennery, as their lodgings were known. 'That one's for the maid. There's a gold-plated one inside for us.'

Joe laughed. 'Don't worry. We cleared out all the spiders when we heard we had ladies joining us.' He pointed out the flag locker beside the back door then led them inside.

The ground floor of the signal station consisted of a living area with a table and a few chairs. Although there was a row of hooks behind the door where they could leave their coats, the room was so cold that Iris opted to keep hers on. Leading off from the living area was a tiny galley and a bunk room.

Opposite the galley doorway a metal ladder led up through a hatch in the ceiling. The girls followed Joe up into the signal room. The moment Iris put her head through the hatch, she was bathed by the heat from a cast

70

iron stove. Two more men were in the room. One jotted a note in a log book at a rickety table while the other stood at one of the long windows that formed three sides of the room. There was a large telescope mounted on a swivel at the window looking out to sea. There were smaller fanlights above the main windows, and these were open to allow the telescope through.

The rating at the desk flung down his pen. 'You girls are a sight for sore eyes. I'm Andy McCall. Freed for the fleet, thanks to you. Welcome to Kyeness.'

'Are you all being transferred to ships?' Sally asked, tearing her gaze away from a chart pinned to the back wall.

'The three of us are,' Joe replied. 'Andy and Ollie to destroyers, the lucky sods, while I'm stuck on a mine-sweeper here in bloody Orkney. Pardon my French.'

'You won't think us lucky if we end up in the Arctic convoys,' Andy said with a theatrical shiver.

'True.' Joe gave Mary a wicked grin. 'And I can't deny there are compensations for staying.'

Mary narrowed her eyes and said, 'Since this is the last time we're seeing each other, perhaps you could describe the routine at Kyeness.'

Andy chuckled. 'Bad luck, pal. Better luck next time.'

But Joe didn't look defeated. 'This isn't the last time we'll see one another. We don't leave till Friday, and the WVS have organised a Christmas party on Thursday night. You've got to go. It'd be bad form to let these lads leave for their ships without seeing them off properly.'

'Of course we'll come,' Sally said. 'We look forward to it. Don't we, girls?'

Much as she shrank from the thought of an evening spent with rowdy ratings, Iris agreed, unable to think of a reasonable excuse. Mary also muttered, 'Of course,' although looking as reluctant as Iris felt.

'Now that's sorted,' Joe said with a grin, 'let's get to your duties. The main thing is to send the code of the day challenge to all naval vessels passing this point, and the unknown ship call to international vessels.'

The girls nodded. This had all been covered on their course.

'Then there are the loops.'

'The what?' Iris asked.

Joe beckoned them to the window and gestured at the sea. 'This is Hoy Sound,' he said. 'One of the entrances to Scapa Flow. It's your job to make sure only friendly vessels go through. We can't afford a repeat of the *Royal Oak* incident.'

Iris didn't have to ask what he meant by that – it had been a shocking event and made all the headlines. At the start of the war, the battleship *Royal Oak* had been anchored in Scapa Flow. A German U-boat had somehow made its way into Scapa Flow through what had been considered an impassable channel and torpedoed the *Royal Oak*, causing huge loss of life.

'But how are we supposed to see the subs?' Mary asked, her voice oddly strained.

'That's where the loops come in. There's an anti-submarine indicator loop laid across the Sound of Hoy. No idea how it works, but when a vessel crosses – either on or under the water – it sends a signal to the station at Lower Skaill.' Joe pointed at a phone connected to a box with a handle. 'They will then call on this phone to ask us to identify it.'

It was only now that Iris saw there were two phones on the wall. One was the phone connecting to Lower Skaill and she assumed the other connected to headquarters. It was all starting to sound rather complicated, and she felt a twinge of apprehension. Her misgivings increased when Joe went on to explain how a motorcycle messenger would carry messages to and from the signal station should the phone lines be damaged. It hit her just how far she was from the security and comforts of home.

Just then, the phone connected to Lower Skaill rang. All three girls jumped. Much to Iris's relief, Andy picked up the receiver. She had been terrified she would be asked to answer.

Andy spoke into the receiver. 'WSS.'

He put down the phone then went to the window. Iris followed his gaze and saw a ship sailing down the Sound of Hoy, towards the main anchorage. Remembering her ship identification, she thought it was probably a mine-sweeper although she would need to look through the telescope to be sure. The rating picked up his Aldis lamp and sent a signal to the ship. Iris couldn't see the response from where she was standing. The rating returned to the phone. 'Minesweeper HMS *Troy*, inward.' He replaced the receiver.

Iris felt as though everything she had learned had flown out of her head. Glancing at Sally and Mary, it was a comfort to see her anxiety reflected in their expressions.

Joe crossed to a list pinned above the desk. 'Tredwick and Griffiths,' he read. 'Which ones are you?'

Iris and Mary put up their hands.

'You two are on watch from 0800 tomorrow. Hartley' – Joe looked at Sally – 'you'll be paired with one of the ratings until more Wrens arrive. You're on at 1300.'

Iris listened to the watch system with growing dismay. Why did she have to be paired with Mary? She would rather have been paired with a rating than Mary, who made her disdain clear. As Joe went over the hours, it hit home just how much time she and Mary would have to spend together. They did two watches a day for two days, with a long night watch at the end of the second day. On the third day, after being relieved at eight in the morning, they had the rest of the day off and weren't back on watch until eight the following morning when the whole rotation started again. Factor in the walk to and from the signal station, and it was clear they would hardly be apart.

She glanced out of the window and shivered. The signal station, perched on the cliff top, was exposed to the elements. If a thunderstorm struck, there would be no escape from it. At home, she had always retreated to an alcove behind a bookshelf in the library and sought comfort in one of her favourite books. If she cowered in the bunk room during a storm, Mary would never let her forget it. Joining the Wrens was definitely not one of her better ideas.

The sun had already sunk below the horizon by the time they left the signal station, leaving a dark orange glow upon the sea. As Iris stumbled through the gloom, it struck her with growing horror that it would still be dark the next morning when she and Mary needed to walk the track on their own. How would they find their way in the dark with only the dimmest of torches to help?

Once they were back in the safety of their cabin, she couldn't hold in her dismay any longer. 'What do the navy think they're playing at, sending women out to such an isolated spot?'

'They think they're freeing up men to serve with the Fleet.' Mary hung her greatcoat in the wardrobe and slammed the door. 'What did you think you were joining the Wrens for? To do fancy embroidery and go to dances with the officers?'

Stung, Iris couldn't think of a reply. Mary had been too close to the mark for comfort.

Sally spoke up before the silence became uncomfortable. 'I think it's wonderful here. I love being so close to the sea.'

'But won't you be scared walking all that way in the dark, three or four times a day?'

Sally shrugged. 'I lived up in the North York Moors. I'm used to the dark.'

'I suppose I'd hoped for a livelier posting,' Iris said. 'I wanted to see a bit more of the world.'

'And meet handsome officers?' Mary's voice was caustic.

'So what if I did?' Iris said. 'There's nothing wrong with wanting to enjoy myself as well as helping the war effort. There's no law against that, is there?'

'Course not. But seeing as we're here, why not try to look for the positives about the place?'

This was such common sense that Iris was forced to see Mary's wisdom, no matter how much it pained her to agree with her.

Sally added. 'The Home Fleet is based here, so there's bound to be plenty going on. And as for meeting men, practically the first thing you did when you arrived was to fling yourself into the arms of a handsome man.'

It was on the tip of Iris's tongue to point out that the man had not been an officer. Definitely not the kind of man her mother would approve of. It was only the thought of Mary's snort of disdain that made her hold back. 'Well, I'm going to put in for a transfer at the earliest opportunity,' she said.

Mary slammed shut the wardrobe door. 'You will do no such thing.'

Iris stared at her in amazement. 'You can't stop me.'

'Maybe not. But think about it. The navy hesitated to post us here because they think we're fragile creatures who shriek and stand on the table if we see a mouse. If you decide you can't cope, the powers that be will take that as confirmation of their prejudices. It wouldn't affect just you but every other Wren who wants to do something more exciting than sitting in a comfortable office, typing all day.'

Iris was surprised by the passion in Mary's voice. This was more than disdain for someone Mary saw as spoiled and self-centred, and Iris was coming to see more and more that she must come across as such.

'You worked hard on the course,' Mary went on. 'I was beginning to change my mind about you. But if you go and ruin it for everyone else just because you can't bear to be out of the social whirl, then I'll never forgive you.'

—

A shrill ringing ripped Iris from a happy dream where she had been at a dance on the arm of a rich but faceless man. She gazed into the darkness, disoriented, until memory returned and reality crashed upon her. She was so far from civilisation she might as well be in the Arctic, and she had just three-quarters of an hour to get ready to leave for her first watch with a girl who despised her.

She tumbled out of her bunk, biting back a squeal as her bare feet hit the icy linoleum. She heard a muffled curse that told her Mary was also getting up. Sally, who was not on watch until the afternoon, slumbered on. Iris had never envied anyone quite as much as she envied Sally at that moment. Iris fumbled for the light switch and clicked it on, flooding the attic room with light. Sally groaned and buried her head beneath her blankets.

Shivering violently, her breath forming clouds in the frigid air, Iris dressed, donning all her warmest clothes, including the bell–bottoms. Then she stumbled down the two flights of stairs to find the mess deck.

Not that the dining area in the Wrennery could compare with the mess deck at HMS *Mercury*. This was, after all, a requisitioned house that only seemed to hold about ten Wrens. There was a serving hatch at one end with a table below it. Jugs of milk and a large tea urn stood upon the table. Behind the hatch, a young Wren with rosy cheeks was stirring the contents of a huge pot. 'Eat your fill,' she said, ladling porridge into a bowl and handing it to Iris, together with a plate of bacon and egg. 'You won't get back in time for the midday meal, so we'll put some sandwiches by for you.'

Iris had already worked out from their watch rota that they would not be in the Wrennery for many of the set mealtimes, so it was good to know provision would be made for them. She didn't feel particularly hungry, what with nerves at her first watch and her growing gloom over her posting. However, knowing she had a brisk walk ahead, she took the porridge and added a slice of toast to her plate. Then she approached the long table in the centre of the room, only to see Mary was already there, stirring her porridge with a scowl. After a brief hesitation, Iris sat in the adjacent seat; they were about to spend a whole watch together, so it was high time they got used to each other's company. A couple of times as she ate she tried to start a conversation, but each time Mary only responded with a few short words and lapsed into silence. Iris's heart sank to the hems of her bell-bottoms. Their watches together promised to be awkward indeed. It was a relief when a glance at her watch told her it was time to leave.

They returned their dishes then dashed out to don their outerwear and set out. The relentless wind was still blowing and this morning – if you could call it morning when it was still pitch dark – it was accompanied by a fine rain that stung Iris's face. The blackout was just as strict here as everywhere else in Britain, so no street lights or light escaping from houses lit their way. Whilst they were on the paved road, the white lines painted upon the kerbs showed up in the dim light of their blackout-compliant torches. However, finding the bit of fence that served as a gate was a problem.

'It must be here,' Mary muttered. 'Look, you can see a flattened patch of grass where people have walked.'

Iris, amazed at Mary's powers of observation, could only just make out the spot where, using your imagination, you could see that the grass was a little flatter than the grass elsewhere on the verge. Mary must have the eyes of a cat. Iris knew she would have walked straight past. She fumbled to find the post that served as the gate and gasped with relief when her groping fingers found the loop of wire that allowed her to lift it clear and open the gate. Once they had gone through, she looked back and made a mental note of a triangular lump of rock on the verge opposite the gate. They would have to do this walk again that evening, and she wanted to find it quickly next time.

As they trudged up the hill and down the other side, the rain making Iris's hair stick to her face, she tried to forget that she would have to do this walk three more times that day. Every journey bar one would be in the dark. It was a relief to see the dim outline of the signal station loom ahead after half an hour on the rocky track.

They were greeted by a pair of tired-looking signalmen. 'Ships going to and fro all night, but you should have a quiet watch,' one of them said as he picked up his coat and gloves from where they were hanging over the stove and put them on. 'Don't forget to hoist the ensign at 0900,' he said as he stumped across to the door.

They were about to leave when the telephone rang. Iris looked at the departing signalmen but they laughed. 'Your problem now,' they said as they strode down the track.

Iris hurried up the ladder into the signal room. The ringing phone was the one connected to headquarters. She reached for the receiver with trembling hands. 'WSS.' It meant War Signal Station, and that was how the signalman had answered the phone the day before, so she supposed it was the correct thing to say. Try as she might to sound crisp and efficient, her voice held a distinct quaver.

A woman spoke in a clipped, upper-class accent. 'This is Second Officer Wendleton. HMS *Plover* was due to return to the anchorage last night and it still hasn't arrived. Keep a watch for her and telephone through as soon as you see her.'

'Yes, ma'am.' Iris replaced the receiver with a grimace. So much for a quiet first watch to break them gently into the routine.

'Anything important?' Mary's head appeared at the top of the ladder and she stepped into the signal room.

Iris relayed the message and went to look out of the window. Although the first hint of pearly grey light could be seen in the sky, the sea was still inky black.

Mary joined her. 'We'll be notified as soon as a ship crosses the indicator loop,' she said.

That eased Iris's nerves somewhat but she still found it hard to settle. She paced up and down beside the window, listening to the rain beating down on the roof. At five to nine she was about to suggest tossing a coin to see who got the miserable task of going outside to raise the ensign when the telephone rang again. This time it was the duty officer from the station monitoring the indicator loop, reporting a crossing.

It was still too dark for Iris to pick out any identification on the ship visually. With shaking hands, realising this was her first action as a fully fledged visual signaller, and not wanting to get anything wrong, she sighted the ship and sent a challenge using her Aldis lamp.

The reply came back: it was the delayed HMS *Plover*. Iris called out the message to Mary word by word, who was noting it down.

Iris, sending the single long flash after receiving the name to indicate she had received the complete word, expected that to be the end of the message. However, it continued. 'Wait, there's more,' she called to Mary who had been about to pick up the telephone receiver to report the *Plover*'s arrival as requested. 'Torpedo strike,' she relayed slowly to Mary. 'Five dead, eight critical. Urgent medical assistance required.'

Mary grabbed the receiver, fumbling a little. Iris found it oddly comforting to see Mary was as nervous as her. Mary relayed the message to Second Officer Wendleton, who said medics would be waiting for them. Iris signalled this to the *Plover*, passing on instructions for anchorage.

At the end of the exchange, Iris peered through the telescope and trained it upon the *Plover*. Although the light was still dim in the stormy sky, she could make out smoke billowing from her stern, and she was listing badly. 'I hope she makes it,' she muttered.

'She'll get there,' Mary said.

Feeling as though her knees were about to give way, Iris sank down at the tiny table and entered the event into the log book.

'I'll go and raise the ensign,' Mary said. 'Then I'll make us some tea. I think we could both use it.'

'Thanks,' Iris said. 'I'll do it next time.'

As soon as the initial shock had passed, she returned to the window to resume her watch. The sun had now risen, and she watched Mary fight through the wind and the rain to hoist the ensign on the flag mast that stood at the front of the station. She and Mary might not be best friends, but it had been a relief to know they could work together when needed.

It was hard to get the plight of HMS *Plover* from her mind. The sight of the badly damaged ship haunted her throughout the watch. It brought home for the first time the dangers the men of the Royal Navy faced at sea. Hearing reports on the radio about ships being torpedoed or reading about it in the newspaper was nothing like seeing the results for herself. She thought of the cheerful signalmen who were looking forward to serving on board ships. Would they survive, or would they become one of the numbers listed in casualty reports? Then she thought of George. Iris had enjoyed the glamour of being the fiancée of an RAF officer but she had never considered what dangers George faced. She cringed to remember how she had expected him to drop everything so he could get leave to marry her. It was distinctly uncomfortable to see herself as Mary – and even Sally – must see her.

'You look serious,' Mary said as she mounted the ladder, carrying a kettle. She placed it on the stove.

'Just thinking.'

Towards the end of the watch, the phone rang again. 'Thought you'd like to know.' It was Second Officer Wendleton. 'HMS *Plover* arrived safely, and all the injured were safely transferred to hospital. Good work.'

Iris replaced the receiver, finding she had to swallow to clear the lump in her throat. She passed the message on to Mary, her voice a little husky.

'I've been thinking,' Iris said after a pause. 'You were right about me needing to consider the other Wrens before I put in for a transfer. I'm going to stick it out.'

Chapter Seven

After their first watch together, Mary's attitude towards Iris thawed a little. However, Iris still felt a long way from the friendships she had hoped for. While she enjoyed Sally's company, they rarely got any free time together with Sally being on a separate watch. She was also finding the relentless watches hard going as they only got a full night's sleep one night out of every three. On her second day, she had hoped to spend the morning exploring Stromness before going on duty and getting to know the place she would be staying for who knew how long. However, after arriving back at the Wrennery soaking wet at midnight after the long walk in the rain, it had been one in the morning before she had hung up her clothes to dry and had a wash. She had slept late, barely making it to breakfast before it was cleared away, and then the duty orderly had told them in no uncertain terms their cabin needed a good tidy unless they wanted to spend their day off on mess fatigue. By the time the cabin was spick and span, it was time to set off for their next watch.

Maybe if she had a friend to confide in, she would be able to laugh off the trials and discomforts of this new, strange way of life. However, with Mary's reprimand still fresh in Iris's mind, she didn't dare make any complaint for fear of spoiling the fragile truce.

The morning of their third day saw Iris and Mary at the end of their first night watch. It had, thankfully, been uneventful, with only a few signals needing to be exchanged with the minesweepers patrolling Hoy Sound. The girls had agreed to split the watch so the other could sleep in the bunk room for half the time, and Iris had managed a blissful four hours of uninterrupted sleep, waking half an hour before Sally and one of the new Wrens were due to relieve them. She wasn't sure what had woken her at first, then she realised it was the silence, broken only by the distant boom and crash of the waves at the bottom of the cliff. The wind had dropped. She had grown so used to its constant howl around the signal station, its absence made her ears ring.

'It's going to be a beautiful day,' was Sally's greeting when she arrived. 'The stars are all out, and they are glorious. You won't need a torch.'

Iris left the signal station to a transformed Orkney. Despite being used to the bright stars that could be seen during the blackout, nothing could have prepared her for the dazzling multitude of stars stretching overhead. The Milky Way was a dense band, and the crescent moon was not bright enough to blot out the display. For the first time, Iris saw there was a wild beauty to Orkney.

'I hope the weather holds,' she said to Mary. 'This place might not look too bad in the sunshine. I'd like to go and explore.'

'It reminds me of home a little,' Mary said.

It struck Iris then that she had never bothered to ask about Mary's home. She only knew it was somewhere in Wales. 'Where are you from?'

'Solva in Pembrokeshire,' Mary replied.

'And is it a lot like here?'

'Well, there's no huge natural harbour like we have here, but it has the same wild feel up on the cliff tops. Solva has a long, narrow harbour, with high cliffs on either side.'

'And your father has a fishing boat?' Iris was careful to keep any trace of condescension from her voice. She was genuinely interested in Mary's life before she had joined the Wrens.

'Yes. I know that must sound like the worst kind of life to you, but I can't imagine living anywhere other than by the sea.'

Iris refrained from comment, knowing any remark she made about Mary's life could sound patronising. 'Is that why you joined the Wrens?' she asked instead.

'Partly.'

Then Iris remembered how, back at HMS *Mercury*, Mary had said something about joining the Wrens because she owed it to her dead fiancé. An odd thing to say. Although Iris itched to know more, Mary's closed expression warned her off asking about it, and they walked on in silence.

After breakfast and a couple of hours' sleep, Iris decided to go out and explore.

'Don't forget we promised to go to the Christmas party,' Mary reminded her as she pulled on her bell-bottoms.

Iris had forgotten. In fact, she had almost forgotten it was Christmas next week. She had forgotten everything but the gruelling watch rotation. Even though she hadn't been keen on the party when she had first heard about it, now she found herself looking forward to being in the company of someone other than Mary, and going anywhere that wasn't Kyeness. All in all, Iris felt in brighter spirits as she wandered into Stromness. A low sun gilded the surrounding hills and made the cottages and paved streets seem much more charming than they had appeared through the rain. It was still bitterly cold, and Iris was grateful for the warm garb provided by the Wrens. After strolling around the shops, she found a lane that led down to the harbour. The view took her breath away. Stromness looked across an inlet to hills on another part of the Orkney mainland. Looking out to sea, she could see the flat island of Graemsay out in the Hoy Sound, with the high, snow-capped hills on Hoy looming beyond. The sea sparkled in the sunshine. Orkney looked altogether more welcoming in this weather. Small boats chugged across the water – Iris guessed they were the drifters used to transport men to and from the ships, taking the mail.

For some reason she thought of the man who had helped her on the ferry. Hadn't he said he was based in Scapa Flow on a minesweeper? She looked around the harbour, half expecting to see him, then chided herself. He hadn't been an officer, and she was determined not to get involved with any man lower in rank than a lieutenant commander.

–

That evening, the girls got ready for their first night out. It was fun to wear civvies again, and Iris regarded her reflection with pleasure, admiring the dark green dress with its sweetheart neckline and deep, fitted waist. It was one of her proudest creations. It was only after applying her favourite cherry-red lipstick, that she noticed neither Mary nor Sally were doing more than brush their hair. 'You aren't going out like that, are you?'

'Like what?' Mary put down her brush and folded her arms.

Too late, Iris realised how much like her mother she had sounded. She had been on the point of criticising Mary's clothes – a black knee-length skirt with a cream jumper. The jumper had darned patches on both sleeves, and the skirt had shiny worn patches. 'I… ah… thought you'd want to wear make-up.'

'Haven't got any.' Mary turned her back on Iris and started to brush her hair again with such violent strokes, Iris was sure it must be painful.

'And don't look at my clothes like they belong on the rag-and-bone cart.'

'I wasn't. They're…' Iris flailed for a description that wasn't 'hideous' or 'only fit for dusters', mortified that her thoughts must have shown so clearly. 'Fine,' she said in the end, then grabbed her lipstick and turned back to the mirror.

Mary hadn't finished, though. 'They're the best I've got, but you can spare me your pity. Everything I have was earned through hard work, and I'm not ashamed to admit it.'

In the tense silence that followed, Iris thought of all the clothes left behind in Tredwick Place, stored with mothballs. She blotted her lipstick, wondering if she shouldn't abandon any hope of making friends and instead crawl under her bed covers until it was time for her next watch. If only she had thought of it before, she would have offered to lend Mary some clothes. There was no way of making the offer now without Mary taking it as a deadly insult.

She caught Sally casting a look of longing at her lipstick. Sally was forced to attend the dance in uniform, as she was on night watch later, and wouldn't have time to change. 'My mother would never let me wear make-up,' she said.

Iris offered it to her. 'I promise not to tell.'

Sally darted a glance at the door as though fearing to see her mother standing there. Finally she took the lipstick and applied it. After replacing the lid, she smiled at her reflection. 'It does make me feel daring.'

'You look smashing.' Iris hesitated then dared to add, 'What about you, Mary?'

Mary made a move as though about to take the lipstick, then jerked her arm back. 'No, thank you.'

'You're lucky, Mary,' Sally said, saving them from another awkward silence. 'With your colouring you don't need make-up.'

Annoyingly, it was all too true. Mary's looks were striking. Her porcelain skin and blue eyes were in vivid contrast to her dark, curly hair, and her full lips had plenty of colour even without paint. Iris felt quite pale and insipid in comparison.

'Do you think your saviour will be there?' Sally asked as they headed down the stairs.

'I don't know. I haven't thought about him,' Iris lied. 'Anyway, he's not my saviour.'

Some of the other Wrens from the Wrennery were also going to the party. They all congregated in the entrance hall and pulled on greatcoats, scarves and gloves.

'Have you got late passes?' one of the other Wrens asked the three girls.

While Sally explained about being on night watch, Iris and Mary both nodded.

'Good. That means we don't have to be back until 2300.'

'What happens if we're late?' Iris asked as she tugged open the door.

The Wren wrinkled her nose. 'Mess fatigues. Trust me, once you've spent all your free time peeling spuds and washing dishes, you'll have hardly any skin on your hands. You won't want to be late again.'

The wind had returned, and the girls set out at a brisk walk to reach St Peter's Church Hall before they lost the feeling in their fingers and toes.

The church hall, where the Women's Voluntary Service was holding the party, was on one of the streets up the hill from the harbour; the uphill walk soon warmed Iris up. Once inside and through the blackout curtain, they were greeted by cheers from a group of men clustered around a table near the door. Iris recognised the signalmen she and Mary had relieved on their first watch and Joe, the signalman who had shown them round on the first day. Through a haze of smoke, she saw tables groaning with cakes and sandwiches. At the far end of the hall, a lady was operating a gramophone, and the strains of 'A Nightingale Sang in Berkeley Square' drifted across the room. Despite the serene music, there was a group of men in army uniform who appeared to be vying for the attention of a very few women, and Iris eyed them with apprehension. This was not the kind of party she was used to.

'What'll you have, girls?' Joe asked when they approached. He jingled the change in his pocket. 'There's lemonade or ginger beer. My treat. I'm celebrating the start of two whole weeks of embarkation leave. Buying you all drinks is the least I can do to thank you for getting us into ships at last.'

They all ordered lemonades, and while Joe went to fetch their drinks, the girls peeled off their layers and handed them to a smiling woman in return for cloakroom tickets. Then, seeing a group of chairs by the wall, they made their way to them, hoping they would be out of the biting draught coming through the door.

'Well, well. If it isn't the Wren who flung herself into my arms a few days ago.' Sauntering towards the group was the man Sally delighted to describe as her saviour.

'Oh, hello,' Iris said, making an effort to sound casual. 'I didn't think you'd be here.'

The man – Rob Sinclair, she remembered – took the empty seat beside her. 'You've been thinking about me? Glad to hear it.'

'What? No! I mean, I remember you, of course. I'm very grateful you stopped me from hurling myself overboard.'

Rob clapped a hand to his chest. 'So you only remember me for my help, not for my charm and boyish good looks? You wound me.'

Iris stammered something, she hardly knew what. She wasn't used to being teased by a man. George had always been very formal and polite.

'Oh, dinnae mind me,' Rob said. 'But I'm forgetting my manners. Would you like a drink?'

'Thank you, but someone's already getting one for me.'

Rob gave a sad shake of the head. 'Too late even to shower you with gifts. Is there nothing I can do to impress you?'

Despite herself, Iris laughed. 'Getting a lemonade is hardly being showered with gifts.'

Rob's expression turned serious, although the twinkle in his eye betrayed him. 'Of course not. A classy English

90

lass such as yourself wouldnae be impressed by a mere drink.' He gave a dramatic sigh. 'What chance is there for a poor sailor like me?'

By this time, Iris was feeling out of her depth. She felt like she was playing a game when she had no idea of the rules. 'There's nothing wrong with being a sailor,' she said, then cringed inwardly at how patronising she sounded.

She was rescued by Sally who happened to turn and notice Rob at that moment. 'Iris's saviour!' she cried. 'We'd hoped we would meet you again, didn't we, Iris?'

Iris managed a weak smile, wishing Sally hadn't got it into her head that Iris and Rob were destined to be together. Thankfully, Sally didn't wait for her to reply. 'What are you doing here? I thought you were on a minesweeper.'

Joe returned with the drinks in time to catch Sally's last remark. He handed out the drinks saying, 'Rob's been here even longer than us. We couldn't leave without saying goodbye.' He raised his glass in a toast.

Iris eyed her glass doubtfully, hoping it was clean, before joining in the toast with the others. She caught Rob's sardonic gaze and felt her face heating at being caught out.

'Thank you, all,' Rob said. 'Anyway, I'm still on leave, and I'm staying not too far from Stromness.'

'How long have you been here?' Sally asked.

'Feels like forever,' Rob answered.

'You're looking at one of the few men who survived the *Royal Oak*,' Joe said.

All this time, Mary had been sitting with her back to the little group Iris was with, deep in conversation with the other Wrens. Now her head snapped round. 'You were on the *Royal Oak*?'

Even Iris, who had not taken much interest in any actions involving the navy before joining up, had heard of the *Royal Oak*. It had been sunk by a U-boat in Scapa Flow not long after the start of the war, with the loss of over eight hundred lives.

Rob's face shadowed. 'I was there.' He pushed back his chair, the legs screeching upon the linoleum. 'Anyway, my throat's dry as the Sahara. Excuse me while I get a drink.'

He strode to the drinks table. Iris didn't know if it was her imagination, but Mary seemed to watch him with an unreadable expression.

'Sorry,' said Joe in an undertone that was meant just for Iris and Sally. 'Should have known better than to mention the *Royal Oak*. He's never really got over it. Well, who can blame him? It's not something that can be easily forgotten. The locals all shudder when you mention it.'

When Rob returned with a glass of ginger beer, he seemed to have recovered his good spirits. He laughed and joked with the signalmen and toasted the leaving signalmen's good fortune when they joked about leaving 'Bloody Orkney' at last. Orkney, it appeared, was not a popular posting. As one signalman put it: 'There's nothing to do; it's just a great expanse of cold, dark nothingness where the bloody wind never lets up.' Iris, even though she had only been there three days, couldn't argue with that.

'What about you?' Iris couldn't help asking Rob. 'Don't you want to get away?' Surely anyone in their right mind would want to escape from a place that must bring back terrible memories.

Rob shrugged. 'There's something about Orkney that gets under your skin.'

'Seriously?'

Rob smiled, and the last of the haunted shadows faded from his eyes. It was, Iris had to admit, a very attractive smile. 'Seriously,' he said. 'Even in wartime, there's a special kind of peace here that you don't get anywhere else. I wish I could have seen these islands before the war.'

'Where are you from, then?'

'Glasgow. Not the most peaceful place in the world.'

'What did you do before the war?'

'Oh, I worked in the shipyards with my dad until I turned eighteen, then I joined the navy. I could see the way the world was going, and wanted to join on my own terms.' He took a swig of beer then asked, 'What about you? Where are you from?'

'Buckinghamshire. In the Chiltern Hills.' Just saying it gave Iris a pang of homesickness.

'You're a country lass? Maybe you'll get used to Orkney yet.'

'I doubt it.'

Rob burst out laughing. 'I thought the same when I first arrived, yet here I still am.'

One of the signalmen raised his glass. 'Good old Sinclair. Take care of Bloody Orkney for us when we're gone.'

A group of signalmen linked arms and began a song with lyrics that made Iris's cheeks burn. This was a far cry from the civilised dinner parties and tea dances she was used to. After that, she was joined by a group of Wrens and the conversation moved to where they could buy make-up and nylons, and places to visit on their days off.

Eventually, Sally glanced at her watch. 'Goodness, it's nearly 2100.' Iris couldn't help a smile at how they had become accustomed to using the twenty-four-hour clock.

'I need to get back now if I'm going to be ready in time for my watch.'

Iris happened to look in Rob's direction, only to find him looking at her. She turned away, face burning. 'I'll come with you,' she said to Sally. 'I could do with a good night's sleep.' Not to mention escape from this man who made her feel distinctly jittery.

'What about you, Mary?' Sally asked. 'Coming?'

But Mary shot an odd glance at Rob. 'I'll stick around a while longer and come back with the other Wrens.'

'Don't be late,' Sally said.

Then they were stumbling through the dark streets on their way back to the Wrennery. Once there, Iris went straight to bed, tired out, while Sally gathered what she would need for her night watch and went down to the common room until it was time for her to leave. Iris drifted into a doze, her head full of Rob Sinclair's smiling face.

Some time later, Iris was jolted awake by the sound of the door opening. Her first thought that it was Mary returning was dispelled when torchlight shone into her face. 'Where are Hartley and Griffiths?' It was Third Officer Jean Pardew, making the last rounds of the night. Iris had been in Stromness long enough to learn that Pardew was not to be crossed.

That last tendrils of sleep banished, Iris said, 'Hartley's on watch, ma'am. And Griffiths...' She glanced at Mary's bed. It was empty and clearly had not been slept in. Wherever Mary was, she was officially past the time allowed by her late pass and would get into trouble when she returned.

Chapter Eight

Iris hesitated. She could tell the truth and say that, as far as she knew, Mary hadn't returned from the party. The thought barely crossed her mind before she knew she couldn't do it. While Mary hadn't exactly been her friend, Iris knew she deserved most of the teasing Mary had aimed at her. It was dawning on her that if they were to become friends, Iris was going to have to make more effort to act like one.

'Griffiths is in the ablutions, ma'am,' she said. 'Something she ate.' It was the best excuse she could think of at short notice. She could only pray Pardew didn't go into the bathroom to check, or both she and Mary would be on mess fatigues until *next* Christmas.

'Very well.' The torch snapped off and the door closed.

Iris let out a shaky sigh of relief. Where was Mary? Although Iris didn't know her that well, Mary didn't strike her as the sort of girl to rebel against discipline and stay out late. After all, hadn't Mary lectured Iris just a few days ago about how her behaviour reflected on all the Wrens? A growing dread grew that Mary must have tripped and fallen in the dark and might even now be lying in the cold, waiting for help. Had Iris been irresponsible to pretend she was safely in the Wrennery? Should she go and confess so a party could be sent to look for her? What if she had been hit by a car? In the blackout, in the depths of winter, it was easily done.

A rattle against the window made her jump. There it was again. Her senses jangling, Iris scrambled out of bed and felt her way to the window. She pulled aside the blackout blind and peered out. She could just make out the pale blur of a face looking up at the window from ground level. Holding her breath, praying the hinges didn't creak, she eased the casement open, letting in a blast of icy air.

Iris leaned out over the sill and said in a low voice, 'That you, Mary?'

The answer came in a whisper barely to be heard over the distant roar of the sea. 'Yes. Let me in.'

'How? Pardew's on the prowl. I can't get to the door without her seeing.'

'Hang on.' Iris could dimly make out Mary's dark form groping around the walls. She disappeared around the corner for a moment then reappeared. 'Can you get to the window on the first-floor landing? I can climb up the drainpipe.'

'I'll give it a go.'

Iris closed the window and eased the blind back into place then crept to the door, careful to keep near the wall to avoid the floor creaking. The lino was ice-cold against her bare feet, but Iris couldn't find her slippers in the dark. Her heart thumping, she lifted the latch on their cabin door. It clicked, setting her nerves screaming. For the space of twenty painful heartbeats, she stood poised with her hand on the latch, waiting for Pardew to come storming up the attic stairs, demanding to know what Iris was doing out of bed. When she failed to appear, Iris inched the door open and edged out. In the pitch darkness, she had to feel her way with her feet, sliding them along the floor until her toes curled over the top step. Then her seeking hands found the stair rail and she clutched it as she crept down the attic stairs. She then had to repeat the experience of opening the door at the foot of the staircase, straining her ears for the sound of footsteps that revealed Pardew was still on patrol. When she heard nothing, she paused, trying to visualise the location of the window. As far as she could recall, it was directly opposite the attic stairs, with nothing to trip her. Drawing a shaky breath, she stepped out and walked straight ahead, hands outstretched. She almost sobbed with relief when her hands brushed against thick curtains. Moments later she had pushed them aside and opened the window.

'Mary? Where are you?'

'Coming.'

There followed the sound of scrambling and gasps of exertion. Shivering as the cold wind tore through her thin pyjamas, Iris peered out and saw a dark figure scaling the drainpipe that ran to the right of the window.

'Hurry!' Iris whispered. 'Someone's bound to come and see where this gale is coming from.'

A hand appeared over the sill. Iris grabbed it and hauled Mary inside, supporting her so she didn't crash to the landing floor. Expecting to hear footsteps and raised voices at any moment, demanding to know what was happening, Iris pulled the window closed and drew the curtains.

Then she clutched Mary's hand and guided her to the attic stairs. 'Quick. Upstairs.'

They hastened into their cabin. Iris dived under her covers and waited for her heartbeat to subside, listening to the rustlings of Mary getting undressed. Only when she heard the creak of the bed did she whisper, 'What were you thinking? You could have got us both into hot water.'

'I know. I'm sorry.'

'But why?' Iris wasn't to be appeased by a half-hearted apology. 'Pardew wanted to know where you were. I had to make up some tale about you having eaten something that disagreed with you.'

'I can't explain right now. It's complicated.'

Iris heard Mary's bed creak; presumably she had just turned over. When Mary spoke again, her voice was muffled as though her covers were pulled up over her head. 'I'm too tired to talk.'

If Iris hadn't been afraid of Pardew overhearing, she would have dragged Mary out of bed and demanded she explain herself. As it was, all she could do was gaze into the inky darkness, silently fuming. How dared Mary expect Iris to cover for her, risk getting herself put on fatigues until she died of old age then not have the decency to at least explain why?

She was just beginning to drift into an uneasy doze when she heard Mary's voice. 'Thanks, Iris. You're a brick.'

–

After the escapades of the night, both Iris and Mary woke late. In the rush to get ready for their morning watch, there was no time for Iris to demand an explanation for Mary's behaviour. As it was, there was no time for a full breakfast; all they could do was grab a few slices of toast and butter from the galley to eat on the walk.

'Good thing butter doesn't seem to be in short supply,' Mary said, licking her fingers. By this time, they were marching down the lane by the light of their dim torches. 'You've got to admit, being in Orkney has some compensations. If you were in Portsmouth, you'd be lucky to get a smear of margarine on your toast.'

'If I was in Portsmouth, I would have had a full breakfast. I wouldn't have overslept, thanks to hauling you in through a window in the early hours.'

'Look, I'm sorry about that.'

'I don't want your apologies. I want to know why. It's a bit rich, lecturing me on letting down the other Wrens when you go and pull a stunt like that. Thanks to you, I've missed my only chance of a cooked meal today.' Iris swallowed the last of her toast and licked the salty butter from her fingers. She would never admit it to Mary, but she did enjoy the little luxuries that were available on the island. However, a couple of slices of toast and butter couldn't hope to make up for the bacon and eggs she had longed for, and they certainly weren't going to help her walk to the signal station and get her through the long hours of their watch. It was this irritation at missing a meal that made her press Mary for an explanation.

She heard Mary blow out a long breath. 'You wouldn't understand.'

'Try me.'

Another sigh followed by a silence so long that Iris thought Mary would refuse to explain. Then Mary spoke in more hesitant tones than Iris was used to hearing from her. 'I suppose I owe you an explanation.' After another pause she said, 'I told you my fiancé was killed.'

'Yes.' Iris was confused how this could have anything to do with Mary failing to return to the Wrennery on time. However, at least this time she could offer her condolences. 'I am sorry you had to go through that.'

There was another long pause, this time because they had reached the gateway to the track. There was no speaking while they struggled to lift the gate post without cutting themselves on the barbed wire wrapped around it. It was only when they had closed it behind them and were trudging up the track that Mary continued. She spoke in a voice so quiet it was hard to hear above the blustery wind. 'He went down with the *Royal Oak*.'

'He... oh.' She suddenly remembered Mary's odd reaction when they had heard that Rob had survived the sinking of the *Royal Oak*. 'How awful. I'm sorry.'

'I've never been able to get it out of my head.' Now Mary had begun, her words poured out. 'No one was able to give us any details; just that he went down with the ship. It's haunted me. Was it quick? Was he in pain? Was he frightened?'

Mary's voice hitched at that point. She had been walking ahead of Iris and now she stopped, causing Iris to stumble. In the dim half-light, Iris could make out her form, hunched as though wiping tears from her face.

Iris hesitated a moment then put her arm around Mary's shoulders, expecting a rebuff at any moment. Mary was shaking, much to Iris's surprise. Mary had always appeared so self-possessed. She was the last person Iris would have expected to be overcome by emotion. It just went to show that you never really knew what was going on in someone else's head.

Mary sniffed and straightened up. 'I'm sorry. I didn't mean to get all emotional on you.'

'That's nothing to apologise for. It's completely understandable.' Although, truth to tell, Iris was at a loss. Her upbringing hadn't prepared her for dealing with people who were grieving.

Mary continued up the track. 'Anyway, that's why I was late back last night. When your Rob—'

'He's not *my* anything.'

'Fine. When I found out Rob was on the *Royal Oak*, I knew I had to ask him if he'd known Owen.' Mary sniffed. 'Ask if he knew anything about Owen's last moments.'

'And did he?'

'I don't know. He clammed up when I asked. I thought maybe he didn't want to say anything in front of his friends, so I waited until the party ended and then tried to catch him alone, but he said he didn't know anything, and I should let it go.'

'Well, it was a big ship. They might not even have known each other and they could have been on opposite sides of the ship when it was hit. I expect it was…' Iris tailed off. She'd been about to say how chaotic and frightening the experience must have been for Rob, so it wasn't reasonable to expect him to remember much detail. On reflection, it probably wasn't kind to remind Mary of how terrifying it must be to find yourself on a sinking ship.

There was silence for a while, broken only by the wail of a gull swooping high overhead. At times Mary would draw breath as though about to speak, only to break off and stare into the distance.

It was only when the signal station came into view that Mary broke the silence. 'I'm sorry I've been such a cow.' Her words came out in a rush. 'When we first met it felt so unfair that you'd had everything handed to you on a plate while I've had to fight for everything.'

'I didn't exactly make it easy for you.'

'At least you tried being friendly, even if…'

'Even if I kept annoying everyone by blurting out the first thing that sprang to mind,' Iris finished for her. 'Trust me, I know. It didn't make me all that popular at school.'

'I don't know,' Mary said, the beginnings of a grin forming, 'I think it's one of your more endearing qualities. Makes you more human.'

Iris stared at her in astonishment. No one had ever told her she had endearing qualities.

Before she could think of a suitable reply, Mary stumbled on. 'I… well, I could see that you were making an effort and I should have been more friendly in return. I suppose teasing you had become a habit.'

Two burning red spots glowed on Mary's cheeks, and Iris knew she had to meet Mary halfway or lose what could be their only chance to make friends. 'I appreciate that. I accept your apology.' She winced inwardly – that sounded far too stiff and formal. She tried again. 'You never said anything that wasn't true, you know. I'm beginning to realise that I'm a terrible snob. If you can forgive me for that, then I hope we can be friends.'

Mary beamed; for the first time, Iris noticed that even Mary's eyes smiled, creasing into sparkling crescents. 'I'd like that.'

Iris's heart swelled. Friends. She longed for true friends for so long, and now she'd found two. Not that her mother would approve. She huffed a laugh as she imagined introducing them.

Mary shot her a glance. 'What's so funny?'

'Oh, I was just remembering how my mother insisted on me joining the Wrens because I would meet the right sort of friends. She was right, but not in the way she imagined.'

And now their earlier awkwardness turned to laughter, and they walked the rest of the way arm in arm.

Chapter Nine

'You'll never guess what.' Sally flew into the cabin where Mary stood on a chair while Iris placed pins into the hem and waist of her bell-bottoms. Iris had offered to alter Mary's clothes as she had done for herself and Sally, and this time Mary had accepted. In the three weeks since Iris had covered for Mary and then Mary had made her confession, a friendship had blossomed between them. They had passed a happy, if busy, Christmas, and although the days were getting colder now they were in the depths of a miserable January, the atmosphere in their cabin glowed with a convivial warmth. On the rare occasions their time off fell during daylight hours, she and Mary explored the lanes around Stromness or walked out to the cliffs and breathed in the clean, salty air. In the evenings they would sit in the common room and join in the chatter with the other off-duty Wrens, or sometimes they would go to the NAAFI to meet the other servicemen and women in the area.

Iris glanced up at Sally and tried to answer, but it came out as a mumble around the row of pins she was holding between her lips.

Mary laughed. 'I think what Iris was trying to say was,' she put on an exaggerated BBC-English accent, 'do tell us your news, if you don't mind awfully.'

Iris joined in with the laughter, taking the pins out of her mouth. While Mary still teased her about being posh, Iris didn't mind now it came from friendship. 'I'd be careful what you say when I'm armed with pins.' Raising her eyebrows at Sally she said, 'Don't keep us in suspense.'

'Another five V/S Wrens have arrived to work at Kyeness. They've adjusted the rota to give us more time off.'

'That's marvellous,' Iris said.

'And,' continued Sally, 'it means we're not always working with the same oppo.' This was short for 'opposite'. So far Mary had been Iris's only oppo; if Sally was right, she would get to work with all the other Wren signallers as well. Ironic that just when she and Mary were getting on so well and had worked out a routine, they would be broken up. She could only hope that she got on with the newcomers as well.

'Is the rota up?'

When Sally nodded, they all trooped down to the common room, to where the various duty lists were pinned on a large noticeboard. Iris scanned it and saw that they would, indeed, get more days off to break up the relentless monotony of the watch pattern they had followed so far.

'Look,' she said. 'The three of us get a day off together every two or three weeks. We should use those days to explore the island.'

'Wonderful idea!' Sally's eyes shone. 'I'd love to see more of Orkney. It's so mysterious, with its tales of Vikings and ancient tombs.'

Mary shrugged. 'Plenty of ancient tombs where I come from, and you don't need a two-day train trip followed by a ride on the ferry to get there.'

'Spoilsport,' said Sally, but she was laughing. Iris and Sally had both grown used to Mary's refusal to see the romance in anything. 'Anyway, since we're now a ferry trip and a two-day train journey from your home, we should make the most of Orkney while we're here.'

'I suppose I wouldn't mind seeing the place,' Mary said. 'I could do with a trip to Kirkwall. I can't get any decent hand cream from the chemist in Stromness.'

'Ooh yes,' Sally said, eyes shining. 'We could eat in a cafe, go to the cinema…'

'That settles it,' said Iris. 'We'll go to Kirkwall on our first day off together.' She was pleased Mary had suggested Kirkwall. It was the largest town of Orkney. If she wanted civilisation, that was the most likely place to find it. 'We can visit the shops and see the sights.'

'And forget about the war for the day,' Mary concluded.

As the days went on, Iris found she was looking forward to their first day out. By this time they had been on the Orkney Mainland for a month, yet had seen no more of it than the area around Stromness. It would be good to see more of the island. She eagerly consulted the *Orkney Herald* to find the bus times; there was a bus leaving Stromness at a quarter past nine in the morning and a return bus at seven thirty in the evening. That gave them a whole day to explore and even have an early dinner.

The days dragged in the lead-up to their day off, which fell on the last day of January. There was something about the darkness of an Orcadian winter that made time slow to a crawl. Even though the days were getting gradually longer, with Britain operating under Daylight Saving Time it still meant the sun didn't rise until about half past nine. It then failed to rise far above the horizon and was usually behind thick clouds. She was beginning to wonder if she would ever see it again.

The day of their trip finally dawned, and as Iris walked with Mary and Sally to the bus stop, she was delighted to see stars sparkling overhead. 'Looks like we might actually get some sunlight today,' she said to the others.

'I hope so,' Sally said. 'I've forgotten what the sun looks like.'

Three other women were already at the bus stop. 'Are you girls in the Wrens?' one of them asked. 'I'm sure I've seen you out and about in uniform.'

The friends, who were bundled in their warmest civvies, nodded.

'It's lovely to see you young things around the town.' The woman, who might have been about fifty, greeted them with a beaming smile. She spoke in the soft, musical accent Iris had come to associate with the Orcadians. She had wispy greyish-blonde hair tied into a bun at the nape of her neck, beneath a battered hat that looked like it had first been worn before the last war. She stood tall and straight and was dressed in thick tweeds. Her face was clearly the face of someone who spent a good deal of time outdoors in all weather: brown and creased with lines.

She looked so cheerful that Iris couldn't help smiling back. 'We've got a day off so we're going to Kirkwall.'

'Aye, well, you've got a fine day for it. You'll see some bonny views.'

Sally nodded enthusiastically. 'We hoped we would. We haven't seen anything other than Stromness and Kyeness so far.'

'Kyeness? Are you the lasses working at the signal station?' When they said they were, the woman continued, 'I see you traipsing out there every day, come wind, come rain.'

'Do you live near there?' Iris asked.

'Aye, my husband and I work a croft just around the headland. I look out for the flag every morning. It lifts my heart to know you lasses are looking out for our lads at sea. You must come and visit. You three look like you could do with feeding up. I'm Elspeth Heddle.'

The girls introduced themselves and said they would love to visit.

'You can't miss us. We're the house with the blue door just around the headland from you.'

The bus arrived twenty minutes late, although they were so busy chatting, Iris hardly noticed. The first shafts of sunlight were slanting over the horizon by this time, more than ample compensation for the wait. Elspeth sat next to Iris and took it upon herself to point out all the notable landmarks they passed once the bus set out. Not far out of Stromness, Iris gasped when the road crossed a narrow neck of land between the sea and a vast loch.

'I've not seen anything like it,' said Iris, marvelling at the contrast between the deep blue water and the vibrant green hills rising up beyond. 'I feel like I've fallen inside a book of fairy tales.' The colours were so vivid they couldn't be real. 'What's the name of the loch?'

'That's the Loch of Stenness. Then across the Ness of Brodgar is another loch – Harray. It's a magical place.'

Iris didn't know if she meant magical literally, but she could believe it. The light was so clear, she could pick out all the details of the gently rounded hills surrounding the lochs and the farmhouses dotted around the banks.

The bus followed the lochs for some way. Sally gave a delighted cry at one point and pointed out a standing stone in a field.

'Aye, that's the Barnhouse Stone,' Elspeth told her. 'And look, see that peedie hill beyond? That's Maeshowe.'

Iris looked out and saw a dome-shaped green mound that looked a little like the round barrows dotted around her native Chiltern Hills, only much bigger.

With the frequent stops the bus made, the trip took nearly an hour. However, Iris didn't begrudge a single minute of the ride, as she gazed out of the window and drank in the scenery. Elspeth made an entertaining companion, telling her stories about all the places they passed.

When the bus finally reached the Bay of Kirkwall on the north side of the island, Iris craned her neck to look at the huddle of buildings that clung to its shores. A tower with a squat spire dominated the skyline; Iris guessed it must be the cathedral. When the bus stopped, Iris got off, eager to explore. The town looked much bigger than Stromness, and she was impatient to see what the shops here had to offer.

They waved goodbye to Elspeth, promising to visit soon. Then, after a brief walk around the harbour, the lure of the shops grew too strong to resist. They soon found a narrow passageway, Bridge Street, that seemed to lead in the right direction. It looked very much like the main street in Stromness with its paved surface and tall grey buildings looming over them on either side. Soon the passageway widened, and the first shops appeared. They had obviously arrived on a popular day, for the streets thronged and echoed with footsteps and the hum of voices. Above all, however, was the constant wailing of the gulls which soared and dived overhead.

Bridge Street led onto Albert Street and the larger shops. 'I wish I had more money to spend,' Sally said with a regretful sigh, looking at a bookshop. 'I could spend all day and all my money in there.'

This made Iris uncomfortable. Not only did she have her pay from the Wrens but also a generous allowance from her father. She hadn't considered before that Mary and Sally would only have their pay which, at the princely sum of one shilling and sixpence a day, wouldn't get them very far.

Then she remembered that Sally had her birthday in February, and it gave her an idea. 'Let's go inside, anyway,' she said. 'I'm getting cold and I love browsing in bookshops.'

The others agreed and they pushed open the door, the little bell above it giving a merry ring as they did so.

Sally took a deep breath and closed her eyes. 'I just love that smell, don't you?'

Mary gave a little shake of the head as though from despair. 'Polish and just a hint of damp, you mean?'

'I mean that new book smell, as well you know.'

Soon Sally was browsing books of Orkney folk tales, and Iris made a note of the book that Sally lingered over the longest, only returning it to its shelf after what seemed to be a great struggle, giving the spine a final stroke before moving away.

After they left the bookshop, Iris was able to execute the second part of her plan within minutes. Walking a little further along Albert Street, they soon found themselves outside St Magnus Cathedral. Built with red and yellow sandstone, it made a colourful contrast with all the grey stone buildings surrounding it. When someone opened the door, Iris glimpsed a forest of vast columns in the gloomy interior, candles providing the only pinpricks of light. Sally and Mary both expressed a desire to look inside, and Iris leapt at the chance.

'I've got a bit more shopping to do,' she said. 'Why don't I meet you in that cafe we passed earlier?'

As soon as Sally and Mary disappeared through the imposing arched doorway, Iris hurried back to the bookshop and picked out the book of folk tales Sally had seemed so enamoured with.

She had just left the shop when a familiar voice hailed her. 'If it isn't Iris Tredwick! I do believe you must be following me.'

Iris turned to see Rob jogging down the street towards her. 'I could say the same about you.' She didn't understand why she couldn't keep the smile from her face. 'I'm here with my friends on our day off. It might surprise you to learn we planned it without considering you at all.'

Rob staggered as though he had been wounded. 'And there was me thinking you considered me at all times. You know how to hurt a man's pride.'

'A rather over-inflated pride if you're hurt that I don't think about you at all after only meeting you twice.'

What was she doing, flirting with a man she had no interest in? Still, she had to admit it was fun. She'd never experienced the same thrill when faced with George's dignified manners, and found herself wishing for more than just a quick chat in passing.

'Ouch! You do know how to wound a man.'

'I'm sorry. I didn't realise a man's pride was so fragile.'

'Well it is. And if you're truly sorry, you can show it by allowing me to treat you to a bite to eat.'

Unlike at the Christmas party, this time Iris's enjoyment of Rob's company overcame her nerves, and she didn't feel the same urge to flee. When he offered his arm, she took it, saying, 'I suppose it would be impolite to say no.'

—

Rob's breath caught in his throat as Iris turned her blazing smile upon him and thanked his lucky stars that today of all days, he had bumped into Iris again. And this time she was alone.

'It would indeed,' he said. 'It's an Orkney tradition that when a man offers to buy a woman a meal, she cannae say nay.'

Iris arched an elegant eyebrow. 'That's funny, because I met a lady on the bus this morning who I could swear regaled me with all the old Orkney traditions and folk tales, and she never once mentioned that.'

'Ah, but this is a new tradition. They all have to start somewhere.'

'Well, I'll go along with it, but we have to go to the Copper Kettle, because that's where I've agreed to meet Mary and Sally.'

A little dismayed that their time together would be limited, he led her to the cafe and they took their seats at a table nearest to an ancient cast iron stove that was giving out blessed heat. Iris took off her coat and held her hands to the stove. 'My fingers have been frozen since December. How do the islanders cope?'

'You'll get used to it in time. And you have to admit, Orkney has its beauties.'

'On a day like today, I can't disagree. The view from the bus was glorious. But when I'm trailing to the signal station in the wind and rain, it doesn't feel quite so wonderful.'

'Orkney has a way of getting under your skin. You wait. You'll go home on leave and find you're missing the place.'

'I can't see that ever happening. Don't you miss the life and bustle of Glasgow?'

'Ah, so you paid enough attention to me before to remember where I come from.' Rob was delighted to see a faint blush colour Iris's cheeks.

'I listen when someone is talking to me. It doesn't mean I start composing love poetry about them.'

Rob briefly considered making up an impromptu poem but couldn't think of any good words that rhymed with either Rob or Iris. 'Anyway, to answer your question, there's plenty of bustle in Orkney. You'll soon get invited onto the ships. Trust me, there will be more than enough activities to fill your time when you're off duty. And I like being able to escape from time to time.' When the memories became too much, for instance. 'I like that we're never too far from a quiet place where you can get away from it all for a while. To be honest, I can't think of a place I'd rather be. When the war is all over, it's my dream to set up my own boatyard here.'

'How lovely.' But Rob could tell from the tone of Iris's voice that she wasn't particularly impressed. He felt a lurch of disappointment. He had never dared to confide his dream to anyone else before; he cursed himself for revealing it to Iris. Of course she wouldn't be impressed. He didn't know anything about her background, but she was clearly a classy girl who was probably used to being with men who could lavish her with expensive gifts. She would not be won by the idea of a simple boatyard in a place she considered to be the end of the world.

The waitress arrived, saving him from making a reply. They ordered tea and flapjacks. Once the waitress had left, Rob did what he could to salvage the conversation. Up to this moment he had been thanking his lucky stars that the job that had brought him to Kirkwall had allowed him to meet the pretty Wren who had caught his eye from the first time he had seen her on the ferry. However, if he was going to impress her, he should show her there was more to him than a man who wanted nothing more in life than to tinker with engines. He needed to show her he could bring a bit of class into her life.

What did his mother like to do?

It was then that a poster in the window caught his eye. It was advertising an organ recital at the cathedral. Now that was something his mother would approve of.

'Don't suppose you're free next Saturday?' he asked.

'I am, actually, why?'

Rob pointed at the poster in the window. 'There's an organ recital at the cathedral. Would you like to go with me?'

Iris looked at the poster. Putting her hand to her mouth she breathed, 'Oh, they're playing a piece by Elgar.'

'You like his music?' Rob tried desperately to think what Elgar had written. His mother loved classical music and always tuned into any concerts on the wireless, all the while bemoaning that his father couldn't take her to concerts.

'I love it.' There was a wistful light in her eyes. '*Enigma Variations* is my father's favourite music. Just thinking about it makes me feel homesick.'

'Then you'll come?'

The waitress chose that moment to return with a pot of tea and the flapjacks. Rob was forced to wait in suspense while she set down their teacups and the milk and sugar. Rob managed to bite back the impulse to tell her to get a move on, but did she really have to place the tea strainer so precisely?

At long last she placed the sugar tongs upon the saucer holding the sugar cubes and went back into the kitchen.

Rob looked at Iris. 'Well?'

Iris cut a corner off her flapjack, and looked at her plate, biting her lip. Finally she smiled and met his gaze with a smile that winded him. 'I'd love to go.'

Chapter Ten

Sally was almost as excited about the date as Iris. 'I knew it had to be fate when he caught you on the ferry,' she said at least ten times a day. She said it again now, a few days after their Kirkwall trip, as they walked around the headland to visit Elspeth Heddle after their morning watch. Mary, who was on her day off, had arranged to meet them there.

Iris shook her head and laughed. 'Don't get your hopes up. I like him, but not in that way. He's a friend, that's all.'

'A friend who makes your eyes sparkle every time you see him.'

Iris opened her mouth to protest, only to break off at the sound of running footsteps behind them. She turned to see Mary approaching, muffled against the ever-present icy wind by a thick scarf wrapped around her face.

'What's this about sparkling eyes, Sally?' she said when she caught them up. They all stopped to allow her to catch her breath. 'Don't tell me you're talking about Iris's young man.'

'He's not my young man. We're going as friends. Because I wanted to hear the Elgar.' She ignored the tiny voice that reminded her Rob had asked her before he'd known of her love of Elgar's music.

'I didn't notice him asking us,' Mary said.

'I'm sure he would have done if there had been time, but he had to get back to his ship.' For shortly after Mary and Sally had arrived at the cafe, Rob had said he needed to leave and paid the bill, generously paying for Mary and Sally's order as well, despite their protests. Not something George would have done, despite his considerable wealth.

'Funny how he was suddenly in a hurry to leave once he couldn't have you to himself,' Mary said.

'It was just a coincidence.' Iris firmly squashed the little thrill she felt at Mary's insistence of Rob's interest in her. To be honest, she had surprised herself at how readily she had agreed to Rob's invitation, considering he wasn't at all her type. Both Mary and Sally were on watch on Saturday, though, so she would have spent the day alone if she hadn't agreed to go with Rob. She would continue to believe that was her true reason for accepting, and nothing to do with the shiver of anticipation she felt whenever she thought of him. 'I promise you, this is nothing more than friendship,' she said, pleased at how reasonable and level-headed she sounded. 'I'm not looking for a boyfriend yet. I still haven't recovered from the embarrassment over George.'

'Probably sensible,' Mary said. 'We've got enough work to do without men getting in the way.'

'Honestly, I don't believe either of you,' Sally said. 'Don't you want romance in your lives?'

'I had it,' Mary said in a flat voice. 'I don't expect to find it again.'

There was a brief silence, and the girls continued their walk. For a while there was no sound but the pounding of the waves at the foot of the cliffs and the wails of the gulls.

Finally Sally said, 'I'm sorry, Mary. I forgot.'

'I wish I could.' Mary marched ahead, her back ramrod straight and rigid.

Sally looked like she wanted to speak, and Iris was sure it was to say something like she was sure there was someone else out there. Iris caught her eye and frowned and was relieved when Sally closed her mouth and gave a little nod.

The Heddles' croft soon came into sight. The house was perched on the edge of the cliff. Iris realised she had caught glimpses of it from the balcony of the signal station; she had always been too busy looking out to sea to pay it much attention before. It was of the same grey stone that so many of the Orkney cottages seemed to be made from. However, the window frames and door were painted in a beautiful shade of teal. A few goats grazed nearby, and a plot of land was fenced off with the same wire fencing that was used all over the island. Iris had soon learned that there were few trees in Orkney, so wood was in short supply and too precious to be used on fencing.

A herd of cattle stood in the farthest corner of the field, and Iris could just make out a man scattering bales of hay around them. Elspeth, her head wrapped in a shawl, was in the yard outside the house, scattering feed to a flock of chickens.

Elspeth glanced up at the sound of their approaching footsteps. 'Welcome! I'm fair blithe to see you. I hoped you'd come today. I've just made a batch of bere bannocks, and they're best eaten warm. Let me finish feeding the hens and I'll be with you.'

Sally stepped forward. 'Let me help. I used to enjoy feeding the hens when we had a farm.' She took the basket from Elspeth and scattered the remaining seeds around the yard. Iris smiled at the way the hens squabbled and fought to be the first to reach the grain.

Once Sally had finished, she handed the empty basket back with a smile.

'You're a kind lass,' Elspeth said. 'Thank you, my dear.'

'It was a pleasure,' Sally said.

'Well, come in out of the cold, all of you.'

The door led straight into the kitchen, which was dominated by a huge range. Iris took a deep breath, smelling a rich, earthy aroma, nothing like a coal or log fire. Strange, black oblongs were stacked on either side of the range, and Iris realised they must be peats.

Looking around, she could almost believe she had been transported into the past. The kitchen was lit not by electric lights but by kerosene lamps, one suspended over the large oak table in the middle of the stone floor, others perched upon shelves. A large cast iron cooking pot stood on the range next to a blackened kettle with steam curling from the spout. There was one window overlooking the sea, a threatening dark grey today, with white horses springing from the waves. A stone sink occupied the space beneath the window. There didn't appear to be any plumbing, so Iris supposed Elspeth had to fetch water from a pump or well. The kitchen shelves mostly held crockery and tins of food. However, in pride of place was a framed photograph of two young men in uniform.

'I expect you must be hungry. I see you girls traipsing across to the signal station at all hours. When do you get time to eat?' As she spoke, Elspeth raised the lid of the pot and gave the contents a stir. A delicious aroma of chicken and sage arose from it, making Iris's stomach rumble.

'It is hard to fit in meals sometimes, although it's getting better now there are more Wrens assigned to Kyeness,' Iris said, pressing her stomach to muffle a sudden gurgle.

'My Archie will be back in a moment – he has an uncanny ability to sense when the food's ready. Then we can eat. Chicken soup and bere bannocks. I made plenty, hoping you'd be along today.'

'Bear bannocks?' Iris knew she must have misheard. An image of a huge brown bear flashed into her mind.

'Bless you, it's the grain we grow in Orkney. Makes a much tastier bread than the rubbery stuff folks eat away south.'

Iris had been in Orkney long enough to know that 'south' covered everything from Dunnet Head on the northern tip of Scotland and southwards. The 'Mainland' always referred to the largest island in the Orkney archipelago.

'Everything smells delicious,' Iris said. Mary and Sally murmured their heartfelt agreement. 'We'd love to eat if you can spare it.' Since the start of food rationing, she had always felt awkward eating someone else's food.

'Lord bless you, dear. We're not short of food. We're so much better off up here than the poor city folks in the south. We have our own ways of trading with neighbouring crofters that bypasses the ration books.'

Just then the door opened, and the man they had seen working in the upper field strode in, bringing a blast of cold air that caused the lamps to flicker. He kicked off his boots and crossed to the sink, eyeing the girls. 'You must be the three Wrens Elspeth was telling me about.' He appeared to be in his mid-fifties or early sixties, with a weathered face and grizzled hair and beard. He was stocky with broad shoulders and powerful limbs. To Iris, he looked like an ageing Viking.

'Aye, that's right.' Elspeth introduced them while her husband scrubbed his hands and arms in the sink.

'Pleasure to meet you.' Mr Heddle dried his hands then flung the towel beside the sink. A moment later he caught Elspeth's eye, picked the towel back up and hung it on a hook beside the sink. 'Always a comfort to know you girls are on the lookout for all vessels out there.' He waved an arm towards the sea. 'I got into difficulties when a storm blew up last year. The signallers saw me and called the coastguard. I might not be here today if they hadn't been on the lookout.'

'Do you fish then, Mr Heddle?' Sally asked.

'Aye, although not as often as I'd like. And call me Archie. No call to stand on ceremony.'

While Elspeth placed a round flat loaf and a dish of butter on the table, he opened a drawer and pulled out knives and soup spoons and started to lay the table. 'I keep a yole down in the geo.' He pointed in the vague direction of the headland. Iris remembered seeing a narrow inlet on one of her walks and guessed this was the geo Archie was referring to. She had seen a large rowing boat pulled up onto the rocks, beside a steep path that climbed up onto the headland. She supposed that had to be Archie's 'yole'. 'I used to take it out with my sons to put out the creels.' He nodded at the photograph Iris had noticed earlier. 'They're both in the navy now, so I must bide ashore until my friend in the next croft can come out with me.'

'I'll know to look out for fishing boats, too, when I'm on watch from now on.' She had only considered the naval boats and ships before, with the fishing boats being an inconvenience that set off alerts along the indicator loop. To learn Archie might have drowned had it not been for an alert visual signaller gave her a fresh perspective.

'It's a comfort, knowing you lot are up on the cliff top. I always like to see the signal light flashing. Lets me know there's someone looking out if I need help.'

'Oh aye.' Elspeth began to dish out bowls brimming with soup. 'When Archie's out in the dark, I like to walk out on the cliff and watch for the signals. It makes me easier in my mind, so it does.' She placed the last bowl on the table. 'Now come and sit down and eat before the soup gets cold.'

The soup was every bit as delicious as its aroma had promised. It seemed to be mostly vegetables with barley, cooked in a flavoursome chicken stock. The bere bannock turned out to have a wonderful nutty flavour. Spread with the butter that Elspeth proudly told them she made herself, it tasted like a feast.

After the meal, which was rounded off with another slice of bannock, spread this time with more butter and carrot marmalade, Iris, Mary and Sally insisted upon clearing up and washing the dishes. Archie put back on his boots and coat. 'I need to get my work finished before more bad weather blows in,' he said. 'There's a storm coming.'

'I didn't think the forecast looked bad,' Iris said in surprise.

'There's a storm on the way, all the same. I can feel it in my teeth.' And without explaining that curious remark he left the cottage.

Elspeth ladled the remainder of the soup into a bowl and then made them all a fresh pot of tea. While they drank, she told them of the other crofters nearby. 'The arrival of so many servicemen and women had turned our island upside-down, as you can imagine,' she said.

'But everyone's grateful you're here. If you ever need help, you'll always find a welcome in the crofts.'

'You've certainly been a wonderful hostess,' Iris told her. 'I can't think when I've had such a delicious meal.'

'It was a pleasure,' Elspeth told her. 'It does my heart good to see so many young people. You're welcome any time.'

–

Despite what she repeatedly said to Sally, Iris found she was looking forward to the organ recital. It was definitely the music she was looking forward to, more than seeing Rob. She had to remind herself of that several times as the days passed.

Still, when Saturday finally arrived, and once she had seen Mary and Sally leave for their morning's watch, Iris found herself taking extra care with her appearance. Rob had warned her it would get cold sitting in the cathedral, so she chose to wear her uniform. She was half-tempted to wear her bell-bottoms, having heard the wind whistling around the attic roof all night. In the end, she opted for the skirt. It felt strange wearing a skirt and stockings again after days of wearing bell-bottoms and a seaman's jersey while on duty. She had washed her hair the day before, and now it was too limp to style into victory rolls. In the end, she braided it on either side of her head and fixed it into a pleat at the back to keep it above the collar. To make up for the less than fashionable hairstyle, she applied a generous quantity of cherry red lipstick. She hesitated over rouge, but examining her face in the mirror, she saw that even the small amount of sunlight she had been exposed to had been enough to bring her out in freckles. Now a broad stripe of freckles dotted her cheeks and the bridge of her nose. She knew from bitter experience that no amount of rouge or face powder would cover them, and she knew exactly what her mother would say: 'They make you look so common, darling.' Still, she comforted herself with the thought that she would have got even more freckled in Portsmouth.

They had arranged to meet at the bus stop to catch the eleven o'clock bus for Kirkwall. As soon as the bus stop came into sight as she walked down the lane, she saw Rob's tall figure among the group waiting for the bus. At that moment he turned his head and saw her. He smiled, and it was as though a break in the clouds allowed the sunshine to fall on just him. She couldn't help it. She felt her own lips curve in an answering smile, and her footsteps quickened. That was why she felt quite out of breath when she reached him, of course. Her raised heartbeat was nothing to do with Rob.

'You came,' Rob said.

'Yes,' Iris replied. She felt suddenly awkward, which was strange seeing as she had felt so comfortable in his company when they had met in Kirkwall. It was Sally's insistence that they were destined to be together. It meant Iris didn't know how to behave around him. When she had gone out with George she had kissed him on the cheek when they met at the start of a date. But of course, she had been all wrong about George, and maybe she was mistaken about Rob's intentions, too. She'd better not assume it was a date. Rob had probably meant them to go out as friends, and it would be awful if she presumed too much. In the end, she gave an awkward wave, aware that everyone in the queue was now watching them.

'I thought we'd get a bite to eat first,' Rob said, not sounding at all like his usual confident self. 'Does that sound good to you?'

'Sounds lovely. Where?'

Rob scratched his cheek. 'Erm...'

'You can't go wrong with the Kirkwall Hotel,' a lady standing two places ahead of them in the queue said. She wore a green felt hat with a pheasant's feather in the brim. 'Not too fancy and they always serve good, warming food. What do you think, Meg?'

'Aye, the Kirkwall Hotel. My Fergus took me there when we first started walking out. Forty years we've been married now.'

'Thank you, ladies.' Rob gave a bow of the head in their direction. 'The Kirkwall Hotel it is.'

'Ooh, such a charmer!' The woman in the green hat leaned towards Iris and patted her arm. 'You hang on to this one. He reminds me of my John, and he's the best man that ever lived.'

Iris's cheeks burned. She was saved from answering by the bus, which rolled up. Iris and Rob stood back to let the others board first, and Iris met Rob's eye. They both burst out laughing at the same time, and that broke the awkwardness between them.

'Shall we?' Rob offered his arm and escorted her on board the bus as though he were accompanying her into a ballroom.

Chapter Eleven

The weather was nowhere near as good as on Iris's last bus ride. A low cloud hung over the islands, veiling the hills of Hoy across the bay and draining the land of much of its colour. A fine rain hung in the air, making visibility poor. Iris didn't mind the lack of scenery, however, as the company on the bus was so entertaining. Instead of everyone carrying on with their own conversations, they all seemed fascinated with Rob and Iris's plans for the day. It turned out that many of them already knew Rob, for in his spare time, he would help the local fishermen with any repairs they needed on their boats.

'Wait. You spend your days keeping the engines running on your ship, and then instead of resting when off duty, you find more boats to work on?' Iris stared at Rob in disbelief.

Rob shrugged. 'I love it. I find it relaxing.' He snorted. 'Well, maybe not relaxing when some jumped-up lieutenant is telling me to get something fixed yesterday. But that's why I like helping on the fishing boats. Besides, the Orcadians have a lot to put up with, now the navy, army and air force are swarming all over the islands. It's good to give something back. Thank them for providing us with real eggs instead of the disgusting powdered stuff everyone has to put up with away south.'

One of the women nodded. 'That's how it works on the islands,' she said. 'We all look out for each other and lend a hand where we can.'

Iris nodded, remembering Elspeth had said something similar. Rob, it seemed, had taken to the way of life in Orkney in a way she couldn't imagine doing herself. She was too used to having staff who did all the menial jobs for her. While she was forced to do things like keeping her cabin clean and tidy, she couldn't wait for the war to be over so she could go back to the way things had always been.

She found herself gazing at the hand he rested lightly on the seat in front. She had always admired George's hands, which were long-fingered and elegant. A gentleman's hands, she had always thought. Rob's hands were nothing like that. They were broad and strong, with square-tipped fingers. His nails were clipped short and although he clearly cleaned his hands thoroughly, there was a hint of ingrained oil around the nails. They were the hands of a man who worked for a living. She shivered a little, imagining her own small hands enclosed in their grip.

When they arrived in Kirkwall, the other passengers bid farewell to Iris and Rob with many well wishes for their date. Iris took Rob's arm feeling highly self-conscious, not to mention flustered at the interest total strangers were taking in their relationship, and said very little on the walk to the Kirkwall Hotel. The hotel turned out to be an imposing Victorian building overlooking the harbour. Iris sighed with pleasure as they walked into the warm dining room and were met with an appetising aroma of roast meats and rich sauces. This was promising to be a much more enjoyable date than she'd expected possible in Orkney.

As they studied the menu, Rob picked up the conversation they'd had in the cafe, as though there hadn't been a week's gap. 'Anyway, I've told you all about my dreams of running a boatyard after the war. What about you? What do you see yourself doing?'

Iris was taken aback by the question. 'I don't know. I mean, I was brought up to expect to marry and run a household.'

Rob raised his eyebrows. 'What do *you* want?'

What kind of question was that? Of course she wanted to marry. The only reason she was in the Wrens was because George had callously broken off the engagement. She should be mistress of her own house by now instead of sharing a cold attic room with two other girls in the back of beyond. She was sure she would meet another suitable man soon. At least in Orkney, there were many more men than there were women. She couldn't say that to Rob, though.

She studied her menu. 'I think I want the fish pie.'

Rob grinned. 'Very well, keep your secrets.'

Iris frowned. 'What's wrong with wanting to get married?'

'Nothing, if that's what you really want.'

'Do you want to marry?'

Rob glanced up at the approaching waitress at that point and gave their orders. When the waitress had gone, he leaned back in his chair and regarded her with a glint in his eyes that made Iris's stomach perform a little swoop. 'I want it all,' he said. 'I'd like my own boatyard and a house with a spot of land, and I'd like a bonny wife and bairns to come home to.' Then he grinned. 'Although maybe

I should concentrate on building up my business first so I can get a larger house and pay for servants. Apparently that's what fine women expect these days.'

Iris felt her face heat. 'It would have to be a very big house if you want to persuade a woman from the mainland to come to Orkney.'

'Then I'll just have to work all the harder. Oh, and I'd like a dog, of course. No family is complete without one.'

'Oh, a dog would be a must,' Iris said. 'I always wanted a dog, but my mother wouldn't allow one in the house.' Then she realised she had sounded like she expected to be with Rob and get a dog with him. Feeling her face burn all the hotter, she said, 'I didn't mean...' She tailed off, not knowing what to say without making it worse.

Rob laughed and waved his hand in a gesture of dismissal. 'What kind of dog would you like?'

And as Iris launched into the relative merits of Labradors and red setters, she forgot her embarrassment and only knew how much she enjoyed Rob's company. Of course she and Rob weren't suited for each other – they wanted completely different things out of life. But he was fun to be with and had earned the liking and respect of the Orcadians. That wasn't something to dismiss lightly. She and Rob might not be fated to be lovers, as Sally insisted, but there was no reason why they couldn't be friends.

Rob couldn't remember the last time he had enjoyed conversation with a woman so much. Once he had decided not to press her further on her views of marriage, at least. Seeing her face shine when she spoke of her ideal pet dog, and the simple pleasures of walking in her native Chiltern Hills, allowed him to see beneath the polished veneer of rich society girl turned Wren, through to the real woman. He wondered what had happened to her that made her so adamant she needed to make a so-called good marriage. He didn't think it was just because she had been brought up to expect to marry a wealthy man, although he was sure that was a factor. Sometimes he had glimpsed an almost fearful expression when she had spoken of the need to marry well.

The meal passed quickly, in laughter and happy reminiscence; soon it was time to go to the cathedral for the recital. Rob paid for lunch, waving away Iris's protests that she should pay her share. He was glad she had offered, though. It showed that she wasn't so spoiled that she expected everything to be provided for her. He remembered the books she had bought for her friend. Yes, there was a generous soul lurking beneath the surface, someone who valued her friends.

'Gosh, it's cold,' Iris said, pulling up the collar of her coat as they stepped out of the hotel. 'Don't you ever wish you'd been posted somewhere warmer?'

Rob offered her his arm. 'Like everything in life, it's a trade-off,' he said.

Iris placed her gloved hand in the crook of his elbow, and he felt a quiver of pleasure at the feel of her fingers pressing his arm, even through the many layers he was wearing. 'True, Orkney will never get as warm as the weather you have down south. However, on a sunny day, when the curlews are singing, and the colours of sea, land and sky are brighter than a stained glass window, you'll be glad you're here. Who knows, one day you might decide you cannae leave?'

Once they were settled in their seats in the dim interior of the cathedral, Rob let his attention drift from the melodic chords of the organ. If he was honest with himself, he would never have chosen to come to an organ recital. Anything to do with classical music was a reminder of being forced to go to concerts with his mother in freezing churches or crowded town halls, kicking his heels against his chair in boredom whilst his mother listened in rapt attention. Although those memories weren't as painful as the arguments that ran up to these concerts, when his mother would rail at his father, telling him if he would only make more of an effort, he could make something of himself. She had never understood that his father was perfectly happy as he was.

Iris was the kind of woman who would appreciate being taken to recitals, though. Was he mad to pursue her? Was he making the same mistake as his father, who had been bowled over by a pretty face and blinded to the differences between himself and Rob's mother? Rob's maternal grandparents had fallen on hard times and although his mother, Eileen, had been poor, she had never forgotten that she had been brought up to expect the finer things in life. She had never forgiven her husband for not wanting to better himself.

Rob shook his head impatiently. He liked Iris, enjoyed her company. That was all there was to it. It was far too soon to start thinking long-term. For all he knew, she could be posted away from Orkney within a few weeks. In the meantime, he would enjoy her friendship.

The music faded into silence, and the audience clapped. Startled from his musings, Rob joined in.

Iris leaned closer, giving Rob an enticing scent of roses. 'That was lovely, wasn't it? Thanks for inviting me.' Then more notes started in a minor key, and her eyes widened. 'Oh, this is the Elgar.' She leaned forward in her seat, her attitude one of keen attention.

Somehow, the knowledge that this was a special piece to Iris made Rob want to listen too. His mother's liking for classical music had always been a source of discontent between her and his father, so Rob had been determined not to like it. However, now he allowed himself to truly listen, he found the music beautiful. Beautiful but stirring a deep melancholy within. The slow, sad melody sounded like a farewell. He found himself thinking of the waters just off the beach at Scapa where the *Royal Oak* now lay submerged, the graveyard for many of the friends he had served with.

His throat ached, and he gripped the back of the chair in front, willing himself not to cry. Drawing several deep, shaky breaths, he glanced at Iris. She was still leaning forward, her eyes glistening with tears. She seemed to appreciate music in a different way from his mother. Eileen had always been aware of how she appeared, and had listened with a rapt smile as though showing the world how much she loved a particular piece. Iris seemed unaware of how she looked, and gazed into the distance. Rob decided she was lost in her imagination, roaming her beloved woods and hills.

When the last notes of the 'Adagio' drew to a close, Iris blinked as though surprised to find herself in the stone interior of the cathedral, surrounded by broad sandstone columns instead of the pastoral landscape of her home. There was a brief silence while the last chord seemed to hang in the air. Then the audience burst into applause. Rob clapped out of relief that he had managed to get through it without shedding tears.

Iris turned to look at Rob and gave him a smile that pierced his heart. 'That was beautiful.' She pulled a handkerchief from her pocket and dabbed her eyes. 'It made me so homesick, though.'

'It was beautiful,' Rob agreed, surprising himself. He would never have believed he could have ever appreciated classical music. He had Iris to thank for opening his eyes – or possibly his ears – to it.

He found much to enjoy in the remaining pieces, although nothing that tore at his heart in the way the Elgar had.

'Thank you so much for bringing me,' Iris said again when they left the cathedral and walked out into the dusk onto Broad Street. She tucked her arm into his, and Rob couldn't help thinking how right it felt to have her beside him.

'Thank *you*,' he said. 'I would never have got to hear it if it hadn't been for you. The Elgar was wonderful.'

'It was, wasn't it?' she replied. 'You should hear his cello concerto.' She spoke with such enthusiasm that Rob decided there and then that if he ever got the chance to hear it, he would go. Preferably taking Iris with him.

But what about a smoky pub, listening to an old man play the fiddle? Rob enjoyed that, too. Would Iris like it? His mother had always turned up her nose at such entertainment, and he was sure Iris came from a far wealthier family than his mother's had ever been.

He would take it slow, stick to being friends. If Iris ever gave any sign of wanting to improve him, he would take it as a warning sign.

Iris didn't get a chance to catch up with either of her friends until the next day. She was on watch in the morning but had arranged to go to the Heddles' for Sunday lunch straight afterwards. Mary and Sally met her outside the signal station.

'Tell me all about your date,' Sally said. 'Going to a concert together sounds so romantic.'

'For the millionth time, Sally, it wasn't a date.' Iris paused, feeling a small smile tug at her lips as she thought back over the day. 'It was fun, though. He's so easy to talk to. With George I always used to talk about flying or his house. Quite boring, really.' Her mother had always told her she should take an interest in a man and let him know he was the most important thing in her life. Her own concerns, Letitia had always stressed, took second place. It had seemed to work with George, who had been only too willing to tell her about managing the estate, and the pros and cons of keeping Hereford cattle compared to other breeds. At least, it had worked until Felicity had come along.

'I missed you at the kirk today,' was Elspeth's greeting when they arrived at the little croft.

'I was on watch,' Iris said. The visual signallers were excused church parade owing to their irregular hours, although she attended church when she could. It was engrained into her psyche that being seen at church was expected of her. But she had to admit, the lure of sleep had proved too powerful on several of the Sundays she had been free to attend. Then she thought of Rob, and how he had been accepted into the community because he made an effort to involve himself in local concerns. 'I will try to come more often, though.'

'Us too,' said Mary with a glance at Sally, who nodded. 'We'd just come off night duty this morning, so we were too tired.'

'Bless you, I know how hard you all work. I see the lights flashing up at the signal station at all hours. It will be good to see you when you can make it, though.' She ushered them inside. 'Come in out of the cold. We've got another visitor for lunch.'

They trooped inside and shed their outer gear. Mr Heddle was at the table, speaking to a young man who appeared to be in his late twenties or early thirties. After getting used to seeing every young man she knew in uniform, Iris was surprised to see he was dressed in a smart but serviceable tweed suit. He had close-cropped dark brown hair and handsome, chiselled features. He carried an indefinable air of refinement that immediately grabbed Iris's attention.

'This is Dr Irvine,' Elspeth said. 'He kindly came out to look at Archie's ankle. He twisted it walking up from Kye Geo yesterday evening.'

'No lasting damage, I'm happy to say,' Dr Irvine said, his eyes crinkling as he smiled. 'It's good of you to invite me to lunch, there really was no need.' He spoke with only the faintest trace of a Scottish accent.

'There now, Dr Irvine, we couldn't let you go home to your empty lodgings. Not on a Sunday.'

'Well, it's much appreciated. And it does give me the opportunity to meet these lovely ladies.' He turned his twinkling smile onto the girls. Iris was sure his gaze lingered on her the longest, and felt a flutter of pleasure. A doctor, and by the sounds of it, one who lived alone! Now this was far more the kind of man her mother would approve of.

Elspeth introduced them, and when they sat down, Iris was pleased to find herself placed beside the doctor. Mary entered into a spirited conversation with Archie about his fishing boat, and Sally asked Elspeth what she fed her chickens on. Feeling unable to contribute to either discussion, she turned to Dr Irvine. 'Do you come from Orkney, Dr Irvine?'

'Do call me Stewart. No, I'm from Edinburgh.'

'How long have you been here?'

'Only a year. I wanted to join the army when I qualified, but didn't pass the medical – heart trouble.'

'I'm sorry to hear that.'

Stewart accepted her condolences with a nod of the head. 'Nothing too bad, but it prevents me from joining up. My doctor recommended I move somewhere quiet with plenty of fresh air. When I heard they needed a doctor in Stromness, I jumped at the chance.'

'There's certainly no shortage of fresh air.'

They both laughed.

'Don't you miss Edinburgh? I've never been there, but I've heard it's lovely.'

'I must admit, I find it all very wild here. And I miss the entertainments you can find in Edinburgh.'

'I know how you feel.' Iris gave a sigh. 'I mean, I lived in the country, but I could easily get to Oxford or London for the theatre or a concert.'

For some reason, she felt slightly disloyal as she spoke. After all, hadn't she had a lovely afternoon listening to Elgar only yesterday? But that had been a rarity. Her calendar had been packed when she had lived at home. She eased her conscience by adding, 'Of course, I'm on duty most of the time. I'm here to work, not go to society events. I'm sure it must be the same for you.'

'Naturally. There aren't many doctors on the island, so I'm kept busy, even though the population is small.' After a short pause, Stewart added, 'So are you the girls who work at Kyeness?' He jerked his head in the direction of the signal station. When Iris nodded he said, 'Don't you feel very isolated out there?'

'I did at first, but it's not too bad. We work in pairs, so we're never there alone, and HQ is only a phone call away.'

'I'm glad you don't feel alone out there.' And Stewart gave her such an intense look that Iris felt a flutter of pleasure.

She was saved from answering by Elspeth, who placed a cookpot on the table, from which a tempting aroma drifted. She started to dole out liberal quantities of a vegetable and barley stew while Archie cut triangles of bannock for everyone and handed around the butter dish. After saying Grace, they tucked in.

'This is wonderful, Elspeth,' said Sally. 'It certainly beats the fare we get served in the Wrennery, although they do their best. I wish there was something we could do for you in return.'

Elspeth beamed. 'Just having your company is return enough. It's wonderful to have young folk sitting around our table again, isn't it, Archie?'

'Aye, that it is. With most of our youngsters serving with the forces, it's a pleasure to have you here.'

But Iris was struck with an idea. She had been unable to forget Rob's insistence that the way to become involved in island life was to join in with whatever jobs needed doing. 'But isn't there something we can do to help? I was reminded the other day that living on an island means lending a hand wherever you can.'

Elspeth looked pleased. 'I see you've been talking to Rob Sinclair. He's a good lad.'

Iris felt a hot blush rise up her face. Honestly, what was it about any mention of Rob's name that set her off like that? It must be Sally's continued comments about fate and destiny. 'He might have said something. But my offer holds.'

Elspeth frowned as she spread butter onto her bannock. 'Can you knit? There's a drive in Stromness at the moment to knit socks for sailors.'

'Yes, I can knit. I'm not very fast, but I'll do what I can.' She was pleased to see Sally and Mary nod in agreement. She remembered reading about the knitting drive in the *Orkney Herald*. It had struck her that in many ways, life wasn't so different whether you lived in Buckinghamshire or Orkney. The women at home had busied themselves with the war effort, picking fruit and bottling it so none went to waste, knitting socks, packing parcels for prisoners of war and collecting paper. It seemed the same activities went on in Orkney. Possibly with the exception of picking fruit from the hedgerows; from what she had seen, woods and hedgerows were non-existent on the island. 'Is there a shop in Stromness where I can buy yarn?'

'Aye.' Elspeth told them where to find it. 'Be sure and say it's for sailors' socks. The yarn for that doesn't require coupons.' Elspeth put down her knife and beamed at the girls. 'It's good of you to help when you're so busy already.'

'It's no trouble. It'll be something to keep me from nodding off on night watch.' Despite early attempts to divide the watch with their oppos, none of the girls found they were able to get much sleep on their hours off. The bunks were hard and the signal station was icy cold. To add to the discomforts, the never-ending wind moaned and swooped through every gap with a shrill cry that set the nerves of even the bravest Wren on edge. Many of the girls, Iris included, now used the quiet hours of the night for getting on with tasks they had not had time to do before. Now the rail guarding the stove was often hung with laundry, which the girls did in the sink in the tiny galley, and Iris would often carry bags of laundry and mending with her on the walk to the signal station.

As they discussed patterns and estimated how many pairs of socks they would be able to knit in a month, Iris marvelled once again at the welcome that had been extended to them. At home, incomers tended to be regarded with suspicion, and she had expected to be treated with a similar, if not deeper, suspicion by the islanders. Instead, they had been welcomed with open arms, invited into Elspeth and Archie's home and given hospitality that put the far wealthier inhabitants of her home county to shame.

After a while, Mary glanced at her watch and gave a gasp. 'Buck up, Sally. We're on watch in fifteen minutes.'

Everyone hurried to pull on coats and scarves, Iris doing likewise, deciding to return to the Wrennery to catch up on some sleep.

'Are you walking back to Stromness on your own?'

Iris paused in the act of winding her scarf around her neck to glance at Stewart. 'Yes. Well, I'll go as far as the signal station with Mary and Sally then pick up the Stromness path from there.'

'Then permit me to walk with you. I can't let a young lady walk all that way alone.'

Iris bit back her answer that she walked the path as many as four times a day, often in the dark. She couldn't deny the flutter of pleasure she felt that the handsome doctor had singled her out. She gave him a gracious smile. 'I'd like that. Thank you.' She wasn't being disloyal to Rob – they were just friends, after all.

Chapter Twelve

After thanking Elspeth and Archie and bidding them farewell, the visitors headed out into the cold. The clouds had lowered since they had been in the croft. When Iris looked towards the hills of Hoy – the landmark she always used to get her bearings since she could see them from just about anywhere on Mainland – she saw their tops were shrouded in grey cloud. Looking west, out to sea, a grey curtain obscured the view, allowing visibility for no more than a mile or two.

'Looks like more rain's on the way,' she said as she followed Mary and Sally along the rocky path around the headland, head lowered against the wind.

'It's days like this I wonder why I didn't look for a job in a milder climate,' Stewart said, keeping pace with her.

'I was thinking that,' she said. 'I didn't have any choice about coming to Orkney, but you could have chosen anywhere.'

'Where would you recommend, then, if you had to live by the coast?'

Iris thought back to her childhood holidays. 'Cornwall. It never gets too cold there. I can't imagine why you would want to come to somewhere as bleak as Orkney.'

'Maybe I'll look into Cornwall after the war.' Stewart pulled up his collar with a grimace. 'It doesn't seem right to leave Orkney when they need me here, but once the war's over there should be plenty of doctors returning to civilian life.'

'So you don't see yourself staying?' Iris thought of Rob, who had fitted into island life so easily and didn't seem to want to leave. He had predicted that Iris would feel the same way, given time. Well, here was Stewart who had been here a year and didn't seem to be in love with the place.

Stewart gave a shiver and pulled his coat closer around him. 'I can't wait to leave.'

'Maybe now the Americans are in the war, it will end quickly.'

'Let's hope.'

They shared a grin, united in their desire to get off this wind-swept island.

Then Stewart glanced sharply ahead. 'Ah, so this is the signal station.'

Iris was startled to see they were already at Kyeness. There was the squat, concrete signal station, its stark outline even bleaker than the rocky headland. Mary and Sally said their goodbyes and hastened to relieve the Wrens on watch.

Stewart, despite his earlier insistence that he was freezing, didn't seem to be in a hurry to leave. Instead, he said, 'Let's look at the view from the cliffs. I've always thought you must get a fine view out to sea from here.'

Iris agreed, although she doubted they would see anything in this weather. She was aware that the two Wrens currently on watch would be about to leave and return to the Wrennery. Now she had this handsome and very eligible doctor all to herself, she didn't want to share him. 'Look,' she said, leading Stewart to a point that would be hidden from anyone leaving by the bulk of the signal station between them. 'You can see Curlew Croft from here.'

'So you can.' Stewart, bless him, seemed delighted with this information. Iris smiled to herself, knowing he couldn't really be that bothered about being able to see the Heddles' house from here. It must be her company he was enjoying. As she gazed at the croft she said, 'It's a shame you can't see so far today. You usually get wonderful views across Scapa Flow on one side of the headland and across the Atlantic on the other. On clear days I swear you can see all the way to Canada.'

'Shame you don't get many clear days, then.'

Iris laughed. Oddly, even though Stewart was only saying what she thought, she felt a little disloyal. Maybe Rob's love of the place was starting to rub off on her. She had to admit, even on a day like today, when storms threatened, there was a grandeur to the view. She had become used to seeing the towering, rounded hills of Hoy, and realised it was a sight she automatically looked for. For a brief moment, a ray of sun slanted from behind the clouds, lighting up the hills with a golden glow. It was over in an instant, and she looked at Stewart to see if he had noticed. He was looking that way, but didn't appear impressed. Iris had the fleeting thought that she wished she had been with Rob. He would have loved the sight, and she would have enjoyed sharing the moment with him.

'You certainly get a good view across Hoy Sound from here.'

'It wouldn't be a good location for a signal station if you didn't,' Iris said.

'I suppose not.' Stewart shivered. 'Let's get back before the storm hits.'

Confident that the other Wrens would be well ahead of them by now, Iris agreed and they followed the track to Stromness. 'Didn't you come by car?' she asked. She didn't know why it hadn't occurred to her before. Surely, as a doctor covering a wide area, Stewart couldn't manage without a car?

'My practice is in Stromness, and it's almost as quick to walk to the Heddles' as it is to take the road around. Besides, the roads are so rough, I didn't want to damage the car.'

Iris shook her head. 'If I had the option to drive out here instead of walk, I'd choose driving any day.'

'Walking has its advantages. I wouldn't have been able to walk you back if I'd come by car.'

Iris felt a spark of joy. 'You could have driven me back.'

'True. But then I wouldn't have had the pleasure of your company for so long.'

Iris was too flustered by Stewart's obvious interest to point out that he had previously explained his decision to walk by saying driving took about the same time. She put her hand on his arm, her feet seeming to float some way above the rocky track. For once, the walk seemed to take no time at all; they were so wrapped up in a conversation about music and theatre that she hardly knew they were walking. By the time they parted at the driveway to the Wrennery, she had agreed to meet him for dinner on her next day off.

–

'What about Rob?'

Iris was surprised at Sally's expression of dismay when she told the girls about Stewart. It was the following day, as this was the first time their watches allowed the three a few hours together. It also happened to be Sally's birthday, so they were on their way to celebrate with tea and buns at the Beehive Cafe in Stromness once they had purchased knitting yarn for the sailors' socks.

'What about him?' Iris said. 'This has nothing to do with Rob.'

'But you went out with him. What would he say if he discovered you were going out with another man?'

'I only went out with Rob as friends.'

Mary snorted. 'If you're just friends, why do you always blush whenever someone mentions his name?'

Iris put her hands to her face. 'I don't.' They happened to be walking down Victoria Street in Stromness, and Iris looked into a grocery shop window to try to see if her face looked flushed. It was impossible to tell from the darkened reflection. 'Do I?'

'You're blushing now.'

'I'm not blushing. The cold always makes my face go red.'

'It must always be cold when you see Rob, then.'

Iris glared at Mary. Their friendship hadn't saved her from being the subject of Mary's blunt observations. On the contrary, Mary seemed to view it as permission to offer her opinions more freely than ever. 'It's always cold here.'

Mary just smiled.

'Anyway,' Iris said as she pushed open the door of the little drapery, 'as I said, despite Sally's insistence we're destined for one another, Rob and I are just friends. There's no law against being friends with a man, is there?'

'Not at all, dear,' said the lady behind the counter, who had a round face and sparkling brown eyes.

Iris's face burnt all the hotter at the realisation that the woman must have overheard the last part of her conversation. However nice it was to live on an island where everyone seemed to want to befriend you, sometimes Iris wished people wouldn't be quite so free with their opinions.

'You have fun, my dear. In times like these you have to grasp any opportunity for friendship with both hands.'

Feeling like she was on the point of combustion, Iris ignored Mary and Sally's giggles and asked for the yarn and needles they needed to knit socks. Once they had made their purchases, Iris was actually thankful for the cold wind when they carried their bundle outside. It felt blissfully cool against her hot cheeks. 'Come on,' she said, marching in the direction of the Beehive. 'Afternoon tea is on me.'

'Oh, we couldn't. You already got me that beautiful book.' For Sally had been moved to the point of tears when Iris had presented her with the Orkney folk tales. 'And your gloves, of course, Mary.' Mary had given Sally a pair of gloves that she had knitted herself in a soft red wool.

'I insist,' Iris said. 'You can't possibly be allowed to pay for cake on your birthday, and my present didn't take nearly as much effort as Mary's gloves, so this is the least I can do.' She pushed open the door of the cafe, hopeful that she had diverted the conversation away from Rob and Stewart.

She should have known better.

Once they had ordered, Sally turned to Iris, looking thoughtful. 'Are you going to tell Rob about Dr Irvine?'

'There's nothing to tell. If Stewart comes up in conversation, I certainly won't try and hide the fact that I know him.'

'Interesting,' said Sally. 'You're on first name terms with Dr Irvine, then?'

Iris gave an exasperated snarl and swatted Sally on the arm. 'You seem to have got past your idea that I'm destined to be with Rob, so I suppose I shouldn't complain.'

'Oh, I still think that. I don't think Stewart is right for you.'

'Why not? We share the same taste in music, and books. And he's much more the type my mother would approve of.'

'You don't have to judge every man by their suitability in your mother's eyes.'

'You've never met my mother.'

'Forget about your mother. What do *you* think?'

'I like them both. As *friends*.' She knew Sally and Mary would never understand her need to marry well. They didn't come from such an affluent background. Didn't understand how difficult it would be for her to marry beneath her. Most of all, they hadn't had Letitia warning them over and again that they needed to marry well or risk ending up like Aunt Sybil. No. She couldn't do it. Rob might make her heart beat faster but he would never be able to provide all the luxuries in life that she was accustomed to. Sally and Mary could marry for love if they wanted, but Iris was going to marry for security. She couldn't tell them, though. Not when they came from the lower classes she was snubbing. She had only just made friends with Mary and didn't want to earn her contempt.

Sally shook her head and gave Iris a pitying look. 'Very well, deny your feelings. Just take care you don't end up losing one of the best men in the world because you were too proud to admit your feelings.'

Iris grinned. 'I thought we were destined to be together. If that's true, nothing I do will prevent it.'

'I don't believe that.' Mary spoke for the first time in a while, her voice flat. 'If we all have one person we are destined to be with, what does that mean for those of us who have lost loved ones?'

Shock froze Iris to her seat. 'Mary, I'm so sorry.' How could she have forgotten? Here was poor Mary, forced to live only a few miles from the place where her fiancé's ship had been torpedoed. What kind of friend did it make Iris if she couldn't remember the pain Mary must be in?

Mary gave a brittle smile. 'No need to apologise. It wasn't you who attacked the *Royal Oak*.'

'No, but—'

'Forget it.' Mary reached for the teapot. 'I'll be mother. Pass me your cup, Sally.'

They spoke of other things after that, and although Mary joined in with the laughter and gossip, Iris thought she looked strained. When they left to return to the Wrennery, Mary mumbled something about needing to speak to Pardew and marched ahead.

Iris and Sally exchanged glances.

'I feel awful,' Sally said in a low voice. 'And I was only teasing you. You can see whoever you like.'

'I know.'

They didn't catch up with Mary until they got to the Wrennery. She was waiting for them in the common room.

'Sorry for storming off like that.'

'Don't be an idiot. We didn't mind. I'm sorry for being such an unthinking clot.' Iris unpacked the needles and yarn and sat beside Mary.

Sally, too, said how sorry she was as she selected her needles and wool.

But Mary shook her head. 'Really, there's no need. You were just teasing each other. I shouldn't be so sensitive. I'd hate to have you both walking on eggshells around me.'

Iris squeezed Mary's arm in sympathy, and Sally assured her that they wouldn't. They worked in silence for a while, although it was a companionable silence. Iris found her thoughts drifting to George. How would she have reacted if he had been killed?

She would have been sorry to lose out on being lady of Sherbrook Manor. Would she have mourned George, though? She would have been sorry, of course, but she couldn't honestly say she would have suffered the same grief that Mary obviously felt. Looking back, she found she couldn't remember anything that they had discussed, and she didn't even have a clear memory of his face.

Then, over the click of needles and the occasional tut when one of them dropped a stitch, Mary spoke again. 'I didn't realise how much Owen's death has been preying on my mind since I got here.'

'It's hardly surprising,' Sally said. 'Anyone who was here at the time brings the *Royal Oak* up in conversation sooner or later.'

Mary paused while she started a new row then said, 'I was in the post office the other day, and I overheard a couple of women talking about it.'

Iris put down her knitting. 'What did they say?'

Mary had stuck her free needle through the first stitch on the other needle but didn't wind the wool around. She was frowning at the completed stitches as though trying to decipher a code. 'They said there was a rumour that there was a Nazi sympathiser somewhere in the Orkney islands. That they had guided the U-boat through Kirk Sound.'

'Oh, Mary. You can't listen to those rumours. There's a signal station overlooking that part of Scapa Flow. How could anyone have got a signal to the U-boat without them seeing and reporting it?'

Mary shrugged. 'I know. It sounds far-fetched. But everyone thought it was impossible for a U-boat to steer past all the obstructions. How could they have done it without inside knowledge?'

'It's possible. After all, we don't know how many vessels tried and failed. They could have built up a chart over successive attempts.'

'I suppose you're right.'

'I know I am. Anyway, listen. Rob says—'

Suddenly she was pelted with balls of yarn from two directions. Sally was laughing, and even Mary smiled.

'*Rob says*,' Sally repeated and then put her hand to her forehead and pretended to swoon.

'I'll admit you're right,' Mary said, 'if you admit you manage to bring Rob into every conversation.'

'I do not!'

Her protest was met with another volley of wool.

She was only saved when Tilly Leadbetter, Iris's oppo on her next watch, stuck her head around the door. 'Come on, Tredwick, if we don't leave in the next ten minutes we'll be late.'

Iris gathered up her knitting and dashed off to get ready, relieved to escape the teasing.

Chapter Thirteen

As the days and weeks went by, Sally and Mary gradually tired of teasing Iris about her suitors. Iris had her evening out with Stewart. He took her to Kirkwall in his car and treated her to dinner at the Kirkwall Hotel. She refrained from telling him she had already eaten there with Rob. The evening was all that Iris had hoped for from the date. It was lovely to be with a man who had his own car, so they didn't have to rely on the buses. As a doctor, he had an extra fuel allowance and he told Iris that on an island the size of Mainland, he was never in danger of running out. If using his doctor's allowance for personal use didn't disturb his conscience, she wasn't going to let it bother her, and the slight twinge of guilt disappeared when he presented her with a bunch of flowers on collecting her from the Wrennery. It was lovely to be treated like a lady and have him hold open the passenger door when she was getting in and out of the car. In short, he had the class and refinement she longed for in a man. True, she didn't experience the same flutter of pleasure she felt whenever she saw Rob, but that wasn't important. Stewart was a real gentleman and never went out with oil in his fingernails.

After the date, Iris had finally plucked up the courage to write to her mother and confess that her engagement to George was definitely off. To soften the blow, she hinted at a growing relationship with Stewart. Once that letter was posted it was a weight off her mind, although she didn't look forward to the reply.

Now they were approaching the end of March, the days were growing noticeably longer. She had fewer walks to and from Kyeness in the dark. Now she could see the views across Scapa Flow and out into the Atlantic, she started to appreciate the beauty of Orkney. The sights became more familiar, less bleak and threatening. It didn't get much warmer, though.

'Does the wind ever let up?' she moaned to Sally one day as they stood watch together one afternoon, shivering as the draught whined through the window lights. 'I'd like just one day when I didn't have to spend half an hour combing the tangles from my hair after each trip outside.'

'I know,' Sally said. 'I thought the gales at home were bad, but nothing could have prepared me for this.' She paused as she lifted her binoculars and did a visual sweep of Hoy Sound. When she'd finished she said, 'You have to admit it's beautiful, though.'

Iris followed Sally's gaze. She had a point. On a day like today, when the choppy water sparkled in the sunlight and the islands looked like emeralds upon a turquoise sea, it was hard to imagine a more beautiful sight. The pennants on the anchored ships danced in the wind, and the eerie cries of the curlews fell and rose as though imitating the swell of the waves.

They were interrupted by a lieutenant from base coming to inspect the logs. Iris, breathing a sigh of relief that she had kept them up to date that day, handed them over.

'By the way,' he said, once he'd approved the logs, 'we've had a few reports of a low-flying plane in this area at night. Probably one of our pilots playing the daredevil, but let us know if you hear anything.' The he grinned. 'Anyway, it won't be my problem after today. I'm transferring to HMS *Tyne*.'

'Congratulations, sir,' Iris said. The *Tyne* was the depot ship serving the fleet's destroyers, anchored in Scapa Flow.

The lieutenant, on the point of leaving, halted at the door. 'Actually, you girls could do me a favour. The *Tyne* is hosting a tea dance in a couple of weeks, and I've been charged to invite as many girls as I can muster.' He named the date.

Sally, looking sorrowful, said, 'I'm on night watch with Mary that night, but it's your day off, isn't it, Iris?' When Iris nodded, Sally said, 'And I'm sure she'd like to bring a date.'

'Bring who you like,' the lieutenant said, 'as long as there are more ladies than men in the party.'

After extracting a promise from Iris to invite the other girls from the Wrennery, the lieutenant left.

Immediately, Sally tackled Iris. 'You lucky thing. I wish I could go. Who are you going to invite – Rob or Stewart?'

That was a good question. Iris knew she ought to invite Stewart. When she had first joined the Wrens, she had pictured attending shipboard parties with officers or other well-to-do gentlemen. Stewart fitted in with that picture far better than Rob. Yet she couldn't deny that when she imagined dancing in the arms of a handsome man, it was Rob's face she saw.

In the end, the decision was taken out of her hands. She was walking through Stromness the next day, on her way to buy more yarn, when she ran into Stewart.

'I was hoping to see you,' he said. 'I've been hearing rumours about a party on HMS *Tyne*.'

He was so clearly angling for an invitation, Iris could hardly turn him down. She gave him her best society smile and asked if he'd like to go with her. The reply was an eager yes. However, once they'd parted, Iris was aware of a dull weight of disappointment, which was ridiculous. Stewart was the right one for her, and he was far more suited to a tea dance than Rob.

Anyway, it wasn't as if Rob had ever given any indication that his feelings were anything but platonic. They had met twice since their first date, although their free time hadn't coincided long enough for more than a drink together at the NAAFI and a stroll through Stromness. On neither occasion had he done so much as try to hold her hand, let alone kiss her.

A delicious shiver ran down her spine at the thought of Rob kissing her.

No! She had to stop that train of thought at once. She was going with Stewart and that was that.

Rob had been unable to get leave for a while, and she was able to push the thought of him from her mind for a few days. But that was until she returned from watch a week later, and Sally handed her a note from Rob, delivered by one of his crew mates.

I'm sorry I haven't been able to see you recently, the note read. *I've been seconded to doing engine repairs on the drifters for a month because the engineering team was short-handed. I'm going back to the Kelpie soon, but I've been invited to a dance on HMS Tyne as a thank-you. If you are free on the 11th April, would you like to come with me?*

Iris's heart gave an unpleasant lurch. Not only did she have to turn him down, she would also have to explain she was already going. With another man.

The knowledge that Rob would see her at the party with Stewart spoiled Iris's anticipation of the event. She was starting to wish she had never agreed to go, especially since neither Sally nor Mary could make it. When the day of the party arrived, she was tempted to tell Stewart she wasn't feeling well, but Sally wouldn't hear of it.

'You promised,' Sally said. 'It would be terribly bad luck to break your word. Besides, we're relying on you to tell us all the gossip tomorrow.'

'It won't be the same without you two,' Iris said as she dressed in her tiddly jacket and skirt. Despite her reluctance to go, she couldn't help admiring herself in the mirror; she didn't often get an excuse to dress in her smartest uniform.

'You enjoy yourself,' Sally told her. 'There'll be other parties.'

After promising to tell them all about the tea dance the next day, Iris made her way to the pier with the other Wrens who were going. None of them shared her reluctance, and their excited chatter soon lifted Iris's spirits. The sight of Stewart cheered her even more; he looked very dapper in a suit that was tailored to perfection. Yet it was Rob that made her heart give a jolt.

'I didn't know you were taking the tender from Stromness,' Iris said to him. The sight of him in his neatest uniform made her feel quite jittery. She found herself reliving the moment when he had caught her in his strong arms on the boat into Orkney that first time. She couldn't help hoping he would ask her to dance so she could feel his arms around her again.

'I got a couple of days leave when I finished with the tenders,' Rob said. 'I'm staying in Stromness tonight.'

Stewart moved to her side and placed a hand on her arm. 'I think this is our boat.'

The proprietorial way he touched her made her flare with irritation. For some reason, she found herself shooting a glance at Rob. He was turning his narrowed gaze from Iris to Stewart and back.

Sudden irritation flared at both men. Stewart was obviously trying to assert his right over Rob. And what right did Rob have to be annoyed she was with someone else? While they had been on a few dates, he had never indicated by word or gesture that he saw her as anything more than a friend. Yes, he had flirted a little, but he had never said anything to indicate he had any serious designs on her.

She shook off Stewart's arm and stalked to the edge of the pier. However, when it was her turn to board, she suddenly remembered how badly she had handled the crossing from Scrabster, and allowed Stewart to help her down into the boat with a grateful smile. She sat on one of the benches and watched as the others boarded. Stewart wobbled as he crossed to join her and nearly lost his balance when the tender lurched beneath his feet. Despite her better intentions, she allowed her gaze to drift to Rob, admiring the easy way he sprang aboard, crossing to his seat as easily as though he was walking on land. It really wasn't fair to compare them. After all, ask Rob to treat someone who was bleeding, and he would probably look as out of his depth as Stewart did now.

Soon the tender was chugging out of the harbour and skirting Graemsay. The HMS *Tyne* was anchored in the waters off Lyness on Hoy, in the shelter of the smaller islands of Fara and Flotta. It would take about three-quarters of an hour to get there, so Iris took in the view, using it as an excuse not to speak to Stewart or Rob. The sun was still up, casting a golden glow over the hills of Hoy, and, much to her relief, the water was calm. Away to the south west, however, black clouds were stacked upon the horizon, obscuring the sunset glow. 'I hope there isn't going to be a storm,' she said. She felt a flutter of fear. 'It's too early in the year for a thunderstorm, isn't it?'

'I'm sure it'll be fine,' Stewart said.

Rob's brow knotted and he cast a dark look at Stewart. 'That's your opinion as an expert sailor, is it?' Then his expression changed when he looked at Iris. 'I'm sorry. I didnae mean to—' He broke off, rubbing the back of his neck. 'It looks like it might get a bit squally, but we should be on the *Tyne* by the time it reaches us, and she's built to glide through an Atlantic storm. A bit of choppy water in Scapa Flow won't bother her at all.' He gave her an encouraging smile, and she did feel reassured.

Thankfully, the weather remained clear throughout the crossing, and Iris was relieved when Rob finally pointed out a large ship in the anchorage. 'There she is.'

In Hoy's shadow, the *Tyne* was no more than a vast dark outline against the water. More an absence of light where elsewhere Iris could see the soft shimmer of the water. She caught her breath at the sheer size. She felt she finally understood how a minnow must feel approaching a whale.

'So this is HMS *Tyne*,' Stewart said, in tones that made it sound like he was speaking more to himself than anyone else present.

When they were within earshot of the *Tyne*, Iris's pulse quickened to hear swing music drifting from the open portholes across the empty water. Then came the moment Iris had been dreading: scaling the ladder. Never had she been more glad of her sturdy blackouts than when she scrambled up the ladder, a young rating calling encouragement from above, and another stationed on the deck directly below her, 'In case you slip.'

'I bet you'd be too busy looking to catch me,' she muttered under her breath as she pulled herself up the ladder, too occupied in getting a secure toehold with each step to worry about what anybody below could see.

'Welcome aboard,' said the rating who helped her down onto the deck. Stewart, who had eagerly scrambled up the ladder before her, was standing a little way off, gazing around the ship with interest. As soon as the whole party was aboard, they were led down to the wardroom, where some Wrens who must have arrived earlier from a different part of Orkney were already dancing in the arms of the officers. The new group was greeted with cheers, and a junior officer handed out drinks. A gramophone was playing 'Don't Sit Under the Apple Tree', and soon Iris's feet were tapping as she sipped cautiously from her glass of sherry. A wave of elation rushed over her. This was a taste of the life she had hoped for when she joined the Wrens. Maybe now she was friends with Stewart, she would experience more evenings like this.

'Will you dance?' Stewart asked, offering her his hand.

Iris took it and they stepped into the cramped space occupied by the other dancers. There wasn't room to be swung around, but it was fun to sway in time with the music. Glancing around, Iris saw happy faces, flushed from the dance.

Then she saw Rob leading Shirley James onto the dance floor. Shirley was another visual signaller, whom Iris had always got on well with. Right now, Iris had to fight the urge to march up to her and slap her round the face. How dare she look up at Rob like that, fluttering her lashes and casting him coy smiles?

The next moment, Stewart steered them to a clearer patch of the floor, and now Iris had her back to Rob and could no longer see him. She was shocked by her visceral reaction to seeing him with another girl. Why was she bothered about who he danced with, when she was with the man of her choice?

After all, Rob wouldn't often be able to take her to smart parties. Stewart was far more at home in these surroundings, graciously collecting glasses of sherry from a side table when the music finished, escorting her to a seat and pulling out the chair. Stewart clearly knew how to behave in good society. Unlike Rob, who was now doing a vigorous Jitterbug with Shirley, his face alight with laughter as several of the other dancers had paused to watch, applauding their skill. She refused to feel jealous.

'I suppose you must get to know the other signallers on board the ships,' Stewart said, taking a sip of sherry.

Iris looked at him, surprised. 'Not really. What makes you think that?'

'Well, they must have their own little quirks.'

Iris wasn't really paying attention to the conversation. She was far more concerned with the way Rob was dipping Shirley, his strong fingers splayed along the small of her back, supporting her perfectly. Iris gave a little shiver; she swore she could feel what it would be like to have his fingers pressing into her own back.

'Do they?' Stewart persisted.

Iris gave a little jump. 'Well, some are faster than others, more confident,' she said, craning her neck to follow Rob as he left the dance and led Shirley to a seat. 'A couple get letters mixed up so I have to keep asking them to repeat a word. Is that what you mean?'

'Can you tell which boat or ship it is by the signaller?'

'Sometimes, although ships have more than one signaller. But there's one minesweeper that—' She broke off when Rob clinked glasses with Shirley and leaned towards her, smiling.

Iris sprang to her feet. 'Anyway, I don't want to talk about work.' She was uncomfortably aware that she shouldn't be talking about signalling to an outsider, no matter how trustworthy. 'Come on. I want to dance.'

She led Stewart onto the floor just as the rating managing the gramophone put on a slower record. She made sure they were standing where Rob could see before she let Stewart lead her into a slow, graceful waltz. Stewart really was an accomplished dancer. Even better than George. He would make the perfect partner at any society ball.

So why did she keep looking over his shoulder to see what Rob was doing?

–

All in all, Iris's first party on board a ship wasn't the exciting, glamorous experience she had anticipated. Stewart monopolised her, meaning she didn't get to meet any new people and, worst of all, Shirley stuck to Rob's side like a barnacle to a ship's hull. When the announcement came that the tenders were waiting to take the revellers ashore, Iris was so eager to leave she was among the first up the ladder onto the deck.

The moment she emerged through the hatch, the wind tore at her hair and ripped the breath from her throat.

The stormy weather they had seen approaching earlier had arrived. Her heart quailed when she saw two tenders rising and falling on the swell and realised that she would have to walk across the first one to reach the one going to Stromness.

Then a distant rumble of thunder sent an icy trickle of fear down her spine.

A hand touched her elbow. She looked round expecting to see Stewart but instead saw Rob.

'You'll be all right, lass.' Although he had to raise his voice to be heard over the wind, there was something calming about his tone that eased her fear. 'I'll help you across.'

No one else seemed at all alarmed about walking across the tenders in a storm. Two Wrens had already descended the ladder and were nimbly stepping across to the Stromness tender as though doing nothing more taxing than walking across stepping stones on a pond.

Encouraged, Iris edged towards the rail. Stewart hadn't waited for her but was already climbing down the ladder.

Rob muttered something under his breath. She couldn't quite catch it, but thought he might have said something like, 'Inconsiderate idiot.'

When Stewart reached the first tender, he shuffled across it, swaying, then stepped across into the next, clutching at the gunwale. Never once did he look back to see if she was all right.

Rob turned to her. 'Would you like me to go first? That way I can help you across.'

Iris peered over the rail. Even in the darkness she could see the tender rising and falling on the swell in an alarming fashion. She nodded then looked past Rob. 'Where's Shirley?'

He shrugged. 'She's coming.'

Warmth kindled in Iris's chest at the news that Shirley could be separated from Rob without recourse to a barnacle scraper. She watched Rob swing himself onto the ladder and slide down with ease. Again, Iris had to chide herself for comparing Stewart's clumsy attempts unfavourably with Rob's.

When Rob was in the boat, he stood at the foot of the ladder. 'Your turn, lass.'

With Rob there, reaching the tender wasn't the terrifying nightmare she had expected. Without looking down, but concentrating on placing her feet and hands, she reached the bottom of the ladder with ease. The difficult bit was stepping into the pitching tender. However, Rob simply grasped her around the waist and said, 'You can let go now, lass.'

There was something about his calm voice that cut through her fear. She released her grip on the ladder. For a moment she was aware of nothing but the feel of Rob's hands on her waist and a rush of air on her face as she was swung round. Then her feet landed in the tender. The boat lurched under her feet, and she clung to Rob's forearms to steady herself. Rob held her a moment longer.

'There you go. All safe,' he said. 'Now take your time. I won't let go.'

Feeling rather breathless, Iris inched towards the Stromness tender. Another rumble of thunder made her dig her fingers into Rob's arms. Her legs quaked beneath her, and she was sure they would give way if Rob let her go. All evening she had wondered what it would be like to be held in Rob's arms, and now she knew. It was the one secure haven in a precarious world. She managed to reach the gunwale just as the tender yawed violently. Spray shot up from between the boats, stinging her eyes. She had a momentary vision of falling into the gap between the boats and being crushed, then Rob's voice spoke in her ear.

'I won't let you fall. The storm won't hurt us – it's miles away.'

Holding her breath, she stepped over the gunwale and down into the Stromness tender. A moment later, Rob was beside her. She had made it. She released her pent breath and smiled up at Rob. 'Thank you.'

'Any time.' There was an intensity to his gaze that sent the blood rushing to her cheeks.

At that point, Stewart intervened. 'Iris, I've saved a seat for you over here.'

Rob let go of her waist, and she dropped her hands from his arms. The cold wind whipped between them, stealing the warmth from her face. The seat Stewart had saved was on the port side, meaning she had to stagger across the rocking tender. Rob moved to put a hand under her elbow to steady her. Stewart lurched forward and knocked Rob's hand aside. 'She's with me, in case you hadn't noticed.'

'Then take better care of her,' Rob replied.

Iris had nearly reached her seat by this time. Another rumble of thunder rolled through the air. She quailed, and in her fear she groped for the gunwale. What happened next was not altogether clear. One moment she was stooping over her bench, the next the boat gave a lurch and something struck her in the small of her back. She staggered forward with a cry, flinging out her hands to hold onto something, anything, to stop herself falling. Then she was in the water, the biting cold punching the air from her lungs. In a panic, she flailed for the side of the boat to save herself, then icy water closed over her head.

Chapter Fourteen

For a moment, Rob couldn't take in what had happened. He stared at the patch of inky black sea where Iris's head had been visible only seconds before. Then one of the ratings gave a cry and flung a lifebelt onto the water. The splash brought Rob back to his senses. Stewart was staring out of the boat with a look of shock on his face, as though he couldn't believe he had just knocked his girlfriend overboard. He gave no sign of moving, so Rob flung off his coat and while he kicked off his shoes, he turned to the tender's skipper. 'Shine a light where she went in.'

'But the blackout—'

'Hang the blackout. Do you want to save that lass or not?'

Without waiting for an answer, he sprang into the water. The shock of the cold was a physical blow. It was a vice, crushing his chest, making it impossible to draw breath. He knew enough not to try swimming yet but to tread water until he could force air into his lungs.

He couldn't last long in this cold. Nor could Iris. He managed to wrench one jerky breath into his lungs, then another, coughing when the choppy water sent a wall of water into his face. The sea closed over his head again, and when he emerged, he blinked stinging salty water from his eyes, straining for a glimpse of Iris.

A light stabbed the darkness. A glance up showed the tender's skipper had obeyed his barked order and was shining a light upon the water. With growing despair, Rob sought for any sign of Iris but could see nothing. He managed to draw a deeper breath and dived beneath the surface. Visibility was practically zero. He could only see where the torchlight lanced the water.

His lungs bursting, he surfaced. 'I can't see a thing,' he gasped to the skipper. 'Move the torchlight.'

He filled his lungs again and ducked beneath the waves. Now the beam of light moved through the darkness. However, it revealed nothing but empty water. He stayed down for as long as he could until his lungs screamed for air, then he surfaced once more, coughing and spluttering.

'Anything?' the skipper called.

Rob managed to unlock his frozen jaw enough to force out a curt, 'Nothing.'

Feeling sick, he dived again. How much longer could Iris last? How long before he would be forced to abandon the search?

He followed the feeble column of torchlight once more, trying to close his mind to the knowledge that this blind search was futile. All the torch seemed to do was emphasise the vast impenetrable darkness pressing around the tiny needle of light.

Then a more powerful beam lit the water. He couldn't for the life of him think where it had come from, but he turned to look in the patch of illuminated water, his lungs beginning to burn. Nothing, save for a feeble tendril of weed, fluttering in the current.

No. Wait. Not weed. A hand! Using every last ounce of his strength, he propelled himself towards the flailing arm. As the strong beam of light moved, he saw more of her arm, then strands of hair drifting in a halo around a white face. Her cheeks were bulging, her eyes wide.

Finding new strength at the sight of her, Rob pulled himself through the water and managed to wrap an arm around her chest. As he heaved her towards the surface, he knew at once why she had been unable to pull herself up: her heavy greatcoat dragged her back. Now he had only one arm to swim with, it threatened to drag them both down. His lungs screamed for air; a grey haze obscured his vision. He kicked furiously with his legs. Iris seemed too far gone to help. She had stopped struggling to swim and hung limply in his grasp. He wasn't going to make it. No matter how hard he fought to pull himself through the water, he couldn't get any closer to the shimmering silver circle that marked the surface. He watched a stream of bubbles rise along the beam but was unable to follow.

Then the light shattered into a cloud of foam. At first Rob was unable to work out what had happened, until he saw a dark form resolve into the shape of a man swimming down the beam towards them. The newcomer grabbed the collar of Iris's coat, and between them, they were able to drag her to the surface. As his head emerged into blessed air, a wall of noise hit him: the splash of water, shouts and his own rasping breath as he heaved air into his starved lungs. He clung onto just enough sense to ensure that Iris's head was above water.

Someone tried to lift her away. In a moment of panic, he clutched her harder until a voice said, 'Let her go. We'll take care of her.'

Steely hands grabbed him under his arms, and he was being dragged aboard the tender, scraping his ribs painfully upon the gunwale. Unable to support his limbs, which felt as though they had been filled with lead, he collapsed to the bottom of the boat, coughing. A weight settled around his shoulders, and he put up his hand and encountered a rough blanket. Finally the scene steadied.

'How is she?' he asked, addressing the group huddled around a form lying upon the decking, water streaming from it. Then the figure convulsed and broke into a fit of coughing and retching. A sigh passed through the group.

'She'll be fine.' It was a young rating who spoke. Water ran in rivulets down his face and he, too, had a blanket wrapped around his shoulders. 'Good job you found her when you did.'

Rob nodded. 'It was the extra light that did it.'

The man nodded. 'I got one of the signallers on the *Tyne* to shine a signal lamp into the water.'

'Good thinking. And thanks for coming in after me. I couldn't have fished her out alone.'

'Don't mention it. We've signalled ahead to Mainland, so there'll be an ambulance waiting at the quay.'

It was only now that Rob saw the tender was moving. The *Tyne* was already some distance away. After another word of thanks to the rating, Rob went to sit beside Iris. She was struggling to a sitting position, still coughing. When she saw him, though, she managed a weak smile. 'Thank you,' she said, her voice hoarse. 'What happened? One moment I was in the boat, the next I was in the water.' She coughed again. 'Did something hit me?'

Rob scowled. In the panic he had forgotten what had happened. Now he glowered at Dr Irvine. 'It was that imbecile doctor of yours.' Now the shock was fading, rage took its place. Irvine simply sat, watching Iris, making no attempt to help her.

Rob advanced on him. 'And what were you playing at?'

Irvine gaped, then said, 'It was an accident.'

'An accident that happened because you were too busy making sure Iris didn't sit with me. If you'd been more concerned with her safety rather than making sure she didn't look at any other men, this would have never happened.' To his dying day, Rob didn't think he would ever forget the horror of seeing Irvine lose his balance and knock Iris overboard as he lashed out to steady himself.

He clenched his fists, struggling with the urge to punch the man and see how he liked being thrown into icy water.

The rating grabbed his arm. 'Sit down, pal. You're going to send someone overboard yourself if you don't calm down.'

Seeing the sense in the man's words, Rob sank onto a bench and clutched the blanket closer. Now the tender was moving at speed, the cold wind seemed to slice into his flesh. His teeth chattered, rendering him unable to talk. He gave an approving nod at one of the Wrens who gave Iris her greatcoat in addition to the blanket. Following her example, a couple of others handed their coats to Rob and the rating who had jumped in to save them. Rob noticed that Dr Irvine hadn't given up his coat. What kind of doctor was he? First his clumsiness had resulted in him shoving Iris overboard, and then he didn't even lift a finger to make sure she didn't succumb to the cold.

Well, tonight's misadventure had shown him one thing. If Dr Irvine had proved himself worthy of Iris, Rob would have stepped back and let Iris go without a fuss. The doctor was the right class for her. Now, however, Rob could see Dr Irvine would never treat Iris with the respect she deserved. He wasn't right for her. From now on, Rob was going to fight to win her.

The next morning, Iris was released from sick bay after a disturbed night's sleep. She had been ordered to take a hot bath, then given a steaming mug of tea before being put to bed and covered with so many blankets their combined weight had pinned her to the mattress. But it hadn't been the blankets that had kept her awake. She had stared, wide-eyed, into the darkness, reliving the moment when the icy water had closed over her head. She couldn't rid her mind of the horror of being unable to draw breath, the cold that burned and the sensation of her heavy garments dragging her into the depths, no matter how hard she struggled to pull herself to the surface. She didn't have a clear memory of Rob pulling her out. She also couldn't remember if she had thanked him. All she could really remember of the journey back to Stromness was the Wrens crowded around her, rubbing her hands and wrapping her in their coats, telling her how brave she was being and what a hero Rob was.

She did remember Rob's verbal attack on Stewart, though. Until that moment she hadn't realised it was Stewart who had knocked her overboard. Now she didn't know if she would ever be able to look at him without remembering the terror of finding herself beneath the waves and unable to draw breath.

The last thing she thought before sleep finally claimed her was that he hadn't made a move to help her.

Now, as she returned to her cabin to change out of her salt-stiffened uniform, she had a whole day to herself, the MO having forbidden her to go on watch that day. Sally and Mary were on watch until the afternoon, which was a shame, as she would have dearly loved to talk over the events of the night with them.

She fingered the salt-stained tiddly jacket sadly. The first thing to do was take it to a laundry in Stromness. Until now she had hand-washed her clothes, but these stains were going to need an expert hand if she was to have any hope of rescuing her smartest uniform. Her mind made up, she was walking out of the Wrennery, her uniform and greatcoat in a bundle under her arm.

'Iris!'

A familiar voice hailed her as she walked out of the gateway. Her heart pounding, she turned to see Rob hovering beside the entrance. For some reason, although she had wanted to find him to thank him, she felt uncertain, lost for words.

'Rob, I… it's good to see you.'

'Are you all right? They said you were out of sick bay, but I wanted to check on you.'

'I'm fine. I…' The next words came out in a rush. 'I wanted to see you today. To say thank you. I can't remember if I said so last night but I don't want you to think I'm not grateful.'

'You don't have to thank me. I only did what anyone would have done.'

Stewart hadn't helped. It was on the tip of her tongue to say so, but she kept quiet, thinking it would be disloyal.

'You don't have to go on duty today, do you?' Rob asked.

She shook her head. 'The MO has put me on sick leave. I couldn't spend the whole day in my cabin though.'

'Same here. Would you like to come for a walk with me?'

She would. Very much. It frightened her, the intensity with which she wanted to be with him. But nothing had changed – he wasn't the eligible young man she ought to be with. On the other hand, the air was warm, the gulls were wheeling through the sky, and a walk with Rob on a rare day of sunshine was too inviting to pass up. She nodded and indicated her parcel. 'I have to find a laundry first.'

Her uniform dropped off, they walked out of Stromness on the Howe Road. The road climbed steadily until, looking back, Iris could see across Scapa Flow. The waters were now still and a clear blue, reflecting the sunlit sky. 'It's hard to believe it was so stormy out there last night.' With the daffodils dancing in the breeze along the verges and even the barrage balloons gleaming in the sunshine, Iris felt the lingering fear of the night fall away. Far across the bay, she could see the faint outline of ships at anchor. At that distance, the water looked like silver, the ships set upon the surface like toys. Thoughts of yesterday's stormy weather and those terrifying moments when she was being dragged beneath the water were fast fading like a half-remembered nightmare.

It took a while to notice that Rob wasn't looking at the view but regarding her with a level of concentration that she usually only devoted to reading distant flashes of Morse. 'Is something wrong?' she asked. Being the focus of his steady gaze scattered her thoughts, and she felt a prickle of self-consciousness. Had she forgotten to brush her hair? For the life of her, she couldn't remember. She put a hand to her head, half expecting to encounter salt-encrusted tangles, rather than her usual smooth, neat rolls, off her collar as required by regulations. But all was well. Why, then, was he staring at her as though he had never set eyes upon her before?

A faint smile played on his lips. 'Nothing's wrong. Nothing at all.'

Something about the tone of his voice set her insides aflutter, and she was beset by two conflicting urges: one to run away and the other to step closer. Caught between the two, she remained unmoving.

'It just hit me,' Rob went on, 'that here we are, totally alone for the first time.' He made a wide gesture that took in the fields, road and distant water. Following his hand, Iris saw that they were, indeed, alone, apart from a few sheep eyeing them from behind a wire fence, and the curlews on the hillside, their presence revealed by their plaintive whistling cries.

'We've—' Her voice shook, and she licked suddenly dry lips. She tried again. 'We've been alone before.'

'Alone in a crowd.' Rob took a step nearer. So close she could raise a hand and place it on his chest, push him away. She didn't want him to move away, though. 'This is the first time we've been somewhere with no one else around to see us.'

She had a sudden flash of returning memory from the night before, when her head had broken the surface. After she had dragged air into her lungs and realised she wasn't going to drown after all, it had gradually dawned on her that the strong arm supporting her had belonged to Rob. She should still have been scared, with the waves breaking over her face and being unable to see far in the darkness. Instead, she had trusted him absolutely, knowing she could rely on him to get her safely back aboard the tender. What she remembered most of all was how bereft she had felt after being helped back onto the tender, when she had been separated from Rob and taken into the care of a group of Wrens. She also remembered that Stewart hadn't lifted a finger to help.

The view faded; her vision tunnelled until she could see only Rob's warm brown eyes. She could no longer hear the curlews' calls or the sheep. All she could hear was her own heart, thumping so hard against her ribs she was sure Rob must be able to hear it too. Nothing stopped her from moving away, breaking the spell. Nothing but her own will.

'I could kiss you,' Rob said, 'and there would be no one to see but a handful of sheep and a few birds.'

'I—' She should be shocked. She should pull away – not that he was holding her with anything but the power of his gaze. There was a reason she shouldn't let him kiss her, only she couldn't seem to bring it to her numb mind. And there were a hundred reasons why she wanted it, the foremost being that she wanted to feel his arms around her again. Wanted to relive that wonderful moment of security.

'I won't if you don't want me to,' Rob said. 'I—'

Before he could say another word, Iris raised herself onto her tiptoes and pressed her mouth to his. For a moment he stood, frozen, not responding. Confused, Iris made to pull away. That was when his arms wound around her shoulders, pulling her close until she could feel the rapid beat of his heart in time with her own. He deepened the kiss, and she gasped against his lips. Instinct took over. She didn't think but looped her arms around his neck, pulling him to her even as he pulled her into a closer embrace. The sensation, the feel of him, the faint rasp of stubble beneath her lips, the scent of coal-tar soap, the roar of blood in her ears, all became all-consuming. The sensations were so overwhelming that she closed her eyes, her reeling mind unable to process sight on top of everything else. It was only when the need to breathe asserted itself that she drew back and opened her eyes.

Rob's mouth curved into a slow smile. 'Now that's something I wasn't expecting.'

A blush heated Iris's face until she was sure she must be glowing even brighter than the sun. 'You're the one who introduced the subject of kissing.'

'I thought I would be the one to kiss you. Or, rather, I thought I was going to have to use all my powers of persuasion for you to let me. I wasn't expecting you to throw yourself at me.'

'I didn't!'

'Maybe not throw yourself, but you definitely started it.'

She hadn't thought it was possible for her face to get any hotter, but she was convinced she was about to burst into flame. What had possessed her to be so bold? 'I was just… just thanking you for saving me.'

Rob gave a crooked smiled that made her fight the urge to throw herself at him again. 'If that's how you thank people, remind me to do you more favours.'

'That's not what I meant. I… oh—'

This time it was her turn to be surprised by a kiss. She should push him away. She even raised her hand and placed it on his chest. But instead of pushing him, her treacherous fingers traced the lapel of his coat, feeling the firm muscles beneath.

He looked altogether too pleased with himself when he finally broke the kiss. 'I trust this means you've put all thought of that idiot, Dr Irvine, from your mind. The bastard was so busy trying to save himself, he didn't even notice he'd pushed you overboard. Then he stood there like an utter blockhead while others rushed to help.'

All thought of rebuke left her. Stewart hadn't so much as apologised for the risk to her life. Rob might be altogether too pleased with himself, but he had been there for her. Her irritation ebbed. 'I wish I hadn't gone with him. I would have rather been with you.' Maybe Rob didn't come from the same class as her but he was the one who had saved her. She knew now that she could never feel the same way for Stewart as she did for Rob. When she was with Rob she felt as though her heart was wrapped in a warm blanket, and nothing could ever hurt her. She had a fleeting thought of George and what her life would be like if she really had married him. The thought gave her a nothing but horror.

Rob smiled and offered her his arm, and they ambled down the road. Iris scarcely noticed where they were going, her full attention being fixed on Rob. It was so easy being with him. She didn't have to censor her thoughts in the same way she had done with George and Stewart. Instead, she could speak of what was in her heart, of how she was coming to love the wildness of Orkney, of how she missed her father, of how she enjoyed making clothes, something her mother had always sneered at. She had never dared to say any of this to George or Stewart, but Rob listened without laughing, and said missing a beloved parent was nothing to be ashamed of, and if dressmaking was something she enjoyed, she should do it.

They lost all track of where they were until they found they had walked the four miles to Stenness and were approaching the Standing Stones Hotel. It struck Iris then that she was hungry. However, Rob hung back. 'This is where all the top brass stay,' he said.

'Leave it with me.' She stood tall, threw back her shoulders and marched into the dining room. 'Table for two, please,' she said, looking the waitress in the eye and speaking in the accent that only years of elocution lessons could give. Within moments they were shown to a table and handed menus.

Once the waitress had gone, Rob grinned, although Iris spied a shadow behind his eyes. 'I always knew there were advantages to courting an upper-class girl.'

'Courting?' All thought of Rob's strange expression fled.

He raised his brows, and Iris knew he was thinking of their kisses. 'Isn't that what we're doing?'

He had a point. Her thoughts were also straying to their shared embraces, and she could feel another blush stealing across her face. 'I suppose we are,' she said. The beaming smile he gave in answer chased away all her reservations.

Chapter Fifteen

The next day Iris was passed fit to return to duty, and so the week passed in the usual round of watches, knitting and visits to the Heddles. Rob, who had returned to the *Kelpie*, had been unable to get any more leave, and Iris missed him with a pang of longing that took her by surprise. As the days went by, her misgivings about courting him faded until she could only remember their kisses and how wonderful they had felt. She went through the week feeling as though she were enclosed in a warm bubble of sunshine. For some reason, although she told Sally and Mary about their walk, she couldn't bring herself to confess to the new turn in their relationship. It all felt too new, and she wanted to keep it to herself for a while longer without having to endure their inevitable teasing.

Even at the end of the week, when the weather deteriorated into squally showers, it couldn't dampen her spirits. As she walked with Sally to Kyeness for the morning watch, she let herself lapse into a happy daydream.

'Iris, have you heard a word I've been saying?' Sally's voice jolted Iris back to the present, and it was something of a shock to find herself on the hillside with rain stinging her eyes, Sally regarding her with hands on hips.

Iris jumped and gave Sally a guilty look. 'I'm sorry. I was miles away.'

Thankfully, Sally didn't look too cross. 'I take it that wherever you were, Rob was with you.'

It was impossible to hold back the smile that seemed to burst from deep within. 'He might have been.'

'I knew it!' Sally looked almost as happy as Iris felt. 'Didn't I say he was the one for you?'

'You did. Several times.'

'You know what you have to do now?'

'What?'

'You have to write to your mother and tell her about Rob.'

Even that couldn't destroy the glow cocooning Iris's heart. She had gradually been reaching the same conclusion. 'I know.'

'Now I know you've got it bad. Aren't you worried what she'll think?'

'Oh, I know what she'll think. And I've decided there are advantages to being in Orkney after all.'

'Besides the presence of Rob, you mean?'

'Besides that, yes. If I'd ended up in Portsmouth, nothing would have stopped her from storming down there and laying siege to the place until I saw sense. At least I'm safely out of the way up here.'

The thought of writing to her mother about Rob had also reminded Iris of another unpleasant task. She hadn't seen Stewart since the accident in the boat, but if he tried to ask her out again, she would have to tell him that she couldn't see him any more. At least his action on the tender, or lack of action, would make it easier.

–

The wind had strengthened by the time they reached the signal station; Iris and Sally battled the last quarter of a mile with heads lowered. Before they went inside, Iris glanced up. Her stomach clenched when she saw the flat grey clouds giving way to slate-blue towers stacked on the northern horizon.

'Just had a call from base,' Shirley James, one of the Wrens they were relieving, said as she bundled herself in her waterproofs. 'There's a gale on its way from the north and possibly thunder. They want you to put up the storm cone.'

Iris tensed. While she knew it was Stewart's fault she had ended up in the water, she couldn't forget that it was her fear of thunderstorms that had made her so shaky in the first place. If she hadn't been so frightened, she might have kept her head and not put herself in such a vulnerable position. 'I don't know why we ever take it down,' Iris said, trying to make light of her unease. 'We're always either in the middle of a storm or there's one on the way.'

'True. Have fun!' Shirley pulled on her hat and waved goodbye. It was a good thing Iris was no longer jealous of her, or she might have pointed out that Shirley should have hoisted the storm cone herself instead of leaving it for the next watch. With the memory of Rob's kisses lingering on her lips, Iris was able to smile and withhold the comment. No need to snap and create ill-feeling.

A gust hit the hut, rattling the windows. From outside, she could hear the clang of the halyard striking the flag-pole. She shivered. The storm would hit in a matter of minutes, and she desperately didn't want to go out in it. Still, if she hurried out now, she should be back inside before any thunder arrived.

'I'll do the storm cone if you go out at nine to hoist the White Ensign,' she said to Sally. While she hated herself for her cowardice, she was relieved when Sally agreed without complaint and immediately climbed the ladder to the signal room.

Still in her waterproofs, Iris went straight outside and collected the black canvas storm cone from the flag locker. It took just a matter of moments to clip it on, arranging it to point upwards to indicate a wind from the north. Once she had hoisted it to the top of the pole and secured the halyard, Iris gazed out to sea, holding her sou'wester to stop the brim from slapping her in the face. The rain was falling harder now, lashing her face and eyes. Blinking to clear her vision, she saw with increasing dread that the dark storm clouds had nearly reached the coast. Making a quick decision, she pulled the White Ensign from the locker and set to work hoisting that as well. What did it really matter if it was a few minutes early? It wasn't fair to send Sally out in this. Once the flag was whipping the air at the top of the pole, she went to close the flag locker. She had just locked it when she caught a flicker of sheet lightning in the far distance. Forgetting everything, she fled inside, breathing a sigh of relief as she slammed the door, shutting out the storm. It was only when she had finished stripping off her soaked waterproofs that she thought of Rob. She could only pray he was safely ashore and not out in this weather.

Before joining Sally in the signal room, she filled the kettle and spooned tea leaves into the chipped teapot. Then she carried the kettle up the ladder, only sloshing a few drops from the spout as she managed to hoist herself up using only one hand.

Sally was at the window, a frown of concentration on her face as she peered out.

'Don't tell me there's a boat out in this,' Iris said, placing the kettle onto the stove.

'No.' Sally turned away from the window. 'I thought I saw someone out on the cliffs. You didn't see anyone out there, did you?'

'Not a soul. Though the wind was so loud, someone could have been playing a tuba right behind me and I wouldn't have noticed them. They'd have to be mad to walk on the cliffs on a day like today.'

'I think it must have been a bird or something. I can't see anyone now.'

Seeing the fire within the stove was sinking, Iris shovelled in more coal. She checked the coal scuttle and her heart sank when she saw how little was in it. 'Did you check the coal box downstairs?' she asked Sally.

'Yes, it's empty. Why?'

Iris pointed at the coal scuttle. 'There's only enough here to last us an hour or so.'

The wind struck the windows, howling through the gaps. The black clouds filled the sky, and rain lashed down. Iris shuddered when she saw another flash of lightning. The coal bunker was outside and couldn't be accessed from inside.

Sally moved to the ladder. 'It's all right. You did the flags, so it's only fair for me to refill the coal store.'

'Do you want me to help?' Iris failed to inject any conviction into her offer so wasn't at all surprised when Sally shook her head.

'Anyway, someone needs to stay up here in case we're needed.' Sally stepped onto the ladder and dropped out of sight. A moment later Iris heard the rustling of waterproof clothing then a clatter as Sally must have picked up the bucket and shovel they used for the coal. She heard the creaking hinges of the door, and a gust of wind blew through the hatchway and rustled the papers on the noticeboard. Then the door slammed and all was still.

Feeling guilty, Iris looked out of the window. The coal bunker was just outside the door and couldn't be seen from the signal room. As she watched, the rain turned to hail, bouncing off the balcony and railings. The noise of it hitting the roof was overwhelming. She flinched as a rumble of thunder rattled the windows.

Hugging her arms to her chest, she stood frozen in indecision. She should go and help Sally. It wasn't fair to expect her to do battle with the storm alone. On the other hand…

The wind shrieked down the flue of the stove; Iris sprang away from it, barely able to bite back a shriek of her own.

'Pull yourself together, Iris Tredwick,' she muttered. 'You're in the Wrens now. You can't shrink into your shell every time there's a storm.'

She was halfway to the ladder when the sharp ring of the phone cut through the howling wind. Ashamed of the wave of relief that washed over her, she hurried to answer it. 'WSS,' she said, hoping the person on the line couldn't hear the tremble in her voice. It was the officer at Lower Skaill, asking for identification of a ship crossing the indicator loop.

Iris blew out a shuddering breath as she crossed to the window. Peering through the rain-streaked air she saw a little boat bobbing on the choppy waves, spray flying across its bows as it steered a course for Stromness. She was pretty sure she recognised it as a fishing boat that they often saw plying the waters along this stretch of the coast, although she sighted it through the telescope to confirm it was indeed the *Seasnake*. She reported it as a friendly fishing boat then replaced the receiver. Having something to do had helped calm her nerves. She crossed back to the window to check the fishing boat wasn't in any distress. To her relief, it had already made good progress towards the more sheltered waters in Hoy Sound, although she didn't envy the crew trying to remain upright as it pitched this way and that.

She was on the point of turning away from the window when a movement on the cliff caught her eye. Remembering Sally saying she thought she had seen someone, she frowned at the line of gorse bushes growing along the cliff's edge. There was a narrow, rocky path beyond leading down to the geo where Mr Heddle kept his fishing boat. Was someone there? If so, they risked being blown off the path. It was no good, she couldn't see properly from here. She opened the French window, clutching it to stop it being caught by the wind and slamming shut. Hair whipped across her eyes. She was about to step out when a gull rose from behind the bushes, wailing. It was caught up in a violent air current and soared up high until it was little more than a dot. Iris tugged the window closed and leaned against the pane, limp with relief. It was just a bird. No one would be mad enough to go for a stroll along the cliff top on a day like today.

She paused. She would have expected Sally to return with a load of coal by now, yet she couldn't hear any sounds of movement in the room below. Of course, Sally could have come in and left for another load while Iris had been standing in the open doorway. After another quick scan of the water to make sure there were no other boats or ships she needed to identify, she hurried down the ladder. The coal box stood just inside the door, still empty.

Iris opened the door and peered out. 'Sally?' Holding her hair away from her eyes, she could see the lid of the coal bunker was down. Then she saw a bucket rolling away from the rear of the signal station, towards the gate.

Iris bit back a laugh. Sally must have dropped the bucket and was now out searching for it. Well, Iris had managed to quell her fear of the storm enough to identify the fishing boat; surely she could help Sally retrieve the coal bucket. She hurried back inside and pulled on her waterproofs. Then she took a deep breath and went outside.

The first thing she saw when she stepped out was Sally's legs on the ground on the other side of the coal bunker. The gusts of wind caught the coal bunker's lid, making it slam repeatedly; Iris vaguely registered splinters of wood dangling from the side farthest from where she stood, although she was too puzzled by Sally's odd behaviour to pay it much attention.

'What are you doing down there?' Iris asked. 'You'll—'

She broke off with a cry. Sally lay in a huddled heap in the lee of the bunker. Her eyes were closed, and blood poured from a cut on her temple. Her face was streaked with blood. For several seconds, all Iris could do was stare at the blood which dripped onto the wet concrete, staining the puddles with crimson streaks.

Chapter Sixteen

Iris's mouth went dry, and her feet felt rooted to the ground as she stared at Sally's inert body. Then a flash of lightning brought her to her senses. Only her terror for Sally could overcome her desire to escape from the storm. She rushed to Sally's side, kneeling down beside her. 'Oh my God. Sally!' With trembling hands, she pressed her fingers to Sally's throat, gasping with relief when she felt a steady pulse. She shook Sally by the shoulder, although as gently as possible. 'Sally, wake up. What happened?'

Sally's eyelids quivered but she didn't open her eyes. Iris took it as an encouraging sign, however. She remembered being told that hearing was the first sense to return to unconscious patients. Even though she had no idea if this was true, she kept up a steady stream of talk while she fumbled beneath her voluminous waterproof coat to pull out her, thankfully clean, handkerchief. 'I'm so sorry, Sally. I should never have sent you out alone. This is all my fault. If I wasn't such a coward this would never have happened. Whatever it was that *did* happen.'

As Iris dabbed at the cut with her handkerchief, she scanned the area, searching for any clue to what had happened. Gradually, a persistent banging sound broke into her consciousness; the coal bunker's heavy lid was gently rising and falling with each gust. Looking at it properly for the first time, Iris saw that the damaged section she had noticed previously had been torn off. This was letting the air get under the lid, causing the remainder to rise and fall. Looking around, she saw the torn off piece lying a few yards away. It must have broken free when Sally opened the lid, striking her in the head.

She shook Sally's shoulder again. 'Please wake up, Sally. I need to get you inside.' When Sally didn't stir, Iris slid an arm under her shoulders and tried to lift her, but Sally was a dead weight, impossible to move.

Filling her lungs, Iris staggered to her feet and cupped her hands around her mouth. 'Help!' she cried. 'I need help.'

She didn't know what she expected. The nearest house was the Heddles', and they were beyond earshot, even on a calm day. So when she heard footsteps she gasped in surprise and relief. Squinting through the rain, she saw a tall figure approach from the direction of the Heddles' croft. It was Stewart.

She ran to meet him, shaking with relief. 'Quick!' She beckoned him on, then pointed back towards the coal bunker, which currently blocked Sally from his view. 'Sally's hurt.'

Another rumble of thunder drowned her voice so she waited long enough to be sure he would follow, making frantic signals urging him to hurry. She bounced on her toes, casting frequent glances over her shoulder at the coal bunker. Why was he so slow? Couldn't he see that only the direst emergency would force her to be outside in this weather? 'Hurry!' she called when he was finally close enough to hear, then she dashed back to Sally's side. Finally, it must have dawned on Stewart that this was an emergency, for he quickened his pace and was soon stooping over Sally.

'What happened?' he asked, placing his fingers upon the pulse point of Sally's throat.

Iris shook her head. 'I wasn't there to see.' A fresh wave of guilt washed over her. 'I think part of the lid broke off in the wind.' She pointed at the coal bunker. 'It must have struck her on the head.'

'When?' Now Stewart gently raised Sally's eyelids in turn and peered into her eyes. He shook his head with a muttered oath. 'Can't see a blessed thing in this murk.'

'I don't know exactly.' Iris looked at her watch and forced her jittery brain to calm enough for her to think. It felt as though hours had passed since she had let Sally go out alone into the storm; it was something of a shock to see it had only been a few minutes ago. 'No more than fifteen minutes, I think.'

'It's safe to move her. We should get her inside.'

Between them, they managed to lift Sally's limp form; Stewart did most of the lifting while Iris supported Sally's head and guided her through the doorway to prevent her from picking up any further knocks.

'Through here,' she said, indicating the bunk room with a jerk of the head.

Once they had laid Sally upon a bunk and wrapped her in blankets, Stewart went back into the main downstairs room and turned this way and that as though looking for something. 'Do you have a telephone or radio in here?'

'A telephone. Why?'

'We need to get Sally to hospital. I think she'll be fine in a day or two, but she ought to be kept under observation for a while.'

'Oh. Of course.' Iris pointed up the ladder. 'There's a telephone up there.'

Stewart moved towards the ladder but Iris clutched his arm. 'I'll go. You stay with Sally.' She was unsure if Stewart, as a civilian, should even be in the signal station. While she was sure her CO would understand when she explained the circumstances, she didn't like to think of the row there would be if she let him use the phone linking Kyeness with the main base.

Without waiting for his reply, she scrambled up the ladder and picked up the telephone receiver with shaking hands. 'There's been an accident,' she blurted as soon as the call was answered, forgetting all protocol. 'My oppo's been knocked out.' In as few words as possible she explained what had happened, and nearly cried with relief when she was told an ambulance was on its way.

'We'll send another V/S Wren to stand the remainder of your watch with you,' said the second lieutenant who had taken over the call.

'Oh, yes, thank you.' Iris had imagined she would accompany Sally to the hospital but of course the signal station couldn't be left unmanned.

She replaced the receiver, then a sound coming from the hatch made her look round. Stewart was standing on the ladder, peering through the hatch.

'What are you doing? You should be with Sally.'

'I wanted to know how long the ambulance will be. She's waking up.'

'Then you should be with her. The ambulance has to come from Stromness, so it will be about a quarter of an hour.'

Stewart nodded and ducked back out of the hatch. Iris listened as the sound of his feet on the metal ladder receded and waited until his footsteps had retreated to the bunk room, annoyed at their unhurried pace. While she was no expert at first aid, she was sure an unconscious patient shouldn't be left alone, and couldn't understand Stewart's apparent lack of concern. She fought her own urge to return to Sally while she went to the window, picked up the binoculars and made a thorough check for signs of any boats. The last thing she needed was being disciplined for abandoning her post. Much to her relief, she saw a lighter band of clouds on the northern horizon. It looked like the storm would be short-lived. Hopefully the ambulance wouldn't encounter any difficulty in getting here.

She remained at her post until the growl of a motor engine could be heard over the wind. Looking down the track towards the Heddles' croft, she saw a military ambulance lurching towards the signal station. The path she and her sister Wrens used wasn't suitable for vehicles, but it was possible to take a track from Stromness to the Heddles' croft then follow the track from there to Kyeness. After a final scan of the waters to be sure she wasn't needed, she slid down the ladder.

'The ambulance is here,' she said, putting her head around the bunk room door.

'I'll show them where to come,' Stewart said and strode out.

Iris took the spot vacated by Stewart and held Sally's limp hand. Unsure if Sally could hear her, she said, 'Don't worry, Sally. They're going to take good care of you.'

Much to Iris's relief, Sally turned her head slightly, frowning, her eyelids fluttering.

'Sally? Oh, thank God!' This last exclamation came when Sally opened her eyes, squinting as though the light pained her. Iris dithered between running to fetch Stewart and not wanting to leave Sally alone.

She made up her mind to stay when Sally gripped her hand. 'Iris?' Sally winced and put a hand to her temple. 'My head.'

Iris pushed her back down when she tried to sit up. 'Lie still. You've taken a knock to your head. You're going to be fine, but we're taking you to hospital to get you checked over.'

Sally nodded, closing her eyes for a moment. Then she opened them again and said, 'Stewart... He was outside.'

'He's been here, taking care of you. That bang on the head must have got you confused.'

'Probably. It aches like fury.' Sally shut her eyes again. At that point Stewart returned with a stretcher team, Mary following, her face pale and anxious. While they loaded Sally into the ambulance, both Iris and Mary assured her they would come to visit as soon as they were off duty. It was only once the ambulance had gone, taking Sally and Stewart with it, that they climbed to the signal room and Mary demanded an explanation.

Iris launched into the tale. When she reached the part when Stewart had appeared, Mary frowned. 'What was he doing here? And in the middle of a storm?'

Iris shrugged. 'No idea. It's a good thing he was, though. I could never have got Sally inside without his help.' She paused and thought for a moment, remembering how he had wanted to follow her into the signal room. 'Maybe he wanted to see me. To apologise for knocking me in the water.' The more she thought about it, the more she became convinced this was the correct explanation.

Mary's face cleared. 'I bet he heard about you and Rob.'

Iris felt her cheeks burn. Really, she didn't know why everyone thought being a blonde was such an advantage.

All it meant was that you had a complexion that displayed your every emotion for the whole world to see. 'Is everyone talking about us?'

'You really think you can go for a long walk with a handsome young man and return with stars in your eyes, and him with a smear of lipstick on his cheek, without the whole town discussing it for a week?'

'I thought I got it all off!' Iris was horrified. She had only noticed the lipstick on Rob's jaw minutes before the end of the walk, not long before they reached the town. She had made him stand still while she dabbed the spot with her handkerchief, giggling each time Rob took advantage of her standing close to him and stole more kisses.

Mary gave a triumphant laugh. 'Ha! You don't deny it, then.'

'You...' Iris couldn't think of an epithet bad enough. 'You tricked me!'

Mary looked smug. 'Only about the lipstick. It was obvious what you had been up to when you returned from your walk all lit up inside.'

'And the bit about being the main topic of conversation?'

'True. But I knew it would take trickery to get you to reveal what happened.' Mary leaned forward. 'So are you in love?'

Iris opened her mouth with no idea how she was to answer. She certainly had deep feelings for Rob – she would never have kissed him unless she felt more than just friendship. Was she in love, though? She had thought she was in love with George, but now she knew she had only been in love with the wealth and social standing that would have come from being his wife. Her pride had been wounded by his rejection, not her heart.

She was saved from answering by the telephone ringing. She snatched up the receiver, expecting to be asked to identify a ship entering the Sound of Hoy. Instead, it was her CO with the news that Sally had been taken to hospital in Kirkwall. She was awake and suffering from a minor concussion. The doctors were confident she would make a full recovery.

Iris dropped into a chair, relief draining the strength from her legs. 'That's wonderful news, ma'am. Thank you.'

Mary nudged her. 'Ask when we can visit.'

'I'm sure she'll be glad of a visitor this afternoon,' the CO replied. 'They're keeping her in for a few days for observation.'

When she replaced the receiver, Iris was relieved to find Mary had forgotten all about her and Rob and was far more concerned with discussing how they were to get to the hospital in Kirkwall. As anxious as she was about Sally, her thoughts kept drifting back to Rob. Did she love him? Whatever the answer, she knew she had two unpleasant tasks to perform. First, she had to break the news about Rob to her mother, who would still be reeling from the broken engagement to George. Secondly, she must tell Stewart she was not interested in a relationship. Whether or not she was in love with Rob was something she would need time to work out. What she did know for sure was that she could never feel for Stewart what she felt for Rob.

–

In the event, Iris and Mary managed to cadge a lift to the hospital in an army truck that was going to Kirkwall.

They perched on boxes in the back of the truck, opposite a young corporal who was occupied in rolling a cigarette, flung this way and that each time the driver took a bend too fast. Which happened at every bend in the road.

'I hope that's not ammunition.' Iris eyed a box that had slammed against the side of the truck during a particularly vicious lurch. She and Mary had gathered a bunch of flowers from the path as they had walked back to Stromness, and now she held them with extra care to ensure the fragile petals weren't damaged.

'Nah,' said the corporal, looking up from his tin of tobacco, speaking for the first time. 'It's supplies for the prisoners of war.'

'Prisoners in Orkney?' Iris asked.

'Yeah, haven't you heard? There's a load of Italian POWs arrived. Gawd knows what they must think of bloody Orkney.'

Iris, thinking of her own reaction to the cold, windy islands, felt a twinge of sympathy for the Italians who were surely used to a far warmer, gentler climate. Although she had to admit, recent events had made her view Orkney with more fondness. While she doubted she would ever come to enjoy the frequent storms, she couldn't think of a more beautiful place than Orkney in the sunshine. Especially when walking hand in hand with a certain engine room artificer.

The driver dropped the girls outside the military hospital. After a bit of a search, they found the hut where Sally had been taken. She was propped up on pillows, her face as pale as the bedlinen, but she greeted them with a smile.

'How are you feeling?' Iris asked, perching on the edge of the bed and presenting Sally with the flowers.

'Not too bad. Bit of a headache.'

'Can you remember what happened?' Mary asked, taking the flowers from Sally to arrange them in a vase she'd persuaded one of the ward nurses to provide.

'Why does everyone keep asking that?' Sally pressed her fingers to the dressing, winced and jerked her fingers back. 'In the ambulance, Dr Irvine kept asking me what I remembered. I think he was trying to keep me awake.'

'What did you tell him?'

'That I couldn't remember. Then I was sick all over him.'

Mary snorted. 'All in all, he's not had a good day.'

Sally massaged her temples. 'I wish I could remember what happened. I just get vague images of Dr Irvine and then seeing you in the bunk room, Iris.'

Iris patted Sally's shoulder. 'It'll come back in good time.'

'You've remembered the important bit, though,' Mary said. 'I wish I could have seen Dr Irvine's face when you threw up all over him.'

Iris bit her lip, torn between laughter and sympathy, then pushed thoughts of Stewart from her mind for the time being. 'From what I can tell, the coal bunker lid tore off in the wind and hit you on the head.' She plucked at the blanket, twisting it between her fingers. 'I'm so sorry, Sally. I should never have let you go out alone. It's all my fault.'

'Don't be silly,' Sally said. 'We needed coal, and it was obviously an accident.' She pushed herself into a more upright position. 'Anyway, I think I know why it happened, and it's all my fault.'

Mary glared at Sally. 'How can it possibly be your fault?'

'You're going to laugh.'

'No we're not.' Iris nudged Mary with her elbow. 'Are we?'

'No.' Mary dropped into a chair, rubbing her arm. 'Go on, then. Explain how a door flying off its hinges can possibly be your fault.'

'When I was getting dressed this morning, I dropped my hat on the bed.'

There was a pause. Iris waited for Sally to elaborate but she appeared to think she had said enough. Iris exchanged a glance with Mary, who looked equally mystified. 'I don't follow.'

Mary, however, was more blunt. 'Is this one of your superstitions?'

'A hat on the bed means bad luck. I thought everyone knew that.'

'I've never heard of it,' Iris said. Having promised not to laugh, she was now forced to bite the inside of her cheek.

'Me neither,' Mary said. 'Besides, I must have put my hat on my bed loads of times, and I've yet to be knocked out by flying lumps of wood.'

Sally's brows drew together. 'I knew you wouldn't believe me.'

'Because it's coincidence,' Iris said. 'Look, it can't be doing you any good sitting in this stuffy hut, brooding. Why don't we have a bit of a walk?'

They had brought Sally's dressing gown and slippers with them, so helped her on with them. Sally had a moment's giddiness when she rose from the bed and clutched Iris's arm, her face turning even paler, but the colour soon came back to her cheeks. 'It feels good to be on my feet again,' she said.

A nurse came in at that point and scolded the girls for getting Sally out of bed. 'She needs her rest,' she said.

'I just want to stretch my legs,' Sally said. 'We won't go far.'

'Oh, very well. Don't blame me if you make yourself worse.'

Setting a slow pace, they walked through the hut, Mary and Iris supporting Sally on either side.

'How do you feel, Sally?' Iris asked when they reached the door.

'Not too bad. Let's get a breath of fresh air.'

Iris held open the door then they helped Sally down the wooden steps. There was a bench a little way along the path with a view onto fields, and Sally managed to walk that far. Trembling, she sank onto the bench; Iris and Mary sat beside her.

By this time, the storms had died away to be replaced with sunshine, and Sally drew a deep breath, looking around with a smile. 'That's better,' she said. 'I thought I'd go mad, staring at the walls in the hut.'

Just then, the door of the next hut opened and a young, dark-haired man in a dressing gown hobbled down the steps and approached the bench. He was hunched over, hugging his middle and didn't appear to have seen them. When he glanced up, he gave a start. '*Mi scusi*,' he said.

Iris stiffened. Was that Italian? Then she forgot her suspicion when she looked at the man's face and saw how pale he was. Beads of perspiration shone on his forehead. Enemy or not, this man was clearly in no condition to do them any harm.

She sprang up. 'Sit down before you pass out.'

'Thank you,' said the man, his legs folding the moment he reached the bench. His accent was definitely not British.

It fell to Mary to ask the question. 'Are you Italian?'

The man nodded. 'I am Aldo Vanni.'

'A prisoner of war?'

'*Sì.*'

'What are you doing here?' Iris asked.

'I had' – he frowned – '*appendicite.*'

'Appendicitis?' Iris asked.

'Ah, yes. That is what the doctor say.'

Iris gave a little laugh. 'I meant what are you doing outside this hut?' Shouldn't he be under guard? On the other hand, he didn't look dangerous.

Aldo glanced over his shoulder at the hut he had just left. 'They will look for me soon,' he said. 'I wanted some time alone.'

'Then why join us?' Sally asked with a smile.

Aldo smiled back, his cheeks dimpling. 'I am Italian. I cannot resist pretty girls.' He laughed then winced, putting his hand to his side.

'Are you sure you're well enough to be out?' Sally said, frowning.

'Absolutely. If I do not walk, how can I get strong?' He tapped his forehead. 'And you? What happen?'

'A silly accident,' Sally said.

'You will be well?'

'Oh, yes. They're just keeping me in for observation. How long will you be here?'

'Another week.'

Sally tilted her head. 'I've always been scared of getting appendicitis. Did it hurt terribly?'

Aldo nodded. 'It was bad. But I was ill for some days before the doctor would believe I was not trying to… what was the word he used? Shirk. He say I try to get out of work.'

'That's awful,' Sally said, her eyes wide.

Aldo grinned. 'I get last laugh. The surgeon is very angry. Says I might have died. So I get more time here before he send me back.'

'How long have you been in Orkney?'

'Only a few weeks.' Aldo hugged his arms to his stomach and shivered. 'Is very cold. Not like my home in Tuscany.'

Iris stirred, feeling uncomfortable. While Aldo didn't appear dangerous, she was conscious that he was a prisoner of war, an enemy. Sitting on the steps in the sunshine, chatting as though there were no gulf between them felt wrong. With a glance at Mary, she saw a furrow between her brows, and guessed she wasn't comfortable, either.

She rose. 'Well, I'm glad you're on the mend.' Iris turned to Sally. 'We ought to get you back to your ward before the nurse comes after us.'

They were halfway back to Sally's hut when the door Aldo had come through slammed open and a man in army uniform dashed down the steps. Mary grinned. 'Looks like he's been missed.'

Chapter Seventeen

Iris and Mary clambered off the bus in Stromness and strolled towards the Wrennery, only to bump into Rob, coming from the other direction.

'Iris, thank God.' He grasped her hands and kissed her cheek. Iris, aware of Mary's gaze, felt her face redden. 'I heard horrific tales about a Wren having her head stoved in up at Kyeness.'

'I'll see you back at the Wrennery,' Mary called and dashed away.

'I do like your friends,' Rob murmured, not releasing Iris's hands. 'Anyway, seeing as you clearly haven't had your brains dashed out, perhaps you would like to come for a drink with me?'

'Oh, Rob, I'd love to.' Iris was torn. 'But it was Sally who was injured. We've just come back from the hospital in Kirkwall.'

'I'm so sorry. Is she badly hurt? What happened?'

'Just a concussion, thank goodness, although she gave me a terrible scare.' She explained what had happened, shuddering when she remembered the shock of seeing Sally lying in a pool of blood. 'She'll be in hospital for a couple of days,' she concluded, 'but she's going to be fine.'

'How awful.' Rob put an arm around her shoulders. 'Come and have a drink. It'll help take your mind off the shock.'

But Iris didn't deserve an enjoyable evening when her cowardice had caused Sally's suffering. Sally might have forgiven her for sending her out alone in the storm, but Iris couldn't forgive herself. Not yet. 'Maybe we can go for a walk tomorrow?' she said. 'I promised Sally I'd wash the blood out of her collar.' She lifted the cloth bag holding Sally's uniform, which she had taken away from the hospital. 'I'm on night watch tomorrow, and I'm going to visit Sally in the afternoon, but we could meet when I get back.' Just the feel of his arm around her shoulder and the lingering warmth on her cheek where he had kissed her was a comfort. Part of her longed to spend more time with him, relive the happiness she had experienced on their walk. But Sally's accident was her fault, and she couldn't spend the evening enjoying herself when Sally was in bed in hospital. The least she could do was wash the blood off the collar and put together a package of toiletries and other things Sally would need.

'I'll meet you off the bus,' Rob promised and after a last kiss on the cheek, they parted. Iris directed her steps to the Wrennery. Once she had finished washing Sally's collar she had one other unpleasant task to complete. She had to write to her mother and tell her about Rob.

Once Iris had finished her chores and sat with her pen poised over the page, however, she pondered how much to reveal. Part of her wanted to say no more about Rob than to mention he was serving on board a minesweeper, leaving her mother to infer he was an officer. That would be the easy thing to do, but it felt wrong, a betrayal of both Rob and her own heart. No. She didn't want to hide the truth any longer. She dipped the pen into the ink and started to write, profoundly grateful for the many miles between her and home.

–

Rob watched Iris dash after Mary, a prickle of doubt intruding into his happiness. Of course she was worried about Sally. It was only natural. And he couldn't expect her to spend every free moment with him when she had plenty of other things to occupy her time.

All the same, he couldn't help wondering if she regretted kissing him the other day. It didn't help that his memory of the day held a sheen of unreality, like a dream that slowly fades after waking. Maybe he wouldn't feel so insecure if she came from the same class as him, but it was hard not to wonder if she was making excuses not to see him.

He pushed those fears aside when he saw Iris wave at him through the window of the bus the next day. Her face was beaming, and when she sprang from the bus and greeted him with a kiss on the cheek, there was no sign of being embarrassed to be seen with him. Mary was with her but, after greeting him with a nod, she departed with a wave, saying she had errands to run before they started their night watch later. Rob had to admit he was relieved to see her go. Not just because he wanted to be alone with Iris but also because he felt a little uncomfortable around her. She was a painful reminder of the friends he had lost on the *Royal Oak*. Although she had never mentioned the subject since she had approached him all that time ago at the Christmas party, he knew she wanted to talk about the night the ship had been torpedoed. But what could he say?

The horrific sights and sounds of men dying around him would stay with him until the end of his days, and the last thing he wanted was for Mary to know what her fiancé might have endured before he died.

Iris laid a hand upon his arm, recalling him to the present, bringing him back from the choking sensation and the reek of oil. 'You look awful,' she said. 'What's the matter?'

He bit back a smile. While it was her looks that had first attracted him, what fascinated him more now was the way she always spoke her mind. It might make for uncomfortable listening, but he always knew where he stood with her. It was a refreshing change from the clouded expressions he would see on some people's faces when they learned he had survived the *Royal Oak*, when he could tell they were wondering how badly he had been hurt. They never asked him directly, yet he could sense them talking about him behind their hands the moment his back was turned. No, give him someone like Iris any day.

The least he could do was return Iris's honesty with some of his own. 'I was thinking of the *Royal Oak*.'

Iris looked thoughtful. 'Is it Mary? Has she been asking you about it again?'

'No.' Rob rubbed his forehead. 'But seeing her brings it all back, because I know she associates me with the night she lost her fiancé.'

They had wandered rather aimlessly towards the piers. As ever, they were a hive of activity with vessels being piled up with vital supplies for the ships anchored in Scapa Flow. Soldiers who were off duty from the nearby gunnery posts ambled around the water's edge, laughing, smoking and complaining about the cold. Suddenly it all became too noisy. Rob turned to Iris. 'Have you eaten yet?' When she shook her head, he said. 'Let's find a cafe and grab a bite. My treat. If you're on night watch, you'll need to eat.'

They found a table in a cafe in Victoria Street, where they ordered fish stew. While they waited for their food and drinks to arrive, they spoke only of Sally's progress (she was doing well and due to be discharged the following day) and how they looked forward to the longer days now spring had arrived. It was only when they were scraping the last of the delicious stew from their bowls that Iris reintroduced the subject of the *Royal Oak*. 'Is it very painful to talk about?' she asked, mopping the last of the sauce with a hunk of bannock. Then she looked down at her plate with a chuckle. 'If my mother could see me now, she'd have a fit.'

'They don't teach you the correct way of mopping up sauce in finishing school?'

A flash of laughter lit her eyes. 'I'll have you know I went to a very forward-thinking school. I'm sure I'd be highly commended for making the best use of the tools at my disposal.' She finished the last of the bannock then said, 'But let's not discuss my terrible manners. We were talking about you.'

Rob nodded although he finished the last of his bread before replying. 'I know. I'm not trying to avoid it. Well, not much.' He leaned back in his chair. 'It's painful to talk about the *Royal Oak*,' he said finally. 'There are parts of that night…' He shuddered as the memories threatened to drag him under again. 'Well, I wouldn't wish that knowledge on my worst enemy. It's best forgotten.'

'But *you* can't forget.' Iris's logic was relentless. 'So why not tell me? I'm not Mary. I didn't lose a loved one there. You can tell me without upsetting me.'

'I…' It was hard to explain his reluctance. Iris represented all the people the crew of the *Royal Oak* had been trying to protect. By telling her, he felt like he was contaminating her, somehow. He wanted to preserve her innocence.

Iris watched him with an unwavering gaze for some time. When he didn't say more, she pressed her lips together and nodded. 'Very well. I won't press you. But the offer stands if you ever want to unburden yourself.'

He nodded, feeling as though he had let her down. Then a thought struck him. There was a burden he could share without having to force her to see the horrors the world could hold. 'There is something,' he said.

Iris's eyes widened, and she leaned forward. 'Go on.'

'I don't know if you ever heard about the rumours surrounding how the U-boat got into Scapa Flow.'

Iris shook her head then frowned. 'No, wait. Mary did say something. A rumour about someone local guiding the U-boat past the obstructions. But I didn't think anyone seriously believed it.'

'I keep thinking about it,' Rob said. 'I didn't believe it at first. Didn't want to believe it.'

'What changed your mind?'

Rob drained the tea from his cup before answering. 'I didn't know Scapa Flow so well at the time. We hadn't been here for long when it happened. But I know it better now. The channel the U-boat must have sailed through was barely navigable, even then.' All access to Scapa Flow had since been blocked with wrecks, and Churchill had ordered barriers to be placed across the channels between the small islands that formed the eastern side of Scapa Flow. 'I've been there several times. It would have taken expert navigation and even then, they could only have got through at high tide.' He looked at Iris. 'How did they know the exact route to take?'

Iris shrugged. 'Maybe they didn't. They might not have known how difficult it was and just got lucky.'

'Perhaps.'

'But you don't believe that.'

'I don't know. I can't get the idea out of my head, though. I mean if someone with local knowledge did help them, what if they're still on the island? What if they're waiting for the opportunity to do it again?'

A pucker formed between Iris's brows. 'But it was nearly two years ago, and no U-boat has managed to get into Scapa Flow since then. Doesn't that show it was simply bad luck that they got through last time?'

'Or maybe they're biding their time. For all we know they could still be passing information and don't want to reveal their presence by guiding another U-boat through.'

'But Scapa Flow's been blocked since then.'

'That side has. There's still a way in through Hoy Sound.'

Iris snorted. 'Trust me, we have to alert the navy whenever an otter takes a swim through there. Nothing could get through without our knowing.'

'I know. I still worry, though. There are other ways of harming the fleet.'

'What do you mean?'

Rob hesitated, then decided it was time he shared a worry that had been weighing on his mind. 'Maybe I've let my imagination get the better of me, but the enemy always seems to be a step ahead when it comes to laying mines. It seems like no sooner have we cleared a channel than we find new mines there. I did speak to my CO about it, but he said it was just coincidence.'

To his relief, Iris didn't laugh. 'Do *you* think it's a coincidence?'

Rob shook his head. 'I think there's a spy on the island, reporting on the minesweepers' routes.'

–

Iris felt extra alert all through the following night watch.

'What's eating you?' Mary asked her when, for the second time when she was supposed to be having a sleep in the bunk room, she put her head through the signal room hatch.

'Can't sleep.' Iris joined Mary beside the window. 'I can't stop worrying about what my mother is going to say when she gets my letter, and I keep thinking about what Rob said.' She had told Mary of Rob's suspicions on the walk to the signal station.

Mary sighed. 'I keep thinking about it too. I can't take my eyes off the sea in case something is trying to slip through Hoy Sound.' Even now she leaned against the sill, gazing out into the darkness.

The words were hardly out of her mouth when the telephone's shrill ring made them both jump. Mary grabbed the receiver. 'WSS.'

Iris could hear the voice speaking from the other end of the line, but she couldn't make out any words.

Mary glanced up at her. 'They want identification of a vessel crossing the loop.'

Iris pulled on her coat and went out onto the balcony. It was a clear night, and the stars reflected upon the calm sea with an eerie glow. The moonlight bathed the breaking waves with a phosphorescent haze, and it was just possible to make out the ragged shape of the shoreline. Nerves jangling, Iris leaned over the rail and strained her eyes as she scanned the water for signs of movement. Then she saw a darker shape against the water – it was certainly not the sinister cigar shape of a U-boat and not big enough to be a threat. Picking up the Aldis lamp, she sighted the vessel through the crosshairs and flashed a signal, requesting identification.

The reply came back, and she could have laughed with relief. 'It's the *Seasnake*,' she called to Mary. This was a fishing boat they were familiar with. 'Incoming.' She heard Mary relay the information and replace the receiver. The boat flashed another message and she called to Mary once she'd jotted it down. 'They've got Archie with them – he cadged a lift to check his creels, and they were delayed by engine trouble.' Sighting the fishing boat again, she sent a further message. 'If he caught a lobster, tell him I'm coming for lunch tomorrow.'

Soon after, the boat went out of sight. Laughing at herself for letting her imagination run away with her, she went back into the signal room and sat in front of the stove and buffed her hands to warm them. No matter how she tried, however, she couldn't get Rob's fears from her mind. What if he was right? What if there was a spy sending information on minesweeping operations?

Mary must have been reading her mind. 'You've let Rob get you thoroughly spooked, haven't you?' she said.

Iris gave a shaky laugh. 'I've got to admit, until I found out it was the *Seasnake*, I'd managed to convince myself there was an enemy vessel patrolling the waters.'

Mary dropped into the other chair and nodded. 'I suppose I thought the same.'

Iris's gaze drifted to the desk and the log book. The sight of it jogged her memory; She sat up straight. 'Did you hear any more about the mystery low-flying aircraft?' She'd made sure the other signallers had been told to keep an eye out after the lieutenant had asked her to report any sightings.

'No. I assumed it was a pilot pulling a prank.'

'So did I. But what if it's an enemy aircraft dropping mines?'

'How would they know where to place them?' Mary sounded sceptical.

'I don't know.' Iris slumped back in her seat. 'I'll keep a watch for it though. Just in case.'

Mary nodded and gazed at the fire but judging from her expression, her thoughts were miles away. 'I was glad to be posted to Orkney because it made me feel closer to Owen,' she said after a pause. 'But now I wonder if it was such a good thing. I can't get his fate out of my mind.'

The fire was burning low, so Iris donned gloves and shovelled more coal into the stove before answering. 'I don't think it's such a bad thing. Not if it makes you extra-vigilant. There's no undoing what happened to the *Royal Oak*, but we can do our utmost to ensure it never happens again.'

Chapter Eighteen

The next day, an unwelcome delivery clouded what should have been an enjoyable day off: a letter from her mother. Iris had never had such a speedy reply to a letter from Letitia before; she could only imagine she had sat straight at her desk to tear off a reply once she had read the news about Rob.

Deciding this was best read in private, Iris took it outside and walked to the harbour. Sitting on a stone wall with the wash of the waves forming a calming background, she finally plucked up the courage to read her mother's reply.

I can't imagine what you're playing at, Letitia had written, her usual elegant, angular handwriting more spiked than usual.

> *George Silverwood was perfect for you: from an impeccable background, with extensive property and capable of supporting a family in the greatest of comfort. Felicity has left to join the WAAF, so I'm sure George could be persuaded to forget her. You must be due some leave soon.*

Iris still had some time to go before she would be granted leave. Besides, even if she went home tomorrow, she didn't want to see George. The memory of her humiliation was still too fresh. She would be happy never to see him again.

Even if you can't persuade George to take you back, her mother continued, *there must be many more suitable men in Orkney. An officer at the very least. What happened with that nice doctor you told me about?*

Iris had to admit life would be easier if she preferred Stewart to Rob. Stewart could give her the life she had always craved, while Rob's determination to build a life in Orkney didn't suit Iris's plans at all. Although it wasn't an issue now, she would be faced with hard choices if she ended up falling in love with him. Maybe it would be kinder on them both if she broke it off with Rob now, before they got hurt. Her stomach twisted in knots the instant the thought crossed her mind. No. She couldn't bear the thought of giving Rob pain, and for all she knew, Rob might change his mind about settling in Orkney long before she had to make any choices about their future. She pushed her worries from her mind and returned to the letter.

Don't think marrying for love will do you any good. Iris's fingers tightened on the paper, and she braced herself for the tale she knew was about to follow.

Never forget what happened to your Aunt Sybil. When she first started seeing Jonathan Brownlow, all she could say was that she had never felt this way before, that she couldn't imagine life without him. I would understand, she said, when I fell in love. Well, she wouldn't listen to our mother's warnings, and married him without a thought. She's had plenty of time to rue her decision now she's left struggling to pay her rent every month from her pitiful widow's pension.

The remainder of the letter continued in the same vein. There was no doubt her mother felt strongly that Iris was making a huge mistake.

Iris folded the letter into her pocket and gazed out to sea. Marry Rob. Was that what Letitia thought would happen? But that was part of the future she had already decided she wasn't ready to contemplate.

On an impulse, she pulled the letter from her pocket again and reread the part about Auntie Sybil. She had never met Sybil; she only knew what Letitia had told her. From what she had heard, she imagined an unkempt, half-starved woman who was unable to look after herself and who frittered away what little cash she had on drink. Certainly her mother always spoke of her as someone totally unsuitable for an impressionable young girl to meet. Never in all the times her mother had used Sybil as a dire warning, had she said that Sybil had been in love with the man she had married. It made Iris regard Sybil in a different light. No longer air-headed and swept off her feet but someone who'd loved deeply enough to defy her parents and turn her back on a life of wealth. Had she felt the same elation that Iris felt whenever she saw Rob? Whatever she had felt, it had ended badly. Iris would be a fool not to learn from her aunt's mistake. It struck her that however Sybil might have turned out, she had started life just like Iris – a young, pretty woman of good family and education. A slight chill that had nothing to do with the weather trickled down Iris's spine.

'Penny for your thoughts.'

Iris looked up from her letter with a start to see Stewart. She had been so absorbed in the letter she hadn't heard him approach. 'Hello. Just reading a letter from home.'

'Because sitting on a wall in the cold wind is the perfect place for reading news from home.' Stewart perched on the wall beside her.

'It is if the news is from my mother.' Iris gave a light laugh. Unbidden, the words her mother had written about Stewart sprang into her mind. Stewart was far more suitable for a girl of Iris's class. She would never be left destitute if she married him.

'I'm glad I've found you alone,' Stewart said after a pause. 'I never got a chance to apologise for knocking you into the water.'

Iris folded the letter and put it in her pocket, giving Stewart her full attention. Between Rob's kisses and Sally's accident, so much had happened since the night on the *Tyne* that the awful memory of the struggle for air had been driven from her mind. Her memories of the return boat journey from the *Tyne* were somewhat confused. If she was to believe Rob – and she had no reason not to – it was Stewart who had knocked her into the water. However, Stewart was no sailor. It had been an accident and no lasting damage had been done.

Her mother's letter crackled in her pocket as she turned to face him. His body seemed to be rigid with tension and his expression radiated anxiety. 'Please don't fret about it,' she said. 'It was an accident, and all is well now.' Because Rob had rescued her. After the accident, she had been determined to tell Stewart she couldn't see him any more. But now, with the awareness of her mother's letter in her pocket and thoughts of Aunt Sybil looming in her thoughts like a thundercloud, she hesitated to dismiss Stewart wholly from her life.

Stewart's expression eased. 'I am glad.' He reached for her hand which lay on the wall between them.

The touch made her shudder and acting from some instinct deep within herself, she jerked her hand away. She pulled her handkerchief from her pocket to cover her reaction. 'This wretched wind,' she said, dabbing her eyes to give an excuse for pulling away, 'it makes my eyes water.'

Stewart addressed his next words to the ground. 'I don't blame you for being angry. All I ask is a chance to make it up to you.'

This was where she should make it clear she was with Rob now. After all, she never usually had a problem blurting the first thing on her mind. But as she shifted position to look him in the eye, she shoved the hanky back in her pocket, and her fingers encountered the smooth paper of the letter. 'You don't have to make it up to me. It was an accident. We're still friends.'

'You're too kind,' he said with a smile. 'But you must allow me to make reparations for my sake if not for yours.'

'And how do you intend doing that?'

'Dinner. In Kirkwall.'

Iris felt as though she was in the eye of a storm between two warring impulses. One half of her wanted nothing more to do with Stewart but yearned to spend every free moment with Rob. The other screamed dire warnings in her mother's voice about Aunt Sybil. She couldn't have been more aware of the letter in her pocket had it been carved upon lead. Although she had tried to dismiss her worries about the future, they refused to be silenced. Anyway, what harm would it do to remain friends with Stewart as long as she made it clear she had no romantic intentions? 'That would be lovely,' she said. 'As friends, of course.'

'Of course.' He made a movement as though to cover her hand again but pulled it back before he touched her. 'I understand. I can be satisfied with that. For now.'

The right thing to do would be to tell him about Rob. Make it clear they could never be anything more than friends because she knew she could never feel the same way about Stewart as she did about Rob. 'I…' she began. 'I don't know…' Maybe if she hadn't just read the letter she would have been able to finish that sentence the way she had intended. 'I don't know when I'll be able to get a late pass,' she said instead. 'I'll let you know.'

She stood and brushed down her skirt. 'Anyway, I must go. I—' She grappled for an excuse. 'I promised Archie Heddle I'd ask Rob if he could take a look at his friend's boat. The engine's been playing up.' She described how Archie had been out late last night in the dark. 'Mary and I were on the point of reporting the signal from the indicator loop as a U-boat,' she finished with a laugh. 'If they hadn't signalled back, the whole wrath of the navy would have descended upon him.'

'Then for Archie's sake, I'm glad you were there.' Stewart jumped down from the wall. 'Well, I'd better get back to the surgery.'

Iris was relieved to wave him off. She was angry with herself for not being completely honest with him. Why, when she usually blurted the first thing on her mind, couldn't she have told him about Rob?

–

Deep in thought as she made her way back to the Wrennery, she didn't see Rob until she nearly walked into him.

'Steady, lass.' Rob caught her around the waist to stop her from stumbling. 'Anyone would think you were making a habit of throwing yourself into my arms.'

Iris leaned into him, allowing herself to enjoy the feeling of being held by him for a moment longer. If she had never met Rob, she would have gone out with Stewart without a qualm, never knowing it was possible for a man to make her pulse kick with excitement. It was strangely intoxicating, and she didn't want to let this feeling go. If only Rob was someone her mother would approve of, she would be perfectly happy. 'I was coming to find you,' she said. She relayed the message from Archie.

Rob nodded. 'I'll try and get up there in the next day or two. But I was coming to look for you. I've just seen Mary, and she said I might find you here.' When Iris shot him an enquiring glance, he went on, 'There's an army truck leaving for Kirkwall in half an hour, and they've got space for you and Mary if you want a lift to see Sally.'

'That's wonderful.' She pulled him into an enthusiastic hug. 'Thank you for thinking of us. Another reason why—' She broke off, her face flaming. *Another reason why you're better than Stewart.* That was what she had been about to say. Rob already had a low opinion of Stewart, she didn't want him to think they were still in competition, even if she had been about to make a favourable comparison. 'Another reason why you're such a good man,' she said finally, congratulating herself on her quick thinking.

The army truck dropped Iris and Mary at the hospital entrance, and the driver said he would pick them up for the return journey in two hours. The girls found Sally in her dressing gown, sitting outside, making the most of the sunshine. The bruise on her forehead had blossomed into a spectacular rainbow of blues and purples, fading to yellow at the edges. To their surprise, she was sitting with Aldo, the Italian prisoner of war. As they approached, he sprang to his feet, saying he had to return to his ward.

Sally laughed as he dashed away. 'I don't know how he manages to get out of his ward so easily. I suppose, being on an island, no one is too concerned about him escaping.' Her face clouded. 'Anyway, I get the impression it was something of a relief for him to be captured. From what he says, he's not happy about Italy being allied to Germany.'

Mary gave Sally a stern look. 'You're not getting sweet on a prisoner of war, are you, Sally? That can only end badly.'

'Of course not.' Indignation wreathed Sally's face. 'There's only one man for me, you know that.'

'Yes, a man who doesn't see you as more than a friend.'

Iris stepped in hurriedly to avert an argument. 'I'm sure there's no harm in showing kindness to a lonely prisoner of war,' she said.

'He is lonely,' Sally said, subsiding. 'He's told me all about his home in Tuscany. It sounds lovely. And look.' She pulled out a silver chain from under the neck of her dressing gown, showing them a silver medallion. 'When he heard about my accident, he gave me his St Christopher medal. Said it provided protection against storms as well as protecting me on journeys.'

Iris shook her head and exchanged a wry glance with Mary. If Sally had found someone as superstitious as herself, it could only be bad news. 'That was kind.' She changed the subject. 'Any news on when you can leave?'

'Tomorrow.'

'Marvellous,' Iris said. 'The Wrennery hasn't been the same without you.'

Sally nodded but Iris noticed her cast a wistful glance in the direction Aldo had disappeared in. Privately, Iris agreed with Mary. It was a good thing Sally would be returning to the other side of the island where she would be unlikely to see Aldo again.

'You'll never guess what Aldo told me,' Sally said.

'You have to hop on your left leg and kiss the St Christopher every morning or something terrible will happen,' Mary said.

'No. Don't be silly.'

'That's rich, coming from someone who once refused to budge from a bench until she had seen a second magpie,' Iris said.

Sally had the grace to blush. 'Maybe something bad would have happened if we hadn't waited.'

'As opposed to us getting mess fatigues for being late to class?'

'This is different, anyway. Nothing like that. Aldo told me more about the doctor who misdiagnosed him.'

'Has he remembered who it is?' Iris asked, glad for a reason to steer the conversation away from Sally's superstitions. While she agreed with Mary, it didn't seem right to lecture Sally on her idiocy when she was in hospital.

'Yes. It was Stewart Irvine.'

Iris stared at Sally in disbelief. 'You're joking.'

Sally shook her head, then winced and put her hand to her head. 'I keep forgetting how much that hurts.'

But Iris was too anxious to defend Stewart to show Sally any concern. 'It can't have been Stewart. He works over on the other side of Mainland. What would he have been doing on Lamb Holm?'

Sally shrugged. 'No idea. But it was definitely Stewart.'

'How do you know?'

'Because we both saw Stewart here yesterday evening, and Aldo pointed him out to me. He said he had been working on the Mainland side of the causeway when he had been taken ill, and someone went for a doctor and brought Stewart back. He'd been visiting someone in St Mary's.'

Iris had to concede that sounded reasonable. St Mary's was the nearest village on Mainland to where work on the barriers was taking place. 'I suppose he could have been visiting friends,' she said. After all, St Mary's was only about twenty miles from Stromness. As a doctor, he would get a fuel allowance, although using it to visit friends twenty miles away was definitely an abuse of the system. Remembering how she had enjoyed the luxury of having Stewart drive her around the island, she felt a prickle of remorse at her tacit approval of his wastefulness.

'I don't know about that,' Sally said, 'but Aldo's positive it was Stewart. He told me Stewart barely examined him before he told the officer in charge that Aldo was malingering and there was no reason why he shouldn't be put straight back to work. Imagine having to do heavy labour when in such pain!' Sally's distress and indignation rang from her voice, and Iris couldn't deny the tale showed Stewart in a bad light.

'There has to be an explanation.'

'Yes,' said Sally. 'Stewart's a bad doctor.'

Iris couldn't accept this. 'He's a *doctor*.' In Iris's eyes, doctors were beyond criticism.

'Really, Iris, you're a hopeless snob.' This was Mary. Iris opened her mouth to protest, but Mary ploughed on before Iris could get the words out. 'You don't want Stewart to be in the wrong because that would involve blaming someone you believe to be of impeccable breeding and education. Instead, you'll go to any lengths to come up with a convoluted explanation that involves Aldo failing to recognise the man who sent him back to work when he was suffering from appendicitis.'

Iris could feel her face burning. 'But there might be a reasonable explanation. At least let me ask Stewart about it before you condemn him. Aldo must have been feverish or something. How can he be sure he remembers correctly?'

Mary snorted. 'That would make Stewart's misdiagnosis even worse if he couldn't even recognise a high temperature.'

'He could have—'

But Mary cut across Iris's feeble protest. 'I don't understand why you're so anxious to defend him. He's the one who nearly got you drowned and didn't even lift a finger to help.'

'That was an accident.'

Sally intervened. 'Please don't argue.' She addressed Iris. 'By all means ask Stewart about it. I have no reason to doubt Aldo, but you don't know him like I do.'

Iris frowned. 'Just how well *do* you know him?'

Now it was Sally's turn to blush, and the conversation turned away from Stewart's failings to teasing Sally. Yet Iris couldn't forget the accusations and resolved to speak to Stewart about it next time she saw him.

–

Sally returned to the Wrennery the next day. Mary and Iris forgot their differences over Stewart and went for a walk to pick some daffodils to make her a welcome back bouquet. On their way back, they went into the NAAFI, pooling their chocolate coupons to add chocolate to their gift.

Sally was still on sick leave but opted not to return to Yorkshire, saying she couldn't face the journey. Instead, she set to work knitting more socks in the common room while Mary and Iris were on duty. Iris, who had neglected her knitting over her worries for Sally, joined her when she was off duty.

Iris had hoped to spend her next free evening with Rob. However, as he had promised to visit Archie's friend to repair the *Seasnake*, Iris, deciding she didn't want to spend the evening covered in engine oil, arranged to have her dinner with Stewart instead. She'd decided to be open with Rob and told him Stewart had wanted to make it up to her for knocking her out of the boat.

'I suppose it's the least he could do,' Rob had said. 'Although jumping in after you would have been a better way to show you how sorry he was.'

Stewart drove them to Kirkwall again. When Iris expressed her surprise about wasting his petrol allowance, Stewart said, 'I have plenty to spare. Orkney's not a big place.'

Iris found this didn't sit very well with her. Considering she had hoarded fabric and soap when she had been at home, it was somewhat uncomfortable to realise she was changing her mind about rationing now. Maybe it was seeing how little the Heddles had to live on and yet were perfectly willing to share what they had. Or maybe something about the island way of life was affecting her – how it was accepted that you helped out where you could and didn't just look after yourself. It seemed selfish to use precious fuel for a jaunt to Kirkwall when they could have stayed in Stromness and offered to run errands for some of the locals who had no transport. Maybe island life was rubbing off on her.

However, she held her tongue for now. But when they were at their table in the Kirkwall Hotel, about to tuck into a very tasty-looking fish pie, she knew there was something she did need to ask him about. 'Sally got to know an Italian prisoner of war at the hospital,' she began.

Stewart paused, his fork poised over his meal. 'I'm surprised they let prisoners mix with other patients,' he said.

'I get the impression he's not supposed to, but managed to find a way,' Iris said with a grin. 'Anyway, he told her something I found concerning.'

'What was that?'

'He said you advised the guards to put him back to work when he actually had appendicitis.'

Iris watched Stewart carefully as she spoke and her heart sank when his gaze flickered slightly. 'Appendicitis?' he said.

She nodded and went on to describe what Sally had said. Stewart listened with a frown of concern, but his initial reaction said it all. He remembered. He *had* been the one to dismiss Aldo as a malingerer.

Stewart rubbed his forehead when she finished. 'You have to understand how imprecise diagnoses can be,' he said. 'It was difficult to examine him with the guards clustered around, and I admit I'd had a glass or two of whisky before seeing him. But the man who came to fetch me said it was an emergency, so I thought it was better for me to examine him rather than wait for a doctor to come all the way out from Kirkwall. The guards were of the opinion he was time-wasting, so I suppose I let that influence me when I should have relied upon my own judgement. I'm sorry I seem to have got it wrong. I hope the fellow's better now.'

'Much better.' Iris relaxed a little. She should have realised there would be a reasonable explanation, and Stewart seemed genuinely contrite.

She enjoyed her meal more after clearing that up. Stewart was good company, entertaining her with stories of his life in Edinburgh. The more she saw of him, the more she was convinced he was exactly the sort of suitor her mother would approve of. A pity, she reflected as she watched him over the rim of her glass, that she felt none of the attraction that she felt for Rob. That she ached for Rob even as she listened to this charming, handsome, engaging man. If someone had told her a year ago that she would prefer a mechanic over a doctor, she would have thought they were mad. She found herself thinking of Rob, wishing she was with him, watching him tinker with a boat engine, even if it meant standing around in a cold, windy cove. What was happening to her?

The question was, should she heed her mother's warnings and allow Stewart to court her in the hope of securing a comfortable life? Or should she follow her heart and risk ending up like Aunt Sybil?

Chapter Nineteen

'Who are you writing to?' Sally looked up from her knitting at Iris, who had settled at one of the tables in the common room and opened her writing case.

'My mother.' Iris sighed. This called for a confession. 'The other day I started to realise how selfish I've been.'

'I don't think you're selfish,' Sally said. She waved the half-finished sock she was knitting at Iris. 'You've given up a lot of time to the knitting drive when you're busy enough with your own duties.'

'If you knew me a year ago you wouldn't say so,' Iris said. 'It's a good thing Mary isn't here, because she would agree with me.'

'I know what you're like now, and that's good enough for me.'

'It might not be when you know.' Iris wrote the date at the top of the page, then put down her pen. 'Something Stewart said about his petrol allowance got me thinking about how I had stored up things like fabric and soap at the start of the war, before rationing kicked in. I was shocked when Stewart said how he'd been using more than his share of petrol for his own purposes.'

'Quite right too,' said Sally, who hadn't forgiven Stewart for misdiagnosing Aldo, even after Iris had reported what he'd said.

'Yes, but I can't criticise him and then not try to make amends for holding onto more than my fair share of goods.'

'You admit you're at fault, and you're sorry for it. That's the important thing.'

Iris shook her head. 'It doesn't feel enough to be sorry. Not when there are people like Elspeth desperate for new clothes and forced to make do with patching old ones.' She picked up her pen again. 'That's why I'm writing to Mother. I'm going to ask her to post some of the cloth lurking in my cupboard. There's a bolt of woollen cloth that would make a lovely coat for Elspeth. Last time I saw her, she told me she has a sewing machine that I'm welcome to use.'

There was a pause while Iris wrote the opening lines of her letter and Sally counted the stitches she was casting on. Finally, Sally said, 'That's why you're too good for Stewart. You're sorry for what you've done and want to do better. Stewart knows it's wrong to misuse his petrol allowance but he keeps on doing it because he gets away with it.'

Iris gave her an exasperated look. 'You're never going to forgive him for missing Aldo's appendicitis, are you?'

'Aldo could have died!'

'It was a mistake, and Stewart's sorry.'

'Not so sorry he's showing any signs of changing his way of life.' Sally punctuated her remarks with stabs of a knitting needle. 'You feel bad about your past behaviour, and you're making changes. I like the person you've become, but when I first knew you, I found you abrasive.'

'That's one way of putting it.' Mary had arrived. She flopped into a chair with a sigh and said, 'The walk from

Kyeness doesn't get any shorter.' Then looking from Sally to Iris, she said, 'What are we talking about – our faults?'

'Only Stewart's,' Sally replied.

'That's a relief. I wouldn't want you to start on mine.'

'Who says we didn't cover yours while you were out?'

'I didn't feel my ears burning. So either you were discussing me, and this is final proof that all your superstitions are nonsense, or you didn't mention me at all.'

Sally threw a ball of wool at Mary, and their bickering continued. Iris took the opportunity to tear off a quick letter to her mother, requesting the cloth. By the time she had finished, the other two had subsided to laughter.

'What's all this about Stewart's faults?' Mary asked when Iris joined them in the comfortable chairs. She nodded when Iris repeated what she had told Sally about his use of the petrol allowance and her own change of heart. 'I hate to admit it, but Sally's right.' Mary dodged a mock punch that Sally aimed at her arm. 'I don't know why you won't give Stewart the boot. It's obvious you're crazy about Rob, so why string Stewart along?'

'You'll think I'm mad,' Iris said. Not to mention snobbish, she thought. But she was starting to learn that her friends were only too willing to help, if only she could find the courage to open her heart. 'It's my Aunt Sybil,' she said, struggling to find the words to explain.

'What's she got to do with anything?'

Stumbling over her words, with many pauses while she tried to express her fears, she told them about Sybil and the unsuitable man she had fallen in love with. She gained in confidence when, despite her fears, her friends didn't laugh or call her a snob but listened carefully, appearing to think hard about what she was saying. Finally she concluded with, 'Whenever I think about Rob, I keep hearing my mother telling me I'll end up like Aunt Sybil.'

'But why should you?' Mary said, her forehead creased. 'You're different people. Just because things didn't work out for your aunt, it doesn't mean the same will happen to you.'

Sally leaned forward. 'Anyway, who says things went badly for Sybil? Have you met her?'

'I... no. I just know what my mother told me.'

'Then you only know your mother's side of the story, and she sets a great deal of store on wealth. She's bound to feel that Sybil threw her life away. It would be interesting to know if Sybil really is the pitiful wreck your mother makes out. I wonder if she regrets marrying for love?'

'But her husband died not long after they married.'

Sally gave a little sigh. 'If it was me, I'd rather have a short time of happiness with the man I loved. I want the kind of love my mother had for my father. Better that than years spent surrounded with comforts but with a man who left my heart cold.'

Mary rolled her eyes. 'Here we go – love conquers all and all that rot.'

'What's wrong with that?'

'I just think you shouldn't pin all your hopes for happiness on a man.'

'You should meet my mother,' Iris said to Mary. 'The two of you would get on like a house on fire.'

'I don't think you should look for happiness in wealth, either.'

'Then what would make you happy?' Sally asked. 'If you remove love and security from the equation, what's left?'

'Myself. When it comes down to it, the only person I can rely on is myself.'

Iris grimaced. 'That sounds bleak.'

'And lonely,' put in Sally. 'Isn't there even room for friends?'

'I didn't mean it like that,' Mary said, looking contrite. 'I just...' She rubbed her eyes. 'When Owen died, I thought my whole world had crumbled. I had nothing worth living for. After a while, though, my mam gave me a good talking to. Told me if I couldn't find the strength within myself to go on, I might as well give up now. We all experience sorrow throughout our lives, she said, and I'd better learn to deal with it.'

'Your mother doesn't pull her punches,' Sally said.

Mary gave a crooked smile. 'Let's say I didn't appreciate her wisdom straight away. And this wasn't the day after Owen died, mind, but after I'd been wafting around in misery for nearly a year. But I gradually came to see her point of view. I knew I had to carve out a life for myself so I wasn't dependent on anyone else. That's when I decided to join the Wrens.'

'But how is that moving on from Owen, when he was in the navy?'

Mary flushed, and Iris, not for the first time, wished she could find a way to stop herself from blurting out the first thought that popped into her head. Mary didn't often speak of Owen, and here was Iris, stamping on her when she had shared something that must have brought back painful memories. She caught Mary's arm. 'I'm sorry. I didn't mean—'

'Forget it.' May rose. 'Anyway, I'm still frozen solid after the walk back. I'm going to have a bath.'

This time Iris did manage to bite back her first thought. The ablutions in the Wrennery were icy cold, and the water was never very hot. Mary was unlikely to warm up in five inches of tepid water. She could only hope Mary would forgive her for her thoughtless remark.

—

Mary didn't seem to hold Iris's remark against her, and was perfectly friendly towards her over the days that followed. However, Iris promised herself to make more of an effort to think before she spoke. She couldn't stop thinking about the conversation that had led up to her careless remark, however. She seemed to have two choices: follow her heart and choose Rob or listen to her mother and choose Stewart. She rejected Mary's suggestion out of hand. It was all very well for someone as capable as Mary to decide to forgo relationships and rely on herself. But Iris didn't have a career or any useful skills to fall back on. She couldn't see her ability at Morse, semaphore or flags to be an advantage in the landlocked Chilterns. Unlike Mary and Sally who had both had jobs before the war, Iris had lived off her parents, and the only skills she had learned involved household management. Somehow, after being in the Wrens, she couldn't see herself giving up her independence to live at home again. She wanted to forge her own life. And to her that meant marriage, even if Mary would argue against it.

She still wasn't any closer towards forming a decision a week later, when she was taking a walk through Stromness on her day off. She was about to go into a cafe when a familiar voice hailed her. But it couldn't be. Not here.

She looked in the direction from where the voice had come from and nearly squealed with delight. There was no mistaking the tall, broad-shouldered figure and the smiling face, even if it was more careworn than the last time she had seen it. 'Daddy!' she cried and ran down the lane to meet him.

'Come here, rainbow.' Charles Tredwick caught Iris around the waist and swung her round.

Giggling, Iris looked round to make sure no one she knew was nearby. She'd never hear the last of it if Mary heard her father's pet name for her. 'What are you doing here?'

'That's a fine welcome from my daughter who hasn't seen me in over a year. Didn't you get my letter?'

Iris shook her head. 'It must have gone astray. I'm so happy to see you.'

'When I heard you were here, I put in for a transfer to a ship based in Scapa Flow. I got transferred to HMS *Snowdon* two weeks ago.'

'That's wonderful. How long are you here?'

'About a week. We've put in for some minor repairs. Fancy something to eat?'

Iris slipped her arm through her father's. 'I'd love it.'

'Good.' Charles pointed towards the harbour. 'There's an army car about to drive to Kirkwall. The driver told me the hotel in Stenness serves good food. He's offered to drop me off on his way to Kirkwall.'

A short time later, Iris and her father were being ushered to a table in the Standing Stones Hotel, the very same table where Iris and Rob had been seated.

Over the main course, they caught up with each other's news, sharing all the things they had been unable to say because of censorship. Iris glowed under her father's approval as she described her work in the signal station.

'You've really done well,' Charles said, putting down his knife and fork.

Iris beamed at him. She had always got on with him better than her mother. While Letitia was always critical, Charles was warm and encouraging. Some of her happiest memories were of strolling through the woods and hills of the Chilterns together. Sadly, his work commitments had always limited the time they had together, and they had scarcely seen each other at all after he had joined the navy.

'Now,' said Charles, 'what's all this your mother has been telling me about you getting mixed up with a rating?'

If Iris had been in any doubt about her feelings for Rob, the way her heart lurched at the mention of him would have cleared it up. She was used to criticism from her mother. However, if her father was displeased, that was far more wounding.

'I don't think "mixed up" is the right term, Daddy,' she replied.

'But you have been walking out with him.'

'Well, yes. I like him.' This was a huge understatement. 'He's in the navy, an engine room artificer. He's a petty officer, not a rating.'

'What does his father do?'

Iris had once seen a film of lions in Africa, where a playful cub had been gently but firmly swatted away from food by a huge adult male. Iris now knew exactly how that cub must have felt. 'He works in the Glasgow shipyards.'

'I see.' Charles tapped the stem of his wine glass. The silence hung heavily between them. Iris gazed at him in anxiety. She pushed her half-eaten fish to the side of her plate, unable to eat any more.

'You have to understand,' Charles said eventually, 'that we have a certain standard to uphold in our family. I want you to live a comfortable life, the life you've been brought up to. Crossing class barriers might sound romantic, but you would not enjoy the reality, believe me.'

Iris felt as though a heavy weight had settled upon her heart. But she didn't want to argue with her father and ruin this all-too-brief time with him. What if…? She tried to bury the thought but it pushed its way to the front of her mind nevertheless. What if her father was killed, and this was the last time she saw him?

It didn't help that his objections to her relationship matched her own misgivings.

She forced a smile. 'Really, Daddy, you make it sound as though I was about to marry Rob. I've only been out with him a few times.' Something seemed to shrivel inside her as she spoke these words. They felt like a betrayal. However, she fixed her gaze on her father, taking in the familiar lines of his face, the aristocratic curve of his nose, the deep blue eyes. She loved him so deeply it was painful to contemplate anything that would displease him.

The furrows on Charles's brow eased as she spoke. 'Your mother did mention something about a doctor.'

Iris seized on this. 'Stewart Irvine, yes. He's taken me to dinner a few times.'

'Well, he sounds much more suitable. You should pay more attention to him and less to this mechanic.'

Iris couldn't let this pass. 'He's got a name: Rob. And when Stewart accidentally knocked me out of a boat, Rob was the one who dived in and saved me from drowning.' She hadn't related this in any of her letters, not wanting to worry her parents. Now, though, she forgot her caution in her need to defend Rob. Hearing Charles dismiss him as 'this mechanic' awoke a roaring lioness within her.

'I'm sure he's a brave man. I serve with lots of sailors of his type. Salt of the earth, the lot of them. The point is, you come from very different backgrounds, and in the end, you'll find the differences are too great to overcome.'

Iris pushed the food around her plate. Her throat felt too tight to force down any food, but wasting it seemed criminal in these days of rationing. 'Would you like to finish my fish? It's delicious but I'm just not hungry.'

There was silence while Charles polished off her plaice and she sipped water, waiting for her knotted insides to ease. This was the conversation she expected from her mother; she had always thought her father didn't worry about such things. He had always said he wanted her to be happy.

As though he were reading her mind, Charles reached across the table and patted her hand. 'You're very young, Iris. You have to accept that your mother and I understand more of how the world works. We just want you to be happy, and you have to trust us that in cases like this, we know best.'

Iris had a sinking feeling she knew what was coming next. Sure enough: 'Don't forget what happened to your Aunt Sybil.'

Maybe it was down to Sally and Mary questioning this well-worn story, but a thought struck Iris that had never occurred to her before. 'Hang on, why did Sybil end up penniless? Mother inherited a lot of her father's wealth. Didn't Sybil get her share?'

Charles raised his eyebrows. 'I thought you knew. Your grandfather disinherited her.'

'Why? Did he stop loving her just because she fell in love with the wrong man?' This seemed callous in the extreme.

Charles shook his head. 'It wasn't like that. He did it because he loved her. He wanted to persuade her to break off her engagement. He was convinced that by disinheriting her, that man would break it off himself, thinking he was a fortune hunter.'

'But he didn't.' Something rankled, but she couldn't put her finger on it for the moment. Then it hit her: 'that man'; 'this mechanic'. These were people with feelings and personalities every bit as complex as hers and her father's. Yet he spoke of them as somehow lesser beings.

'No, well, your grandfather's plan backfired. Just made Sybil all the more stubbornly determined to throw her life away. And your grandfather died not long after, so didn't get the chance to rewrite his will. And before you accuse your mother, she offered to give Sybil her share, but Sybil refused. Too proud for her own good. She inherited that from her father, at least.'

While Charles paid the bill, Iris turned over this news in her mind. She couldn't deny a flicker of admiration for her aunt. That was something she had never expected. Sybil had always been an object of pity, an example of how not to live her life. Now, reviewing the apparently bleak life Sybil led, Iris felt she saw a flicker of light as though from a candle flame. Where the light fell, the scene was warmer, less desperate. It must have taken courage to turn down Letitia's offer of money. Why had she done it? All Iris could think was that Sybil couldn't bear to touch her father's money after he had so ruthlessly cut her off. She was glad her mother had offered, though. Although Iris and Letitia didn't see eye to eye on many things, Iris was heartened to know Letitia hadn't abandoned her sister.

'How far is it to Stromness?' Charles asked, putting away his wallet.

'About four or five miles.'

'It's a lovely day. Why don't we walk back? I could do with stretching my legs after weeks of convoy duty.'

Iris agreed and led the way, painfully aware that the last time she had walked down these lanes she had been with Rob. Her heart gave a little thump as she remembered kissing him. Why had her father had to spoil everything? She had tried so hard to enjoy the present and not think too hard about the future. Now it seemed he was forcing her to make a choice. One she wasn't ready to make.

Her hopes that Charles would let the subject drop were dashed when they stopped to admire the view across the Loch of Stenness. At first they both stood in silence, listening to the curlews as they swooped low over the grass between the road and the loch, their piping whistles filling the air.

'Is that a seal?' Her father pointed to an indistinct grey lump on the shore.

'I don't know. It might be. You get them here.' Iris squinted, trying to make out the shape, her eyes baffled by the flecks of reflected sunlight sparkling upon the blue water. 'I can't tell if it's a rock or a seal.'

It was peaceful standing there together, speaking in hushed voices about the beauty of the island. She could almost forget Charles was disappointed with her and pretend she was a schoolgirl again, revelling in his rare company, wrapped in the warm certainty that she was loved and he would always care for her.

'I hope you mean to learn from your aunt's mistakes,' he said.

She froze. 'Please, can't you let it drop? I haven't known Rob that long. I don't have any plans to marry him. Why can't I simply enjoy his company? Who knows what the next few months and years will bring?'

'I don't want to see you hurt. If you do end up falling in love with him, saying goodbye would be far more painful than if you parted as friends now.' He rubbed the back of his neck, not meeting her gaze. 'That's why I've put certain provisions in place.'

A chill ran down her spine. 'Daddy, are you going to disinherit me?'

Chapter Twenty

Charles shook his head although he still wouldn't quite look her in the eye. 'I would never do that.'

Iris's initial relief faded at the sight of her father's obvious discomfort. 'Then what *would* you do?'

'You're an heiress. As such, you will inevitably attract attention from fortune hunters.'

'Rob's no fortune hunter.' Iris might not have known him long, but she knew that as a fact.

'How do you know?'

'Because I do.' Iris started to walk again, forcing her father to keep pace with her if he wanted to continue the conversation. 'He's got plans for the future. He wants to stay here in Orkney, open a boat yard. He has ambition, just not the ambition to stamp all over other people to get to the top.'

If Iris weren't so upset by what she was hearing from her father, the man she had always considered to be on her side, she would have been amused by the irony at now finding herself defending Rob when only a few days ago she had defended Stewart to her friends.

Charles stopped, grasping her arm and pulling her to a halt beside him. His face seemed to have aged in just a few seconds. 'Is that what you think of me – a grasping tyrant who doesn't mind who he hurts on his way to the top?'

'No, of course not. I know you're not like that. But I thought you loved me.'

'I do. You're my only child. I can't begin to put into words how much you mean to me. It's also my job to protect you. For that reason, I've taken steps to protect you from an unsuitable marriage should anything happen to me.'

Iris swallowed. 'Nothing's going to happen to you.'

'We're at war, Iris. No one is safe.' His voice was gentle. 'I would be a poor father if I didn't consider all eventualities.' He paused, his gaze unfocused as though carefully framing his next words. Iris didn't say anything. What was the point? It was clear he had already made up his mind. A pall of dread settled over her shoulders as she waited.

'I paid a visit to my solicitor before coming here. In the event of my death, I've arranged for your share of the inheritance to be put into a trust. You'll get an allowance, set by the trustees, but you won't be able to access the capital until you make a suitable marriage or are still single when you reach a responsible age. Should you marry a man the trustees consider unsuitable, they will be able to withhold the capital permanently and it will go to any children you might have when they come of age.'

Iris felt too numb to process all the implications. 'Why?' The word came out as a hoarse whisper. She cleared her throat and tried again. 'Don't you trust me?'

'I've seen enough of life to know how love can blind you to another's faults. I'm doing this because I care for you too much to risk you throwing away your fortune. I'm not depriving you of it, I'm ensuring you end up with a man who is capable of taking care of you and not someone who will end up frittering away your inheritance on his failing business.'

'I take it this was Mother's idea.'

'Don't take that tone, young lady. Your mother only wants the best for you.' He didn't deny it, though.

Knowing there was no point in begging him to change his mind, she asked, 'Who are the trustees?'

'Your mother and my solicitor. I've made the conditions of the trust clear in the letter of wishes. Should the trustees consider it necessary, they also have the authority to cut off your allowance. I'm simply trying to protect you from making a choice you'll come to regret – you're so very young.'

Iris drew a shaky breath. 'And what do you consider to be a responsible age?'

'Thirty-five. Old enough not to be taken in by a fortune-hunter.'

Thirty-five? To twenty-year-old Iris, that was a lifetime away. 'And who exactly will be a suitable man in Mother's opinion – would an earl be good enough, or has she set her sights on a duke?'

'Iris!'

'I'm sorry.' She walked in silence while she tried to take in this huge bombshell. The scenery blurred and shimmered as tears welled in her eyes. She blinked them away, suddenly angry, refusing to let her father see how deeply his lack of faith had wounded her. She raised her chin. 'Anyway, this is all academic, as nothing will happen to you. Next time you visit, you'll meet Rob and see that he's the most wonderful man you could hope to know.'

Because if her reaction told her anything, it was that she knew she was falling in love with Rob. The question was, could she wave goodbye to her inheritance?

Iris only saw her father once more before his ship left Scapa Flow; their duties didn't allow for any more meetings. In a way, she was glad. The more she thought about what he had done, the more resentment built up in her heart. How dared he try and regulate her choices in such a way? However, when she saw him, getting off the tender at the pier in Stromness, her anger fell away. It hit her that this would be the last time she saw him for some time. Maybe the last time ever.

She pushed that thought aside, but it prodded her consciousness throughout their time together.

They didn't have so long this time, as Iris was due on watch that night. Deciding not to try and catch a lift anywhere else, they elected to stay in Stromness and eat at a cafe. At first they both skirted around the subject that was uppermost in Iris's mind, and was surely prominent in Charles's thoughts as well. Finally, half an hour before she had to leave, Iris could bear it no longer.

'Please don't let's part with bad feelings between us,' she burst out, interrupting Charles's story of seeing whales while on his last convoy duty. Painfully aware that half the housewives of Stromness were in the cafe, ears flapping, she lowered her voice and leaned across the table. 'I love you, and it pains me to think I've disappointed you.'

Her father's brows twitched as though from a sudden pain. 'I'm not disappointed. Seeing you here, doing responsible work, I've never been prouder. I just worry that you'll make a reckless decision and dive into an unsuitable marriage without thinking through the consequences. What I'm doing is out of love, not any desire to punish you.'

Iris shook her head. 'You wouldn't have done it if Mother hadn't put you up to it.'

'Iris, that's not fair. She wrote to express her opinion, but I happen to agree.'

Despite her frustration, Iris couldn't suppress a smile as she imagined the letter, each word scored so deeply it could be read from the underside. 'I bet there are torpedoes that had less impact.' Then she regretted the comment about torpedoes, remembering that her father would be returning to convoy duty in a few days.

She tried a different approach. 'Look, you haven't even met Rob. Why not try and get your next leave here, and we'll have dinner together, the three of us? You'll like him, I know you will.'

Charles gave a slight shake of the head. Throwing caution to the wind, she said, 'Please, Daddy. Give him a chance. For me.'

He held up his hand. 'There's merit to your suggestion. I suppose I haven't been fair. The trust will still stand, mind, but you're right – next time I'm here, I'll meet this Rob. If I decide he is suitable, I'll write to my solicitor to inform him.'

'Oh, thank you, Daddy.' She leaned across the table to kiss his cheek. 'I know you'll approve. Just ask anyone on the island; everyone thinks very highly of him.'

Charles patted her arm. 'I want you to be happy, my rainbow. I'll do everything in my power to ensure you are safe and secure. Never forget that.'

Iris went on watch that night with her heart lighter than it had been for a week. She couldn't imagine her father disapproving of Rob once he had met him. He would soon be back in Scapa Flow, and once he had met Rob, he would put everything right.

'Is everything all right, Iris? You're very quiet.' Rob shifted the parcel so that he was carrying it under one arm and could offer his other to Iris.

Iris took it gratefully, burdened as she was with her own parcel. 'I'm fine.' She tried to pass off her introspection with a joke. 'I'd have thought you'd prefer me being quiet instead of blurting out the first thing in my head.'

Rob tilted his head to one side and gave her a smile that set a thousand butterflies fluttering in her stomach. 'I like that about you. You've got to admit, I always know where I stand.'

Iris looked away. That might have been right until her father's visit two weeks earlier, but now he could have no idea. When she had returned from her first walk with her father, she had been unable to hold back her distress and, sitting in their attic room, she had poured out her tale of woe to Mary and Sally. Sally, of course, had declared that money should play no part in choosing who she should spend the rest of her life with. Iris had expected Mary to be more pragmatic but surprisingly she had warned Iris not to make any rash decisions. 'Rob's crazy about you,' she said. 'Any fool can see that. If you feel the same way, you need to think very carefully before throwing it away. But losing your inheritance would be huge, too. The knowledge of what you had given up would always be there. Anyway, we're in the middle of a war. It's no time to be thinking about marriage. You can take your time.'

'Iris?' Rob's voice jerked her back to the present.

'I'm sorry. I haven't been getting much sleep lately.'

'Then you are worried about something.'

What could she say? *Actually, Rob, there's a chance I'll end up without a penny if I marry you.* They hadn't even spoken of love yet, let alone marriage. As Mary had said, it wasn't something she was ready to contemplate while there was a war on. Strange, that – she had wanted to marry George to avoid conscription, and now she was committed to her work in the Wrens.

Sunk in thought, she didn't answer. By now they had reached the wire gate, so she shifted the parcel for Elspeth under her arm while she unhooked the loop of wire. She took her time, still trying to work out how to explain her dilemma without burdening Rob with any expectation of love or marriage. Nothing occurred to her, and they continued up the track, the silence between them as thick as treacle.

Finally Rob spoke, each word hesitant as though he were feeling his way. 'I suppose I cannae blame you for holding back. Not when I've kept silent about the *Royal Oak*.'

Iris stopped dead. 'Oh no. I mean, I wasn't thinking about that. I wasn't trying to punish you.' Was that what he thought – that she was giving him the silent treatment because he hadn't confided in her? 'I'd never force you into talking about it.'

'I know, lass. Don't fret.' Rob caught her free hand and gave it a reassuring squeeze. 'The thing is, I want you to know.'

Iris stared at him. Her own fog of worry drifted away, forgotten in her concern for Rob. As far as she knew, he hadn't told any friends or family about his ordeal. His hand still enclosed hers in a warm grip, and she squeezed it in return. 'If you think it would help, I'd like to hear.'

'Let's sit.'

They were at the highest point of the track by this time, and the ground was dry enough to sit upon. They dropped the packages and sat side by side, shoulders touching, looking out across Hoy Sound.

'For the longest time, I hated to think about it,' Rob began. 'And now I want to tell you, I've no idea how to start.'

'Where were you when the torpedo hit?'

'In my hammock. It happened in the early hours, although no one knew it was a torpedo at the time. Someone said something about an explosion in the refrigerating room.' Rob shook his head. 'Looking back, I cannae believe no one thought it was a torpedo. A few men were sent off to check, and the rest of us returned to our hammocks. About ten minutes later, another one hit. It shook the whole ship. That was when we knew we were under attack. We had two more strikes a moment later.'

'It must have been terrifying.'

'Aye. The ship started to list, and there was a scramble for the ladders as everyone tried to get up on deck.' Rob ran a hand through his hair.

Iris felt a surge of protective tenderness when she saw he was trembling. She took his hand, weaving her fingers through his, lending him her silent strength.

'I only made it by the skin of my teeth,' Rob continued after a moment. 'She went down so fast – a matter of minutes. I could feel her sliding away under my feet as I made for the rail – a horrible feeling. There was no time to look for the picket boat. I just hauled myself over the rail, slithered down the side and into the water. God, it was cold.'

Iris looked across Hoy Sound and shuddered as she remembered her own experience of falling into the sea in the dark. She could picture what it must have been like for Rob, in the grip of the icy water as it stiffened his muscles and squeezed the air from his lungs. 'Did you get picked up?'

'Aye, I was one of the lucky ones. I struck out – the sea was covered in oil, and it got in my eyes, nose and mouth. Then after what felt like an age, I heard shouts not far away and saw the *Daisy II*, our drifter. I managed to make it that far, and someone dragged me on board.'

Iris leaned her head against his shoulder. 'Thank God you were safe. I can't imagine being without you.'

'But so many others weren't. And they were just boys, Iris. So young. Many of them weren't even eighteen. That's what I see when I dream about that night. I see the faces of those poor lads trapped below deck, screaming for help that never comes. Those boys who'll never grow up.' His voice hitched and he broke off, his face a picture of anguish.

Nothing in Iris's peaceful, comfortable life had prepared her to hear such a story. Having no idea what to say, she took the only action she could think of, which was to pull him into a fierce hug. 'I'm so sorry,' she said. Tears poured down her cheeks as she wept for all who had been lost and for those who mourned them.

After a moment, Rob hugged her back; he was still trembling, although he seemed to have regained command of himself. 'Thank you for listening,' he said, his face buried in her hair. After a while, he pulled away and sat up. 'You're the first person I've told, and it helps.'

'You didn't even tell the Heddles?'

Rob shook his head. 'I didnae want to frighten them, not with their sons in the navy.'

'So why tell me now?'

Rob scrubbed his cheeks with the back of a hand and drew a breath. 'Because I needed to tell someone, and I want us to be the kind of couple that can say anything to each other. I want there to be trust between us.' A pause, then, in gentler tones: 'Something's worrying you, and I wish you would confide in me.'

There was no avoiding it. 'Very well. Although it's nothing compared with what you went through.'

'Good. I'd hate anything bad to happen to you. And if it's bothering you, then it *is* important.'

'Well...' Iris picked up her cap, which had fallen off during their embrace, and combed her hair back into place while she decided how much to say. No matter how much she agreed in principle about them confiding in one another, nothing would induce her to confess she had considered the possibility of marriage. 'I've been thinking about my aunt,' she said in the end.

'Why – is she ill?'

'No. At least, I don't think so. I've never actually met her.'

–

Rob shifted his parcel again and stared at Iris. 'What, never?'

'No. I've never even seen a photograph.'

This was unbelievable to Rob. While his mother had been an only child, his father had seven siblings, all married with large families of their own. His aunts had all cooed over Rob, pitying him for being an only child. Rob had never minded; having a pack of cousins all living nearby, his childhood had been anything but lonely. He couldn't imagine having an aunt and never meeting her.

'What's made you think of her now?'

Iris sighed. 'Something my father said. I'd always thought she was someone to be pitied, but now I'm not so sure.' She went on to relate a tale that made Rob seethe with indignation. As she spoke, they gathered up the parcels and resumed their walk.

'And you've only just found this out?' he asked when she finished.

'I knew that she was a widow who had married beneath her. But the stuff about my grandfather cutting her out of his will; that was all new. Daddy told me when I met him the other day. He thought I already knew.'

Rob flinched at the reference to marrying beneath her station. That was what his mother had done, after all, and as far as he could tell, not a day had passed that she hadn't looked back at her past life with longing. It had eaten her up to the extent that she didn't seem to be able to concern herself with anyone else's worries. That was why it had become so important to him that he and Iris should be able to confide in one another. Maybe if his mother had taken more of an interest in his father's life, she wouldn't feel her losses so bitterly. It hadn't been easy to talk about the *Royal Oak*, but now he had unburdened himself, he felt lighter than he had done for years.

'Why would he tell you now?'

Iris shrugged. The parcel slipped and she paused to hoist it higher under her arm before continuing her walk up the lane and answering. 'I can't remember. The point is, that all these years, I've pictured my aunt as a foolish woman who threw her life away over a thoughtless passion. But from what Daddy says, she stood her ground when her grandfather threatened to cut her out of the will and stuck to her principles and refused to touch his money even after he'd died.' Iris dropped her voice so that Rob had to strain to hear the next words. 'She sounds like someone I'd like to meet.'

'Well, why don't you? She's your aunt, after all. I bet she'd be glad to meet you.'

Iris brightened. 'Do you think so?'

'Why wouldn't she? I think she'd be delighted to meet her niece. Especially one who is making a life for herself in the Wrens.'

A slow flush spread up Iris's neck. 'I didn't want to be in the Wrens. Not at first.'

Rob's interest was piqued. 'Then why did you join?'

Her flush deepened, and she muttered something. The ever-present wind buffeting Rob's ears drowned her words. 'What was that? I didnae catch it.'

'I thought I was going to be married.' Iris enunciated each word with exaggerated clarity. She stopped, her arms cradling the bundle across her chest, her look seeming to defy him to laugh.

Rob stopped too. This was something he hadn't considered, although God only knew why not. Iris was a real looker. A girl like her would have had a queue of admirers all vying for her attention. 'What happened?' What he really wanted to know was if he should be jealous. He studied her expression carefully, watching for any sign that she was still in love with the idiot who had let her go.

'Too embarrassing to talk about. Let's just say there had been a major communication breakdown.'

Now Rob really was agog to find out what had happened. 'You cannae leave it there. You have to tell me now.' He grinned. 'You know I willnae give you a moment's peace until you own up.'

'Oh, very well.'

She set out again and after a sigh that seemed to express a world of humiliation, she told her tale.

Rob listened with growing incredulity as Iris, with many pauses to cringe and beg him not to repeat the story to anyone else, told how she'd mistakenly thought a former beau was proposing and had accepted without giving the man a chance to explain the mistake. Seeing her mortification, however, he refrained from laughing.

'If you ask me, this George bloke is a complete idiot,' he said, when she'd finished.

'*George* is an idiot? You did understand what I just told you? He dropped a ring from his pocket, and I immediately assumed he'd proposed.'

'Well, and why wouldn't you think he was proposing? He was out with you. You had no way of knowing the ring was for another girl. If you want my opinion, any man who could spend time with you and still want to be with someone else needs his head examined. Anyway, if he was in love with this Felicity, why was he still seeing you?'

'That's what's so embarrassing. I was so set on him – well, more taken with the idea of being mistress of his various residences, if I'm honest – I read more into the friendship than he'd intended.'

Rob was having none of it. 'No, any man who was halfway decent would have made his intentions clear. He's either weak or cruel. Either way, not good enough for you.'

Iris took a few steps in silence before saying, 'Thank you. You're right. I'm still not proud of my behaviour, but you're right about George. He was weak. He should have told me from the start he was interested in Felicity.'

'There you go. You're well rid of him.' But as they walked on, Rob was aware of a heavy weight settling on his chest. Iris had wanted George for the life he could offer. Yet again, he had to wonder, did she see any future with Rob? Having accused George of weakness for not being open with Iris, he could hardly ignore the question now.

They were past the signal station now and approaching Curlew Croft. Before they went any further, Rob knew he needed an answer. He placed the parcel on the ground and took Iris's arm. 'Wait. I have to know. I can't offer you a manor house and a posh house in town. Am I fooling myself to think we have any future together? Exactly what are you doing with me, Iris?'

Chapter Twenty-One

Iris gazed at Rob. Each word seemed to be a tiny dart that burrowed into her heart and twisted. When she'd told him about George, she'd tried to make the tale entertaining, make it appear a joke against herself. Rob, however, had seen to the heart of the matter. Had known she had been drawn to George for his wealth.

All she could do was tell the truth. 'True, I wanted to marry George for what I thought he could offer me: security; a comfortable home; standing in society.'

'All the things I can't give you.' There was a bitterness in Rob's tone. Something she had never heard before.

'I was a fool,' she said. 'Being in the Wrens… being here… it's changed me. I don't deny I've still got a long way to go. But whereas I wanted to be with George for his wealth, I never felt anything beyond a vague liking for him. I never understood what people meant by love until I met you. The way I feel for you, it's…' She stopped. Love. Was that what this was – love? She had spoken without thinking, and now a painful silence stretched between them, heavy with her implied declaration and Rob's continued silence. She became intensely aware of her limbs, of a heaviness in them, and suddenly she didn't know how to position them. A pulse beat painfully in the base of her throat. 'I mean,' she said, when the silence became too awkward, 'I don't expect you to—'.

Rob plucked the parcel from her arms and placed it upon the one already on the ground. Then he wrapped his arms around her waist and pulled her close. He lowered his face to hers so their lips were almost touching. 'That wouldn't be a declaration of love, would it, Iris Tredwick?'

'That depends. Were you planning on making one in return?'

His eyes twinkled. 'I might be at that.' He stooped lower until his forehead pressed hers. 'I love you, Iris.'

Her heart thumped against her ribs as though fighting to meet Rob's. 'I love you too.'

Then he kissed her. A gentle kiss to place a seal on the words they had just spoken.

She felt quite light-headed when Rob pulled away. Then she looked up and saw they were in full sight of the Heddles' kitchen door. She giggled. 'Good thing Elspeth or Archie didn't pick that moment to go outside, or they'd have seen us.'

'Who cares?' Rob hoisted his parcel back into his arms. 'I love you, and I don't care who knows about it.' He gave the package an experimental prod. 'What's in here, anyway?'

'Some bolts of cloth I had at home. I asked my mother to post them. I'm going to make Elspeth a coat, and I'm sure she knows of others who are desperate for new clothes.'

'And that's why you're too good for the likes of that George fellow,' Rob said, approaching the croft with long, easy strides. 'Other women would have held on to good cloth, but you're willing to share it with those who have greater need. Island life's rubbing off on you. I told you this place gets under your skin.'

Iris floated down the rest of the track, not feeling the lumpy, rocky ground beneath her feet. If her father had approached her now and asked her to choose between Rob and her inheritance, she wouldn't have hesitated. She couldn't imagine giving up this feeling for mere money.

–

What with Rob, her signalling duties and all the activities she was now involved in, Iris did, indeed, feel as though she had settled into island life. In particular, she took real pleasure in making a smart coat for Elspeth. Adapting a pattern from a magazine, she made a beautiful knee-length coat in a lovely cerise cloth that she had bought before the war, thinking it would make a perfect winter coat. Seeing Elspeth's delight when she turned this way and that in front of the mirror, admiring the way the colour seemed to bring out the lustre in her skin, Iris couldn't regret giving the cloth away.

'You must let me pay you,' Elspeth had said once the last button had been attached and Iris had completed the finishing touch: a matching belt. 'I feel like royalty wearing this.'

'Absolutely not. It's a gift. To thank you for your wonderful hospitality. I felt quite lost when I first arrived here, and your welcome made all the difference.'

Iris, Sally and Mary were in the kitchen at Curlew Croft on one of their days off together. Once Elspeth had lovingly hung the cerise coat in the cupboard beside the back door, carefully smoothing the collar and sleeves so they wouldn't get crushed, she went to make tea, casting frequent glances towards the cupboard as she worked. Iris was delighted to see how much pleasure Elspeth took from her new coat and felt fired up to find the perfect recipients for the remaining fabric.

'What are you going to make next?' Mary asked, leafing through a magazine.

Iris fingered a pretty cotton fabric, with a lovely print of corn ears and flowers. She had bought it in Liberty the last time she had been to London and although she had loved the design, had never decided upon the right garment to make from it. Now, seeing Sally cast wistful glances at it, she knew exactly what she wanted to do. 'This would make a beautiful tea dress for you, Sally. It will be perfect for you to wear when you're home on leave.'

For Sally had just heard that she would be granted leave next week, and she had already decided to go home to Yorkshire. 'What do you say, Sally? Would you like a new dress in case you bump into that young man of yours?'

Sally's eyes sparkled. 'You can't mean it. I've never had anything as beautiful as this.'

'I do mean it. You deserve something special after that awful accident.' If she was honest, Iris still felt guilty for sending Sally out in the storm.

Sally, looking like she could hardly believe her luck, fingered the fabric, stroking one of the bright red printed flowers. 'Poppies are my favourite flower.'

'There you go. It was meant for you.' Iris grinned at her. 'It's a sign.'

Mary groaned. 'Don't you start.'

'What can I say?' Iris said. 'I've got a good feeling about this dress. This fabric could have been designed especially for Sally. I refuse to give it to anyone but her. And before you complain, Mary, I've picked out this for you.' She pulled out some blue cotton with little red and yellow sailing boats. 'But I'll make Sally's first, because she's the first one to be going on leave.'

Sally had fully recovered from her accident – the bruises had soon faded and she had returned to duty. She still tired easily, though, so the MO had recommended to her CO that as she was entitled to leave, it be brought forward to give her a chance to rest up completely and forget her ordeal.

Sally held the Liberty print against her, her eyes shining. 'If you could make me a dress from this, I'll love you forever. I've never had a pretty dress before.'

'There you go, then. Cinderella, you shall go to the ball.'

The rest of the visit was spent leafing through the magazine, deciding on the best pattern.

'I wish we still had the farm,' Sally said as they walked back over the hill to Stromness and the Wrennery. 'I just realised Uncle Ted had his accident six years ago this week.' Then, her voice so low Iris had to strain to hear, she added, 'I saw a single magpie the morning my uncle had his accident. One for sorrow, they say. It's true.'

Iris glanced at Mary, expecting a tirade. She didn't have long to wait.

'Sally Hartley, don't tell me you blame yourself?'

Sally's answering look made her guilt plain. 'One magpie,' she said slowly, as though teaching a child to count. 'One for sorrow. Uncle's accident brought sorrow. I should have thought it obvious.'

'You're blaming a magpie for your uncle's fall?'

'Of course not. But it was a sign.'

Mary shook her head. 'How can a bird know someone's about to have an accident?'

'It's not the bird, it's… oh, what's the point trying to explain. You'll never understand.' Sally picked up her pace and marched along the path, her back poker-straight.

Mary and Iris exchanged glances. 'I thought I was supposed to be the one who blurted tactless things,' Iris said.

'I know. I just… whenever she implies something bad happened because she only saw one magpie, or forgot to throw spilt salt over her shoulder, I wonder if she thinks the *Royal Oak* wouldn't have been torpedoed if I hadn't walked under a ladder or something.' She shook her head. 'Anyway, we'd better catch her up.'

They broke into a jog and after much puffing and panting managed to draw level with Sally, one on each side.

'Slow down, will you?' Mary said, clutching her side. 'I can't say sorry if I drop dead from lack of oxygen, can I?'

Sally's shoulders sagged. She stopped and turned to face Mary. 'You don't have to apologise. I'm not upset with you.'

'You gave a jolly good impression of it.'

Sally gave a small smile. 'I'm really not. I suppose I've been able to forget about Uncle Ted and losing the farm with all the excitement of joining the Wrens, and then working so hard on the course and coming here. But now I'm going home on leave, only it's not home. Even after six years.'

Mary squeezed her shoulder. 'You'll be with your mam and uncle. That's the important thing. And anyway' – she grabbed Iris's arm to bring her into the conversation – 'you'll have your lovely new dress to wear. You'll have plenty of opportunity to show it off in Whitby.'

Iris, her mind on Mary's loss, and her own father who was about to embark on another dangerous convoy duty, said, 'And I know your uncle's accident was awful, and losing the farm was hard, but he's still alive. You've still got him.'

Sally nodded. She seemed to make a conscious effort to cheer up, raising her chin and her smile becoming more definite. 'I know. I'm sure I'll enjoy my leave when I get there. I've had my wobble. You're right, Mary, I do still have my mum and uncle. I should be grateful for it.'

Iris took her arm. 'I'll measure you up for the dress as soon as we get back. You'll be the talk of the town, you wait and see.'

They walked on, arm in arm. Iris, gazing across Scapa Flow, looked for the main anchorage, where the *Snowdon* would be. Her crew would be preparing to sail, going to their rendezvous with the rest of the convoy. Yes, she could do with working on Sally's dress to try to bury her worries.

'What about you two?' Sally said. 'Your leave must be coming up soon. Where will you go?'

'I'll go home,' Mary said. 'I need to show my mam I've taken her advice to heart and am no longer wallowing in misery.' She glanced at Iris. 'If you don't feel like going home, you could come with me if we get leave at the same time. There's not much more to do there than here, but we could go to a dance in Haverfordwest or something.'

'That's so kind of you, Mary. I'd love to see your home. And yours, too, Sally. And it would be lovely if you could come to stay at Tredwick Place one day. But...' An idea had been forming ever since she'd heard more about her aunt, and she couldn't shake Rob's suggestion from her mind. 'Well, I've had an idea. I think I'm going to visit my Aunt Sybil.'

'Sybil? The aunt your mother keeps warning you about?' Sally looked at Iris with wide eyes.

'That's the one. The Wrens will give me a return ticket to any railway station, won't they? So I'm going to visit Sybil. I want to hear her side of the story.' Iris focused on the distant ships as she spoke. 'Rob suggested I should see her for myself, and I think he's right. My father's threatened to cut me out of his will if I marry Rob.' She gave an exasperated laugh. 'I hadn't even thought of marriage when he said that – it's too early days.'

'You know what I think, don't you?' Sally said.

'Yes, I know. We're destined to be together just because I tripped into his arms on our first day here. But I don't marry someone just because I trip over my own feet near him. Anyway, I've spent my whole life hearing my mother's side of the story, and only recently found out there was more to the tale. I've lived in fear of ending up like Aunt Sybil all my life. I persuaded myself I wanted to marry a man I didn't love because of it.' Iris paused for a moment, struck by what she had said. For the first time she realised how unhappy she would have been if George had wanted to marry her. She might be married by now if he had. Married for all the wrong reasons. Her time with Rob had shown her how empty her life would have been without love.

'It's a wonderful idea,' Mary said. 'It's time you learned the truth. Who knows? Maybe she's leading a fulfilled life somewhere.'

'But do you know where she lives?' Sally asked. 'I mean, I think it's a good idea, but I thought you'd never met her. How will you go about finding her?'

'I'm pretty sure I know where she lives,' Iris said. 'You're right – I haven't met her. But my mother still writes to her sometimes. I remember seeing the address. She lives in York, which is easy to get to by rail, and there's bound to be a hotel where I can stay.' She chewed her lip as she tried to recall the address she'd seen on the envelopes in her mother's spiky handwriting. 'Grosvenor Terrace,' she said finally. 'Number 13B.' She flashed a grin at Sally. 'The number stuck in my mind.'

It felt good to have confided in her friends. It had been a rather nebulous idea, but talking about it made it suddenly seem real. There was no reason not to try and find Aunt Sybil. Besides, she really didn't feel like going home, knowing the visit would be spent listening to her mother haranguing her about Rob. Going to York was far preferable, especially if it meant discovering the truth about Aunt Sybil at last. She could only hope Sybil would want to see a niece she had never met.

Chapter Twenty-Two

Iris looked around wide-eyed with wonder as she walked out of York railway station. She had heard York had been bombed in April but was unprepared for the damage to the railway station and surrounding area. While Orkney might be in the back of beyond, Iris could now see the advantage of living somewhere so protected, if isolated.

Right next door to the station was the imposing Royal Station Hotel – an impressive Victorian edifice in warm yellow brick, overlooking pretty gardens and the river. Thanking her lucky stars she wouldn't have far to carry her case, she hefted it one last time and headed for the entrance. She reached the door just as the doorman opened it to let an elderly woman out. Seeing her expensive pearls and stylish clothes, Iris was glad she had changed out of her uniform into a smart costume, even if it had got rather crumpled from a train journey that had lasted all night.

Two hours later, after a wash and a quick nap in her hotel room, she emerged from the hotel in a light cotton frock and a lime green cardigan, perfect for walking around York on a sunny day. She should probably get something to eat, not having eaten anything bar a bowl of soup that she had managed to grab from a cafe at Edinburgh station. However, now the prospect of meeting Aunt Sybil loomed large, and with no idea what state she would find her in, Iris's stomach tied into knots, and she couldn't contemplate forcing down any food. She wouldn't feel any better until she'd got the visit to Sybil over and done with, so she consulted a map, saw Grosvenor Terrace was within easy walking distance, and set out.

Despite her fears, she couldn't hold back a smile as she crossed the wide bridge over the River Ouse. It being Saturday, it was bustling with women walking into the city centre, shopping bags and baskets over their arms. As she overtook one woman, the woman gave a dramatic shiver and said to her companion, 'By 'eck, there's a bitter wind coming up the river today.' Iris bit back a smile, reflecting that to anyone who had endured Orkney's howling gales for months on end, York was a tropical paradise.

At any other time she would have admired the view over the river as she crossed the wide bridge, and paused to drink in the beautiful minster. Now, however, she could only promise herself she would return later for a longer look before turning into a lane that seemed to be heading in the right direction. A glance at the street sign told her it was High Petergate, which she seemed to remember from the map. It led her through a wide archway that took the road beneath the city walls – another sight she decided to come back to later – and out into the streets beyond. To her dismay, she saw piles of rubble in some streets, marking where houses had been destroyed by the recent raid. A sudden dread overtook her – what if Sybil's house had been hit? As she walked along the wide street, reading the street signs, searching for Grosvenor Terrace, she dreaded finding a crater where number thirteen should stand.

After several minutes where her imagination was seized with several nightmare scenarios, it was a relief to find Grosvenor Terrace undamaged. It appeared to be a respectable street of elegant Georgian brick terraced houses on one side, while on the other side ran a wall alongside a railway line. Some of her nerves eased; surely a woman who could barely make ends meet wouldn't be able to afford even a flat here on a widow's pension. Nevertheless, her legs shook as she found number thirteen and she hesitated outside. It was only the promise of a pot of tea afterwards at Betty's Tea Rooms that gave her the strength to walk up the path.

The card beside the bell for flat B read, 'Mrs S. Brownlow.' The ink was a little faded but it was written in a bold, looping hand. Iris rang the bell, hearing it ring somewhere in the depths of the building. There was a pause long enough for Iris to think no one was in. Then she heard a door slam and the muffled thump of feet descending a carpeted staircase. Iris braced herself when she heard the rattle of the lock, then the door creaked open and a fair-haired woman looked out. 'Hello. How can I help you?' the woman asked in accents that had definitely been honed in the Home Counties.

Iris looked at her aunt, lost for speech for a few seconds. This was definitely her aunt; the resemblance to her mother was too strong for her to be anyone else. Her face was softer, more youthful, but there was no mistaking the arched brows, slanting blue eyes and the aquiline nose that proclaimed a close relationship to Letitia Tredwick.

When Iris struggled for words, the finely pencilled brows twitched closer together. 'Well?' the woman asked.

Iris stepped closer. 'I'm sorry. I'm not quite sure how to begin. I'm Iris. Iris Tredwick. You are Sybil Brownlow, aren't you?' Meeting her for the first time, it felt presumptuous to call her 'Auntie'.

The woman's eyes widened. 'Iris? Little Iris – Letitia's daughter?'

Iris could only nod.

'Oh, my.' Sybil gave a bright smile. 'You'd better come in.' She opened the door wider and stepped aside for Iris to enter into a narrow hallway with a black and white tiled floor. 'I'm up on the first floor.' Sybil indicated for Iris to go upstairs.

Once upstairs, Sybil opened the door on the landing and led Iris inside. Iris found herself in a light, airy living room with long, arched windows looking out onto a wrought-iron balcony and the street beyond. It was comfortably furnished, with a tiled fireplace, and a brocade sofa and armchairs. A crammed bookcase stood opposite the fireplace, and beside it was a desk. There were open exercise books upon it.

'Sit down, sit down,' Sybil said, sounding rather breathless. Sybil patted her hair, which was already smooth and pinned into neat rolls, sat on the sofa then immediately leapt up as though the seat were on fire. 'I'll make us some tea.'

Iris perched on the edge of an armchair, but once Sybil had disappeared through a doorway beyond which Iris could glimpse an inner hallway, she rose and went to examine the framed photographs upon the mantelpiece. The one that drew her eye was a wedding photo. The bride was clearly a younger version of Sybil. Dressed in a plain suit, holding a single long-stemmed rose, she nevertheless couldn't have sparkled any brighter had she been wearing a diamond tiara. She gazed at the camera, radiating joy. The young man beside her wore army uniform with a sergeant's stripes on the sleeve. His expression was one of dazed euphoria. Iris, knowing he had been killed only a short while after the photo had been taken, studied his face with a pang of sadness. It was terrible to think that a man who looked to be in the peak of health and fitness, and seemingly bursting with happiness and pride, could be dead and gone in a matter of weeks. Iris couldn't help but think of Rob with a stab of fear. Beside that photo was a larger photo of the same man, also in uniform, and between the two photos was a little china vase with a single yellow rose. The glass in the frames gleamed, and the silver frames were so bright that they must have been polished recently. From her mother's warnings, she would have expected Sybil to be living in a squalid hovel.

Iris, about to return to her seat, stopped when a photo on the other side of the mantelpiece caught her attention. She stopped and stared. This was a picture she knew well, for a copy also had pride of place on the drawing room mantelpiece at Tredwick Place. It showed a fourteen-year-old Iris, beaming with pride in her school uniform.

A rattle of cups and saucers made her turn. Sybil was back, bringing a laden tray. 'Yes, I should have recognised you straight away,' Sybil said, with a tilt of the head towards Iris's photo. 'You've not changed so very much since then.' She placed the tray upon a low table in front of the sofa and arranged some pretty willow pattern cups and saucers. 'Now come and sit down and tell me all about yourself. It's so lovely to finally meet you. The last I heard you were engaged to be married to a wonderful young man, but your mother hasn't written for a while. I suppose she's busy with war work.'

'Well, she is busy,' said Iris, sitting and taking the cup Sybil handed to her, 'but I don't think that's why she hasn't written. She's rather cross with me, you see.' And she found herself telling the embarrassing tale of George and the proposal that never was to this kindly woman who should have been a large part of her life and yet was a stranger.

'I can see why Letitia's disappointed,' Sybil said, patting Iris's hand when she had finished. 'She must have been thrilled to think you were going to marry into such a wealthy family.'

'She was. It was ages before I could bring myself to write and tell her I wasn't going to marry George.'

'I gather you're in the Wrens now. Your mother told me you'd joined in her last letter.' After Iris had told her a little about being a visual signaller in Orkney, Sybil said, 'I am glad. I do think young women should learn to support themselves.' She paused and looked at the photo of the young soldier. 'I rather fell apart when my Jon died, you know. Your mother and I had been brought up to expect to be looked after, you see. First by our father, then by our husbands.'

'Mother still thinks that,' Iris said. She glanced around the flat again, taking in the signs that while Sybil didn't appear to be rich, she certainly had enough money to support herself in comfort. 'So did your husband leave you with money, then? I always thought he had left you in poverty.'

It only struck her how rude a question that was after she had spoken. 'I'm sorry. I really must learn not to blurt out the first thought that comes into my head.'

Sybil, however, laughed. 'Oh, please don't apologise. It's so refreshing to meet someone who speaks their mind. Besides, you're family, and I don't mind telling you. No, Jon had very little. He wasn't the wastrel my father considered him to be, though, far from it. He was good with his hands and had earned a reputation as a first-class mechanic in the army. He was full of plans to set himself up as a car mechanic after the war, said good mechanics would soon be in demand. He even had plans to start up his own car manufacturing business.'

'He sounds like—' but Iris stopped herself. She didn't want to think too closely about the similarities between Rob and Jon, not when Rob was in danger at sea, and Jon's fate was a heavy presence in the room. 'I'm sorry; do go on.'

Sybil gave a sad smile. 'He could have walked into a good job at somewhere like Morris or Austin, but army life had put him off following orders. He would have done well on his own, though. I had no doubts he would be able to look after me, even if it wasn't to the standard my family expected. When my father told me in no uncertain terms Jon was only after my money, and that he would run a mile as soon as he knew Father had disinherited me, I wasn't bothered. I didn't need riches. I just wanted to be with Jon.' She sighed, casting another glance at the photograph. 'In the event, I ended up with neither Jon nor money.'

'Do you regret marrying him, then?' Another personal question that Iris regretted the moment the words were out.

Sybil didn't seem to mind, however. 'Never for one minute. We had three months of married life, and only ten of those days together. But those were the happiest ten days of my life, and I can never regret them.'

'If you don't mind me saying, though,' Iris said, casting another glance around the room, 'you seem to be leading a comfortable life now. Did you take money from Letitia after all? Daddy said she'd offered but you turned it down.'

'Goodness, Letitia always described you as direct in her letters, and now I know what she means.'

'I'm sorry. You don't have to answer.'

'Oh, I don't mind.' Sybil gave her a shrewd look. 'It seems to me that you must have a reason for coming to see me. I won't pry, but I'm happy to tell you about my life if it will help you with any problems you might be facing.'

Iris felt her face grew warm. She studied her hands in her lap, although she listened with quivering attention to Sybil's next words.

'I think I said earlier that I fell apart when Jon was killed. My father had passed away very suddenly not long before, and in my resentment of the way he had treated me, I had made no effort to be reconciled. Not that I didn't want to, you understand, but because any attempt would have looked like I was trying to get him to change his will back in my favour, and I wasn't interested in his money. It seemed to me that if my father hadn't been rich, there would have been no problem for me to marry Jon, and therefore no family rift.

'Letitia visited me not long after I heard about Jon's death. She saw me in a pitiable state. I had no money, no husband and no apparent way of supporting myself. She, I might add, had hated being torn between me and our father. However, now our father was gone, she had no problem in offering to give me my inheritance.'

'I don't understand why you turned it down,' Iris said. 'No one could deny you had a right to it.'

'It's hard to explain. I was tempted. Oh, so very tempted. But I suddenly saw myself as Letitia must have seen me – a helpless girl who needed a payout from her older sister to get her back on her feet. I knew then that if I took the money, I would always be dependent on my family, and I didn't want that. I had been proud to be Jon's wife, proud that he was going to make something of himself with his brains and his own two hands. I wanted to be like that.'

'What did you do?' Iris was agog to hear what Sybil was going to say next.

'It wasn't easy,' Sybil said. 'The war ended, leaving so many young men dead, and many young widows and single women who had lost fiancés. We were objects of pity. Superfluous women, some called us. But I was fortunate in one way – I'd had a good education. I took what little savings I had and used them to support me through a degree course at London University, working as a waitress to supplement my savings. Three years later, I had a good degree in physics, and became a teacher. Now I'm head of the science department at the Mount School.'

'That's wonderful. I'm so glad.' Iris gave a small laugh. 'Although I don't understand why my mother talks of you as though you are a charity case.'

'Oh, you know Letitia. She's horrified that I have to work for my living. She was brought up to believe that a woman shouldn't go out to work and regards me as an object of pity. Whereas I see it as a kind of freedom. Don't get me wrong; I loved Jon dearly, and would have been happy to have been a wife and mother. But that wasn't to be, and now I have the pleasure of watching girls discover their strengths and helping them achieve their dreams. I wouldn't have Letitia's life for the world. I am glad to have met you, though. I hope we will see a great deal more of each other.'

–

The shrill alarm bell tore through the *Kelpie*, calling the men to action stations just as Rob was leaving the engine room at the end of his watch. His feet took over, and he was halfway up the ladder before his weary mind had taken in what was happening. All around him, above the ear-splitting din of the alarm, were shouted orders and the clatter of feet upon the metal ladders. Emerging on deck, he got a faceful of sea spray, and in the moment before he took up his station beside the magazine flooding valves, he caught sight of a ship in the distance. For a sickening instant, he thought they were under attack from the German fleet. Then common sense took over. The German fleet wouldn't approach this close to Orkney. The ship he had seen was *Snowdon*, on its way to Iceland to rendezvous with the next Arctic convoy, sailing through the channel *Kelpie* and her sister ships had swept the previous day.

In that case, what had triggered the alarm? It wasn't long before he got his answer when he heard the faint growl of aero engines. A split second later came a shout from the signal deck: 'Junkers 88 bearing green oh-four-oh.'

Rob's muscles went rigid as he waited for the attack. Would it go for *Snowdon* or *Kelpie*? His heart hammered so hard he could feel his blood pulsing to his fingertips. Then came the unearthly howl of a diving plane and the rattle of bullets striking the ship. The answering fire from *Kelpie*'s guns shook the deck. Rob dived for cover, making sure he remained within reach of the valves. At times like these, he was grateful to be out on deck, having developed a horror of being trapped below decks after his experience on the *Royal Oak*.

Another line of bullets struck the deck only inches from his face; a spark of pain as something lashed his cheek. His ears rang, assaulted by noise from all directions. Then came another shout: 'Three Spitfires bearing green one-six-oh.' A moment later the gunfire ceased, and the Junkers abandoned the attack. Rob staggered to his feet and joined in with the cheers of the crew as their attacker fled west, pursued by the Spitfires. The chances of the Junkers reaching the safety of the Norwegian coast was slight.

He put a hand to his stinging cheek and decided it was no more than a cut from a flying splinter. Although it smarted from all the salt spray the sea continuously flung into his face, there wasn't much blood. Glancing around, he saw everyone returning to their usual positions. The knot of tension in his chest unwound; he had dreaded seeing the huddled bodies of his dead or seriously wounded shipmates. They had been lucky this time.

As he waited to return below deck, he watched the progress of *Snowdon*. Iris's father was somewhere on board. Rob wondered if he had seen the attack and spared a thought for the man who was courting his daughter. As the destroyer faded into the distance, Rob indulged in a daydream where *Snowdon* came under attack, and Rob sprang into action, swinging on board like Errol Flynn and taking a bullet meant for Charles Tredwick. Quite how he was supposed to swing between ships when neither had any rigging, Rob hadn't quite worked out, but this was his daydream and he could do what he liked. At the end of the little fantasy, Charles Tredwick had been forced to declare Rob was the finest young man he could ever hope his daughter to marry.

Marry. Where had that idea come from? But as he shuffled towards the hatch, he couldn't get it out of his mind. While he hadn't known Iris for that long, he knew he loved her, and couples were marrying after a far shorter acquaintance these days.

'Get your head out of the clouds, Sinclair.'

Rob returned to the present with a jolt and saw it was his turn to go down the ladder. He cast a last glance at the horizon, to carry the memory of the open sea with him down into the depths of the ship. Strange – that looked like a plume of oily black smoke billowing from *Snowdon*.

That was when the dull crump of an explosion reached his ears. The others had seen it now, and men were pointing and shouting. The commander ordered a return to action stations, and Rob raced to take his position again. From there he had a clear view of *Snowdon*, listing to starboard.

It was like the *Royal Oak* all over again, only this time Rob watched from the outside with an eerie feeling of unreality. The *Kelpie* surged towards the stricken ship, and to either side he could see the other minesweepers in their group converging on the same spot. Distances at sea were deceptive, but Rob estimated *Snowdon* to be a little under three miles away. Travelling at their current seven knots, this would take about twenty minutes to cover. The *Royal Oak* had sunk in less time. Yet if they increased speed, it would hamper the ability of the Asdic officer to detect an imminent U-boat attack. Rob was sure it had to be a U-boat; they had swept the channel for mines only the day before. Surely the enemy couldn't have placed new mines since then. His nerve-endings tingling, he kept his gaze glued on the *Snowdon*, expecting to feel a torpedo tear through *Kelpie* at any moment. He was also plagued with a sick feeling of guilt as though his daydream had ill-wished the unfortunate destroyer. Yet, unlike a daydream, the outcome was beyond his control.

By the time they had closed half the distance, it was clear they weren't going to get there on time. The torpedo – or whatever it was – must have broken the destroyer's back. *Snowdon* was sinking fast. They were still a good five minutes away when it disappeared. Rob could see one lifeboat on the water, and he knew time was of the essence. The sea was bitterly cold; anyone in the water couldn't survive for more than a few minutes.

A signal light caught his eye, not from the tiny boat now tossed about on the waves, but from one of the other minesweepers. Rob heard a shout from the signal deck – Joe Pallant, the yeoman of signals. 'It's HMS *Carew*, sir. They've found a mine.'

Pandemonium broke out as the commander ordered a sweep. Rob could hear the agony in his voice, knowing that any delay would cost lives, yet approaching without care could result in *Kelpie*'s destruction. Rob could see the same thought running through everyone's minds: how could there be mines when they had only just swept the area?

It seemed to take forever before they reached the spot where *Snowdon* had gone down. Not having a part in the sweeping operations, Rob dashed to help haul in the survivors. There were only six men in the lifeboat. He examined their faces as he helped them out one by one and wrapped them in blankets, looking for anyone who might share Iris's features. Finally, before they were bundled below, he gripped the shoulder of a man who was shivering violently and blue in the face. 'Charles

Tredwick,' he demanded. 'Do you know what happened to him?'

Through chattering teeth, the man shook his head and replied, 'He was in the Asdic compartment. No one from the lower decks got out.'

Rob turned away feeling sick. Now all he could think of was Iris, on leave, blissfully unaware of her father's fate. Would she even find out before she returned to Orkney? Her mother would receive a telegram, but Rob had the feeling Iris hadn't told her mother she was going to York.

As the search for more survivors continued, the knowledge sank in that he would have to be the one to tell Iris her father was dead. She would be devastated. She was used to having a father around who protected and provided for her. Now he was no longer there, maybe it was time for Rob to step up and prove he could take care of her.

Chapter Twenty-Three

The rest of Iris's leave went by in a pleasant whirl of activities. She saw as much of Sybil as she could, although with her aunt being busy with exams and reports, they couldn't see as much of each other as they would have liked. Between visits, Iris explored York, visiting the Minster and the walls and the narrow medieval streets, marvelling at the overhanging upper floors that nearly met overhead. She was saddened to see the damage caused by the recent raids, however, and vowed to return in happier times.

On Iris's last day, Sybil made her promise to visit again; a promise Iris made with joy. In her aunt she had found someone she could go to for advice without any fear of criticism. Iris took advantage of this before taking her leave.

'I've been thinking a lot about what you said on my first day here,' she said. 'Something about me having the wherewithal to make a living for myself should I need to.'

'That's right. What's the problem?'

Iris leaned forward in her chair. 'I'm not sure if that's true. I don't have any skills. Not that I could make a living from after the war, anyway. What good is the ability to signal ten words per minute in Morse?'

'It's not a matter of having the right skills,' Sybil said, 'although it helps, of course. But you strike me as a competent young woman, able to resolve any problems that stand in your way. I think the Wrens must have given you that. I have every confidence that you could make your own way in the world should the need arise.'

Iris wasn't so sure, but she didn't contradict her aunt. Although the thought continued to niggle at her, it was soon overtaken by the anticipation of seeing Rob again, once she was on the train for the long journey back to Stromness.

This crossing to Stromness was much easier than the stormy voyage she'd had the previous December. The sea was calm, and Iris was able to walk across the deck without fear of being flung into some handsome sailor's arms. She remained outside, leaning over the rails, straining her eyes for her first sight of Hoy. Funny how it felt like going home.

However, Hoy remained invisible. Instead, a grey mist loomed ahead, and presently it enveloped the *Earl of Zetland*, surrounding Iris with chill, wet air. It seemed to drown all the sound, and Iris had the eerie sensation of sailing along the River Styx into the underworld. Still, she didn't want to retreat below deck in case she got seasick, so she remained outside and pulled on her waterproofs. Soon beads of moisture clung to her face, and her hair hung in bedraggled locks upon her shoulders. Not the look she wanted to greet Rob with. Much as she longed to see him, she hoped he wouldn't be waiting for her at the pier.

The mist had lifted a little by the time they reached Stromness, although it hung like a shroud over the hills. Maybe it was the effect of the weather, but a deep gloom seemed to hang over the town. The men and women clustered at the pier, heads drooping, not speaking. Even the gulls were muted.

Rob was waiting for her. The moment she stepped off the gangway and laid eyes on him, she knew something was wrong. She studied Rob's face as she slipped her arm through his; he was pale, with fine lines pulling at the sides of his mouth and eyes.

'What's the matter?' she asked.

Rob squeezed her arm. 'Iris, I wanted you to hear it from me first. Your mother will already have got the telegram by now, but I wanted you to hear it from me, not by letter.'

All the colour seemed to leach from the world until she was surrounded by shades of grey. 'What do you mean?' But she could already read the truth in Rob's grim expression. She was overcome with the childish urge to clamp her hands to her ears. If she didn't hear, then it wouldn't be true. But she couldn't move. Couldn't do anything to hold back the words Rob spoke in a low voice. 'Your father's ship hit a mine. I'm very sorry, Iris, but your father didn't get out.'

Somehow Iris found herself sitting on the verge. Rob was next to her, his arm around her shoulders. She had no idea how she'd got there. She heard herself say in a dull voice, 'Do you know... would it have been quick?'

Rob stirred beside her. 'Very quick. He wouldn't have known anything.'

She put her fingers to her cheeks. There were no tears. Why wasn't she crying? 'How long did you search for survivors? How do you know he didn't escape?'

'Over an hour. No one could survive that long.'

She sat up, knocking his arm aside. 'But what if another ship picked him up?'

'There were no other ships in the area.'

'No British ships. There could have been German ones. He might be a prisoner of war.'

'Iris, there were no other ships close enough. He was in the Asdic compartment when the *Snowdon* hit the mine. There was no way he could have escaped. He's gone.'

Gone. And the last time they had met, he had been disappointed in her. She would have no chance to change his mind now.

—

Iris insisted upon returning to duty the next morning. Sally and Mary had been horrified.

'They'll give you compassionate leave,' Sally said. 'You should be with your mother.'

Iris shook her head, twisting her handkerchief in her hand. She didn't know why she was holding it. She still hadn't managed to shed any tears. 'I'm needed here. Mother will understand.' In truth, she still hadn't forgiven Letitia for interceding with her father to break up her relationship with Rob. Because of her, Iris's last contact with her father had been their disagreement over Rob. 'Anyway, I'd go mad just sitting on that train for two days. I'd rather be on watch.'

But the long hours gazing out to sea didn't help. Even though she leapt at every task available, leaving her oppo very little to do, there was still too much space to brood. She only knew one moment of comfort: watching a team of minesweepers doing a sweep of Hoy Sound. Rob would be on one of them, and it made her feel a little better to know he was within sight.

She grabbed her notepad when she saw a series of flashes from one of the minesweepers, aimed at Kyeness.

'Message for Iris,' the signalman flashed in rapid Morse. With a sudden conviction that they had discovered that reports of her father's death had been a terrible mistake, Iris sighted the minesweeper with her Aldis lamp and sent: 'Iris here.' She waited, dry-mouthed, for the reply.

'Rob says he's thinking of you.'

That was all. No report that her father had been found alive and well. No message from her father to 'his rainbow' apologising for causing so much worry and promising to see her soon. That was when the tears came. Iris sank onto a chair overcome with sobs while her oppo anxiously fluttered around her and plied her with cups of cocoa. She was a fairly new arrival, and Iris didn't know her very well, making it all the more awkward. It would have been much easier had she been on watch with Sally or Mary, although Mary would have probably told her to pull herself together. That incongruous thought made her snort with laughter in the midst of her sobs, throwing the stammering oppo into even greater confusion.

All in all, it was a good thing her watch was nearly at an end. Thankfully, Sally and Mary, who were relieving them, arrived half an hour early.

'We thought this might happen,' Mary said, while Sally crouched beside a still sobbing Iris, patting her hand.

'Take her to the Heddles,' Sally said to Mary. 'I don't mind starting my watch a little early.'

At any other time, Iris would have objected to being spoken about in this way while she was right there. Now, all she could do was meekly allow Mary to escort her to Curlew Croft, one arm firmly around her shoulders.

The walk and fresh air helped Iris recover enough to explain about the message from the minesweeper.

Mary's mouth set in a grim line. 'Honestly, some men have no sense. I'm sure Rob thought he was being caring, but he should have realised what you might think about getting an urgent message. And the signaller should have more sense than to relay private messages. Joe Pallant is yeoman of signals on the *Kelpie*, isn't he? Is the *Kelpie* still out?'

Iris glanced out to sea to see the minesweepers still plotting their methodical path a little farther out than before. She nodded.

'Well, I'm going to give that Joseph a piece of my mind.'

'That does mean sending a private signal of your own.' Iris couldn't resist pointing this out in an attempt to regain some sense of normality.

'It's justified when he's put one of my best friends into a state. I'm going to send him a message that will fry his eyeballs.'

Even in her distress, Iris couldn't help but laugh at that. 'Poor Joe. I'm glad I've got you on my side.'

Mary squeezed her arm. 'Always.'

As it turned out, going to the Heddles was the best thing Iris could have done. Elspeth, on hearing the news, enveloped Iris in a warm hug and told Mary she would take care of her while her friends were on watch.

'Sally and I will collect you at 1800,' Mary said as she prepared to leave. She raised a hand when Iris went to speak. 'And don't even think about standing watch this evening. I'll sort something out with the CO.'

With that, Mary left and Elspeth hustled Iris inside to sit in front of the range, dosed her with Ovaltine, fed her with fruit cake and encouraged her to talk about her father.

Without intending to, Iris found herself pouring out the tale of Charles' visit and his determination that she wouldn't throw her life away over Rob.

When Elspeth heard how Charles had tried to interfere, she shook her head sadly. 'Love does make us do silly things.'

'Love?' Iris slopped some of her Ovaltine over the rim of her mug, only just managing to catch the drops on her plate before they landed on her jumper. 'You think I should have broken up with Rob?'

'Of course not, lass. I was speaking of a parent's love.' Elspeth pointed at the photograph of her older son. 'When Don decided he wanted to move away south, Archie and I were in a terrible state. We had plans, you see, that he was to take over our croft when we got too old to manage it. The Heddles have worked this land for generations, and besides, I couldn't bear the thought of him living so far away. London, can you believe it?'

'You can't find a place more different from Orkney,' Iris said.

'That was part of it, of course. He wanted to find out about life elsewhere. Well, he wouldn't listen to us, even though we warned him he'd never be happy in the big city and was making a huge mistake.'

'And was he?'

Elspeth laughed. 'It was Archie and I who were in the wrong. Don got a good job on the London Underground, met a lovely girl and had three lovely children who are bright as buttons. He knew what would make him happy.' Elspeth patted Iris's knee. 'He followed his heart, and you have to do the same. We parents have to learn that what makes us happy isn't necessarily right for our children.

I'm just sad for you that your father wasn't granted time to come to terms with that.'

'He's only missing. He's not dead.'

Elspeth gave her a steady look and seemed about to say something. Then she obviously changed her mind for she simply said, 'Of course.'

Iris drained her cup and went to wash it up in the sink. 'Anyway, I can't sit here moping. You must have some jobs that need doing.'

Elspeth gave her another penetrating look then nodded as though reaching a conclusion. 'You can help me feed the chickens if you like. Then I must clean the windows. They get so covered in salt spray, I woke up this morning and thought we were in a thick fog.'

Elspeth was as good as her word and kept Iris occupied all afternoon. From time to time, Iris would glance out to sea at the minesweepers that still worked their methodical course around the headland. However, although she took comfort in knowing that Rob was out there, it was also a painful reminder of how she and her father had disagreed the last time they had met. Iris couldn't get past one inescapable fact: her father had only been on the *Snowdon* because he had requested a transfer to be near her. The responsibility for the sinking of *Snowdon* lay with whoever had laid the mine she had struck. The responsibility for Charles being on HMS *Snowdon* in the first place lay with her.

–

Iris's CO told her in no uncertain terms that she was to consider herself on leave for the next two weeks. Despite her reluctance to see her mother, Iris knew it would be

280

heartless to leave Letitia alone in her grief. Therefore, having only just returned from York, Iris found herself yet again on the long train journey to the south. The visit could not have been expected to be happy at the best of times, and she found it even worse than she had feared.

'This is all your fault,' Letitia railed at her on her first evening at Tredwick Place. Iris found her mother's transformation frightening. Letitia had always taken great pride in her appearance, getting her hair waved regularly and never dreaming of coming downstairs in the morning until she had applied immaculate make-up and dressed in a stylish outfit. Now, she didn't seem to have changed out of her dressing gown all day, her greying hair straggled around her face, which was clear of make-up and appeared oddly featureless without her usual crimson lipstick, face powder, eyeshadow and mascara. 'Your father requested a transfer just so he could be attached to a ship that made regular trips to Scapa Flow. And do you know why he did that?'

Iris said nothing. She knew the answer and had thought of little else for days.

'It was so he could put a stop to this foolish relationship with a mechanic. A mechanic! I ask you, what was the good of paying for the best education, buying you the finest clothes and jewellery if you were to end up with a mechanic?' Letitia paced up and down the drawing room as she raged on. 'Well, thanks to the changes your father made to his will, I'm in charge of your money now. And I'll be hanged if you see a penny of it. You can forget about your allowance as well. Why don't you tell that to your mechanic? See how long he hangs around after that!'

'I don't want it. It's your money. Keep it.' Iris twisted her hands in her lap. 'Rob isn't interested in me for my money.'

'Then tell him you're penniless. I dare you.'

'I will. Anyway, this is all beside the point. Daddy's not dead, only missing. He'll be back. You wait and see.' Then Iris sprang up and dashed to her room, unable to cope with Letitia's accusations. She was already carrying quite enough guilt.

The remainder of the visit was uncomfortable, to say the least. Letitia seemed to regret her outburst for she told Iris several times that of course she would always be welcome home at any time. However, she didn't change her mind about the money, and stopped her allowance, saying Iris would only get it again when she promised to give up Rob. If Iris could have returned to Orkney early she would have done so, but there was to be a memorial service for her father the day before she was due to return, and she couldn't miss that. To get out of the house, she joined in with the Women's Institute activities. Her head was so full of her father, she'd forgotten her humiliation over George. However, when Felicity made an appearance, having got a forty-eight-hour pass from the WAAF, Iris found she could look at the rose-cut diamond on her finger without any feelings of regret. Well, that wasn't entirely correct; whenever Iris thought of Felicity at Sherbrook Manor there was a twinge of envy. However, she understood herself well enough now to know that her pursuit of George had been all about his wealth and property and nothing about the man himself. George might be in a social class way above Rob, but she recognised now that she had had no deep feelings for him. She had persuaded herself she was in love because she had been bedazzled by his wealth and the social standing of being his wife. George had never held a place in her heart. Not like Rob.

Now, however, her thoughts of Rob were complicated. While she had no doubt she loved him, would she ever be able to look at him without blaming herself for Charles' presence on *Snowdon* that fateful day?

The day before Iris had to begin the long journey back to Orkney, they held the memorial service for Charles at the local church. It was necessarily a quiet affair, as so many of the people who knew Charles were in the services. They held it at All Saints parish church in the centre of Wycombe, to make it easier for friends and family to get there by train. Iris sat in the front pew between Letitia and her paternal grandparents. It was a shock to see her grandmother – a forceful woman who presided as family matriarch with great energy – shrunken, a mere shell of her former self. She gazed blankly ahead, not seeming to take in any of the service as she listened to the farewell to her only son. Iris slipped her arm through her grandmother's and patted her hand. She hadn't cried since that day spent with Elspeth, but now her vision blurred and sparkled, and she saw the rest of the service through a shimmering haze of tears. For the first time she acknowledged that her father was never coming back. There would be no more strolls through the woods in his company. She would never again hear him call her his rainbow. If he had been picked up by another ship, they would have heard by now. As much as her mind shied from admitting it, she had to accept he was gone.

She would never be able to put their last disagreement right.

'There she is!'

Iris, stepping onto the pier at Stromness, took a moment to regain her balance then looked up to see Mary and Sally waving. They dashed up and relieved her of her bags.

'What have you got in here?' Mary asked, hefting Iris's suitcase. 'It weighs a ton.'

'Don't I know it! I had to change trains at Carlisle and nearly missed my connection. I nearly wrenched my arm out of its socket when I flung it aboard the moving train.'

'But what's in it?'

'More fabric from home.' The clothes she had made before had been received with such gratitude, Iris had not hesitated to bring more.

'You never told us you lived at a drapery.'

The first ray of sunshine cut through the gloom of the past weeks. On an impulse, she hugged Mary and Sally in turn. 'It's so good to be back. I've missed you both. And Orkney.'

'How have you been?' Sally gazed at her with wide, anxious eyes. 'You must have had such a difficult time at home.'

'It was pretty awful. But I'm more than ready to come back.' It had been a relief to get away from Letitia. Although her mother had made a few feeble attempts to withdraw her remarks blaming Iris for Charles' death, the words hung heavy between them. 'I promise not to dissolve into tears on watch again. I hope my absence hasn't created too much extra work for you all.' She forced extra cheer into her voice to deflect further questions. As long as she kept busy she knew she would be fine. It was only when she had nothing to keep her occupied that her thoughts would spiral into endless 'what ifs'. A sudden thought struck. 'You were due to go on leave, weren't you, Mary? What are you doing here?'

'Well—' Mary glanced at Sally as though pleading for help. 'We couldn't both go on leave at the same time. But it doesn't matter,' she went on before Iris could apologise, 'People are still walking on eggshells around me. I don't mind waiting a few weeks.'

But Iris couldn't help feeling that was one more thing to be guilty about.

Still, she couldn't deny it felt good to be back. She drew a deep breath. 'It feels so good to breathe fresh Orkney air after being crammed into smoky trains.'

Mary snorted and led the way towards the Wrennery. 'You must be soft in the head if you call this fishy, oily smell fresh air.'

But Iris turned in a slow circle, taking in the huddled houses of Stromness, Scapa Flow gleaming deep blue in the sunlight, the rounded hills of Hoy. 'Rob was right. There is something about Orkney that gets under your skin. All these months I've been missing the woods and hills of home, but now I can't believe how wonderful it feels to be back here.' Then her heart lurched. 'Rob – is he—?'

'He's fine,' Sally replied. 'He said he'd see you later if you weren't too tired.'

Until that moment, Iris hadn't fully appreciated the burden of worry that she carried on Rob's behalf. Before the loss of *Snowdon*, she hadn't thought much about the dangers of Rob's work. His duties usually kept him around the relatively safe waters of Scapa Flow. But now, knowing his ship had been the closest one to the stricken *Snowdon*, it had started to sink in that not even he was safe.

Accordingly, despite her weariness after the long journey, she made an effort to stay awake and dashed out to meet him as soon as the liberty boat brought him ashore. Yet after the lurch of relief and pleasure brought on by the sight of his familiar figure, a weight settled on her heart. It was what she had feared – she couldn't see him without feeling the burden of blame for her father's death. Would she ever be free of it?

They walked out onto the cliffs and sat gazing out towards Hoy. She leaned her head on his shoulder and entwined her fingers through his. The thrill of being with him again helped push her guilt to the back of her mind. At first their conversation focused on Iris's state of mind and how she had fared at home. Then Rob turned the conversation to Iris's trip to York to see her aunt.

'I'd almost forgotten,' Iris said. 'It feels like a lifetime ago.'

'Did you meet her?'

'Yes. She wasn't at all what I expected.' Iris cast her mind back to the cosy flat in Grosvenor Terrace and related what Sybil had told her about her life. 'She seems so content. There was me, picturing a helpless woman, living in desperate poverty, and the reality is she's got a good job and living a very comfortable, respectable life.'

'But your mother obviously keeps in contact with her. I wonder why she gave you the wrong impression?'

'I think in my mother's eyes, Sybil *is* leading a life of poverty. They come from a very wealthy background.' Iris laughed. 'Maybe if I hadn't joined the Wrens and seen what real life is like outside our privileged bubble, I'd have felt the same way.'

'And now?' Rob's face was grave.

'I'm about to find out.'

'What do you mean?'

Iris sat upright, freeing her hand from his, and shifted so she could look him in the eye. 'My mother's in charge of my money.' Iris paused, clenching her fists so tightly her nails dug into her palms. Part of her desperately wanted to stop at this point, but her mother's taunt about Rob losing interest drove her on. 'She won't give me a penny unless I stop seeing you.'

'What? She can't do that.'

'Oh yes she can.' In a few terse words, Iris explained about the trust her father had set up. As she spoke, she picked at the grass by her knees, ripping it up from the roots and dropping it into her lap.

'Are you going to do what she wants?' Rob held her gaze, and she found herself unable to look away.

'I... of course not.' The lack of conviction in her voice made her wince inwardly. Speaking with all the firmness she could muster, she added, 'I'm not giving in to her this time. She's ruled my life long enough.' A fresh wave of self-reproach struck as she recalled how Letitia's disapproval of Rob had resulted in her father requesting the transfer to be near Iris. Maybe it would help to confide in Rob and try to explain, but she didn't want him to think she blamed him in any way for her father's death. 'I can survive without my allowance,' she said finally. If she focused on her indignation with her mother, it might help her shut out the guilt.

'Then you'd be happy to stay with a humble mechanic?' Rob reached into his pocket and pulled out a small box.

Her stomach gave a sick twist as it dawned on her that he was about to propose. This time she definitely wasn't letting her imagination get the better of her. She couldn't deny she had thought about marrying Rob, especially after the conversation with her father, but coming now, it was another layer to add to her existing guilt.

'Rob, no. Please. Not now.'

'Why not? I know it's too soon to marry after all that's happened, but I want you to know how much I love you.' He gave a wry grin. 'At least you know I'm not after you for your fortune.'

'It's not that. Please, can't we go on as before?'

Only her father had been alive before. Nothing could ever be the same again. Dropping the last handful of grass, she hugged her stomach in a vain attempt to dispel the hollow ache within. Would it always be like this when she was with Rob – moments of happiness that failed to make up for the suffocating remorse and grief?

Rob touched her shoulder, his face wreathed with concern, but she shook him off. 'Don't, please. I need space.' Space to sort out the warring emotions tearing her apart.

Rob went pale. 'Space? Or is this just your way of saying you can't bear to lose your inheritance? You can talk about being content to do without, but it's all hot air, isn't it?'

Iris sprang to her feet, shaking, scattering grass around her feet. She gladly gave in to the anger; it was so much easier to handle than the guilt and confusion. 'How dare you? Of course not. I meant what I said.'

'Not enough to take the irrevocable step.'

Iris clenched her hands into fists at her sides. Rob had always been nothing but understanding. What had changed to make him believe she could be mercenary? Although she had never doubted his regard before, now she wondered if her mother had been right about him only being interested in her money. Her momentary uncertainty, coupled with her flare of anger impelled her to say, 'I... I don't think this is working, Rob.'

Rob was staring at her, white-faced, looking as though he couldn't believe what he was hearing. That made two of them, because she could hardly believe the words coming out of her mouth either.

The only thing that gave her the strength to keep on going was his silence. If he truly loved her, wouldn't he try and persuade her they could make things work? She longed for him to pull her into his arms, make her believe she would one day be able to look at him without feeling that stab of guilt.

After a long pause in which all she could hear was a gull wailing as it swooped over the cliff, Rob said, 'I think I was always waiting for this to happen.'

There was nothing but a lump of ice where her heart had once been. So that was it. When she needed him the most, he wasn't even going to try to persuade her. She swallowed and raised her chin. 'I'm sorry. There are too many differences between us. We should end it while we are still friends.'

Chapter Twenty-Four

'Friends.' Rob had never imagined that a word encapsulating camaraderie and closeness could sound so bitter. He thrust the ring back in his pocket. 'Yes, of course.'

Deep in his heart, he had known this could never work. Iris was right to say there were too many differences between them. What did it matter that days when he didn't see her felt empty and meaningless, that she had brought his heart to life when he had thought himself forever frozen in time after the *Royal Oak* had gone down? All along he had ignored memories of his mother's discontent, told himself Iris was different.

'You're right,' he said, when he could trust himself to speak without his voice cracking. 'We could never be happy together. I was a fool to believe the differences in our station could be resolved.' He gave a bitter laugh, indicating her outfit with a wave of the hand. While he was no expert on women's fashion, the knee-length dress with its delicate blue rosebud print screamed style and expense. 'I could never provide the life you want.'

She gave a tight smile. 'Well, I suppose this is goodbye.'

How could this be happening? He had come ashore that evening expecting to secure his future happiness, not have his heart ripped to shreds. 'Aye, I suppose it is.' He thanked his lucky stars he could still keep his voice steady. 'Shall I walk you back to the Wrennery?'

She shook her head. 'No need.' She took a step towards him, leaning forward. For a wild moment, Rob thought she was going to kiss him. Then her head jerked back as though she'd been slapped. 'Well, goodbye.' She spun on the spot and set off at a brisk walk towards Stromness.

Rob watched her go, not tearing his eyes from her upright figure. A couple of times her feet must have caught a stone or patch of lumpy ground, for she stumbled. Each time, she straightened and continued at the same rapid pace. 'Look back. Please look back,' he muttered. If she did, if she showed any sign she wanted him back, he would sprint after her and beg her to reconsider. But he watched until she was barely more than a pale speck, and she never once glanced back.

–

Rob stood on the cliff top long after Iris had disappeared from view. Finally he stirred and glanced at his watch. There was still two hours before the liberty boat returned to the *Kelpie* and he couldn't bear the thought of going down to Stromness in case he saw Iris. Anyway, he didn't feel like the company of his shipmates, and he wouldn't be able to escape being dragged into one of the pubs by a well-meaning friend.

He took the path away from Stromness, the one that led to Curlew Croft. It was too long since he'd last visited the Heddles. At least there was no worry about being out on the cliffs after dark at this time of year. The sun was a long way above the horizon and would still be there to light his way back to Stromness when it was time to return.

'Come in, come in.' Elspeth, who had been out in the yard, fastening the chicken coop door, greeted him with a beaming smile. 'It's good to see you again.' Then her smile faded. 'Wasn't Iris due back today?'

He had intended to drop it casually into conversation over a cup of tea, to show that he didn't mind overmuch. Instead, he couldn't stop himself from blurting out the truth right there in the yard to the accompaniment of the soft croons of the chickens in the coop settling down for the evening. 'She's ended it, Elspeth. I was going to ask her to marry me, and she told me we had no future together.' To his horror, his voice gave a distinct wobble.

'Oh, there now.' Elspeth clicked her tongue and took his arm. 'Come inside. I was afraid this might happen.'

Rob, halfway over the threshold, paused. 'You thought Iris would never want to marry a man like me?'

'What? No, you silly lad. Come inside and we'll talk about it over a cup of tea.'

Rob allowed himself to be led into the kitchen, where he sat at the table.

'Now,' Elspeth said, placing the kettle on the range. 'Tell me what happened.' She shook her head. 'That poor girl. She's holding onto a lot of guilt. When she came here the other day, I could see she blamed herself for her father's death.'

'That's ridiculous. She didn't have anything to do with it.'

'Well, now, I don't know all the details, but I had this feeling. Tell me what she said to you.'

As much as he wished he could curl up in a corner and forget the whole evening, Rob, fortified with a piece of freshly baked gingerbread, poured out the whole tale. 'I thought she would want me to propose,' he said in conclusion, dabbing up the last of the gingerbread crumbs from his plate. 'She's lost her father, so I thought she would be reassured to know I'll be here to look after her.'

Elspeth raised an eyebrow. 'No doubt a proposal like that would have swept the girl off her feet. Such a tragedy you never got the chance.'

Rob felt his face burn. Now he came to explain it to Elspeth, his reason for proposing did sound feeble. Nothing at all like the powerful burst of feeling that seemed to explode from his chest whenever he saw her. 'I suppose you're right. Do you think I should ask her again?'

'I think it's too soon to confuse Iris with marriage proposals. You weren't planning on marrying right away, were you?'

'No. I mean, I know I love her. I know she's the only lass for me, but I couldn't support a wife on the pay I get from the navy. Anyway, I don't think it's fair to marry her while there's a war on. I know some couples are rushing into marriage, but I wouldn't want to marry until I could be fairly certain I'll be around for her.'

'Why didn't you try explaining all that to her? You probably threw her into a flat panic.'

'She didn't give me a chance. She—' He gave a low groan as he remembered exactly what he'd said. 'Oh no. I said something really stupid. About her not having to worry about me being after her fortune.'

'Robert Sinclair. Tell me you didn't. Not when she's all eaten up over the way she and her father parted.'

'I wish I could, but it would be a lie. I didn't think.'

'But it doesn't sound like you tried very hard to talk her round. Why didn't you apologise and say you'd give her time?'

This was the part Rob really wasn't proud of. 'When she turned me down, I thought maybe it was for the best. That we'd end up like my mother and father.'

Elspeth shook her head and muttered something about foolish young men. 'At least she can't run away. You'll just have to make the effort to show her you're not the idiot lad you appeared this evening. Give her time and I'm sure she'll come round. She's suffered a cruel blow, and she'll need all her friends if she's to get over it.'

The door opened, and Archie appeared, lugging a bucket of water. 'There's a big storm on the way, Elspeth.' He set the pail beside the door, and that was when he saw their visitor. 'Rob. Just the man I want to see. I could do with a hand to take out *Mallimak* and check my creels tomorrow. John Flett was going to help but he can't come now. Would you be free?' The *Mallimak* was Archie's boat and needed at least two to row. Before the war, the Heddles' younger son had helped; now Archie had to rely on friends.

'I'll be out on sweeps but should be able to come tomorrow evening.'

'You're a good lad, Rob.'

'Do you really think there's a storm on the way?'

'Aye. I can feel it in my teeth.'

Rob nodded. While there had been no word of a storm approaching, he'd learned not to argue with Archie's teeth. They had frequently been right when the Met reports had been wrong. 'Looks like I'll be in for a bumpy ride tomorrow.'

It would, at least, take his mind off his heartache. Elspeth's words had given him hope, though. He could see he had said exactly the wrong thing to Iris. He would show her he could be her friend and pray she would eventually change her mind. It was idiocy to think that Iris was like his mother, that their relationship would go the same way as his parents'. There wasn't a single mould that meant all wealthy people were the same, just as his own observation told him how different working–class people could be. His fear had allowed him to think Iris would react the same way as his mother to a little hardship. But remembering how Iris had thrown herself into knitting and making clothes for Elspeth and her friends, he realised she had responded very differently from how his mother would react to being on these islands. Iris had allowed herself to be moulded by the discipline of the Wrens and island life. He didn't think his mother would ever have adapted to change in the way Iris had. He could only hope he hadn't come to that realisation too late.

—

'You've got to be out of your tiny mind.'

Iris winced. They were only at the start of their walk to Kyeness, and it looked like Mary was going to spend the whole of it telling Iris exactly what she thought about her decision to end her relationship with Rob. In truth, part of her agreed, and it was hard to explain how she didn't think she would ever be able to see Rob without remembering how she had caused her father to be on HMS *Snowdon* when it was attacked.

Mary made the most of Iris's silence and pressed her point home. 'I mean, you have to be soft in the head to let a good bloke like Rob go.'

'Well, what am I – out of my mind or soft in the head?'

'Both. That's how bad it is. Why did you do it?'

Iris sighed. She couldn't help wishing she had Sally as her oppo for the afternoon watch. Sally would be more sympathetic. Breaking up with Rob had been like tearing out her heart, and she could use some comfort now rather than being told she was an idiot. She already knew that.

She had been too heartsore to talk to her friends when she had returned from the cliffs the evening before, so she had taken herself straight to bed, pleading tiredness after her long journey. She had lain awake most of the night and only drifted into an uneasy sleep in the early hours. By the time she'd awoken, it had been a mad scramble to get breakfast before the cook had stopped serving it, and Sally had already left for the morning watch. Iris hadn't seen Mary until now, for Mary had spent the morning running errands in Stromness. This was her first opportunity to confess what she had done, and she was beginning to wish she had held her tongue.

They had reached the little wire gate by this time, so Iris took her time unfastening the loop and folding it back to give her a chance to organise her thoughts. In the end, she had to speak from her heart. 'I still love him. I wish you wouldn't scold me. I had to do it.'

'Why?' Mary followed Iris through the gap and refastened the wire loop to the post. She addressed her next words to the wire. 'If Owen was still around, I'd never let him go.'

'I know. I'm sorry, Mary. But you have to understand that my father would never have been with that convoy if he hadn't wanted to be posted nearer to me. And he wouldn't have been worried about me if I hadn't been with Rob.'

Mary turned, and now there was more sympathy in her expression. 'You think it's your fault he was killed?' When Iris nodded, Mary muttered something under her breath that sounded like another insult. 'What's the point of your parents spending all that money on your schooling, if you end up believing lunatic ideas like that?'

'It's not a lunatic idea. I know he tried to get the transfer because of me. Therefore it's my fault.'

'Were you the one who placed the mine?'

'Well, no, but—'

'Then you must have been the one who made the decision to send the *Snowdon* with the convoy, and decided the date and time they would be sailing.'

'Of course not. Don't be ridiculous.'

'All I'm trying to do is get it into your thick head that there was a huge chain of decisions and commands that caused your father to be on the *Snowdon* that day. Most of them were totally out of your control. Anyway, if he had stayed with his old ship, there's no saying he would have survived the war. Don't you think it's a bit arrogant to think that it's all your fault?'

Iris couldn't let herself off the hook so easily. 'You might be right, but I can't help wondering, what if he hadn't come here? What if I hadn't told my mother about Rob so she would send Daddy to try and talk me out of it?'

'What if you didn't come from a family that paid such heed to class and social standing?'

Iris shrugged, not having a good answer. She was pretty sure most families would find it difficult to accept a huge difference in class. She walked on in silence, saving her breath for the uphill walk. Her father would have eventually accepted Rob, she had to believe that. It was more than she could hope from her mother. Letitia had read Sybil's letters, seen how well she was doing without her inheritance, yet still regarded her sister as living in poverty. She would never regard Rob as a suitable husband for Iris.

Her musings were forced to the back of her mind when she paused for breath at the top of the hill. Her heart quailed to see a stack of black clouds looming higher and darker than the hills of Hoy. 'Oh, my goodness. Looks like we're in for a storm.'

Mary drew level and followed her gaze. 'Doesn't look good. I feel sorry for any small boats that get caught out.'

Iris muttered her fervent agreement. 'Let's hope Archie has the sense not to take his fishing boat out. And Rob.' Her stomach twisted. 'I can't remember if the *Kelpie* is out today. I hope she gets back safely if she is.'

She waited to Mary to pass comment on her inability to forget Rob. Mary, however, was gazing out to sea with a frown biting into her forehead. 'Come on. Let's get to the signal station. It's going to be a long, difficult watch.'

–

The storm hit twenty minutes after they relieved the morning watch. A boom of thunder echoed around the headland making Iris jump, then a moment later rain hammered against the windows. Black clouds had swallowed the sun, blotting out the light. Iris spared a moment to pity the two Wrens they had just relieved who would now get a soaking, then a flash of lightning drove out all thoughts barring the fact that she was in the highest place for some miles and in the middle of a thunderstorm.

She and Mary were in the signal room by this time. Determined not to let the old fear overcome her as it had done the day of Sally's accident, she picked up her binoculars and studied the waters. The sea was strangely calm. Funny – she'd expected a huge swell and fifty-foot-high waves. It was inky black, though, and hard to pick out any vessels that might be out there. There were two ships making their way out of the safety of Scapa Flow, through Hoy Sound. They must be making one of their regular sweeps, checking for magnetic mines. Her heart stuttered. It was difficult in this light to identify them, but she was sure one of them looked like the *Kelpie*. Rob's ship. How was he? Was he thinking of her? Was he angry? Hurt? He'd always said before that he took comfort in knowing she was up at Kyeness, watching over him. Did he still feel that way?

'Aren't you going to challenge them?' Mary's voice cut through her thoughts, accompanied by another roll of thunder.

'What? Oh, yes.' Iris picked up the Aldis lamp, only for it to slip through her hands. If Mary hadn't managed to catch and steady it, she dreaded to think of the damage hitting the concrete floor would do to the lamp.

'Here, better let me do it.' Mary took the lamp and sighted the nearest minesweeper. The shutters rattled as she sent the signal, enabling Iris to hear the Morse, even though she couldn't see the light. She looked out at the minesweeper, pad and pencil to hand, ready to take down the reply. *Kelpie* and *Lindesfarne* on a routine sweep. Rob was down there, out in the storm. He would be below decks, though, keeping the engine running. He wouldn't be looking up at her.

Iris was about to enter the signal into the log book when another stream of Morse issued from *Kelpie*'s signal deck. 'Mary: meet me in the NAAFI tonight.'

Iris grinned. 'Shall I enter that in the log?'

Mary muttered something that sounded like, 'Bloody Joseph Pallant. Doesn't know when to give up.'

Iris, bending over the log, still managed to follow Mary's reply even though she was writing. 'You'll have a long wait.'

Iris returned to the window in time to see Joseph Pallant's reply. 'Hello lovely Mary. Would know your flowing prose anywhere.'

That exchange took a couple of minutes; soon after Joe completed the last word, the minesweeper rounded the headland and out of their line of sight – unless Mary wanted to go out onto the balcony to continue the conversation. Unsurprisingly, Mary stayed inside.

More lightning lit the base of the clouds. Sheet lightning. The storm was miles away. Iris took a deep breath. She wasn't going to go to pieces because of a storm. In an attempt to take her mind off her fear, she tried to read the lightning as though it was a Morse signal from the god of lightning. T I. Terrible Injuries. No. Thunder Increasing. Please, no.

The phone rang and she hurried to answer. 'WSS.'

It was only the officer monitoring the indicator loop. Iris was able to report that the signal would have been sent by the two minesweepers. She replaced the receiver only for the phone to ring again almost immediately. This time it was orders to hoist the storm cone. The wind was picking up.

'I'll go,' Mary said with a sharp glance at Iris's face. Iris guessed she must be pale.

Iris shook her head. She had sent Sally out when she'd been too afraid, and she wasn't going to make that mistake again. 'I'll do it.'

Without waiting for Mary's reply, she scrambled down the ladder – the highly conductive steel ladder – and hastened to pull on her waterproofs before grabbing the storm cone from the flag locker. *Keep your head*, she told herself as she pulled open the door. *You've done this a hundred times. The storm is miles away. It can't hurt you.*

The wind had certainly picked up, but it was nowhere near storm force yet. She had been out in far worse. She hastened to the flag mast and managed to hoist the storm cone without much difficulty. Rain pummelled her face, dripping down the back of her neck as she tied off the halyard. A glance out to sea showed her that it was getting rougher, each wave capped with white flecks. The air reverberated with the sound of the breakers pounding the cliffs far below. Her thoughts flew to Rob. It was no use telling herself *Kelpie* could withstand much rougher weather than this, she wouldn't relax until the minesweeper was back safe and sound.

Another flash of lightning came for Iris to decode. M S. Most Scary. Too right. She slammed the door and stripped off her waterproofs, hanging them on the hooks to dry.

Mary's voice drifted down from the open hatch. 'Everything all right?'

'Fine.' Iris drew a steadying breath. 'I'll make some tea.'

'Good idea.'

'We got another call from HQ,' Mary said when Iris climbed the ladder one-handed a few minutes later, balancing the tea tray in the other hand in a manoeuvre she'd perfected in the months she'd been there. 'The thunder will pass over quite quickly, but we've got more wind and rain on the way.'

'Great. So we've got a soggy walk back to the Wrennery followed by another one when we come back at 2300.' The days when they had a few hours between the afternoon and night watches were always the worst. It always felt like they had hardly got in and grabbed some food when they had to leave again. It was getting a little easier now the days were so long. They were heading for midsummer when, so the locals assured them, it never got truly dark. Still, on a day like today, Iris didn't look forward to getting soaked twice more that evening.

'I was thinking about that,' Mary said. 'Why don't we go to the Heddles? We've got an open invitation. If they want to turn in before we go back on duty, we can always come back here and grab a quick kip in the bunk room.'

Iris agreed and accordingly, when their watch ended at six, they trudged along the soggy track to Curlew Croft.

'I'm glad to see you,' Elspeth said when she opened the door to them. 'I've been in a real fret over you lasses going back and forth in this weather.'

'We're hoping it will have eased by the morning. At least the thunderstorm has moved off.' Iris hung her sopping waterproofs on the hooks by the kitchen door and shook out her hair which had been squashed beneath her hat.

'The weather report's wrong,' Archie said. He was sitting at the kitchen table, tucking into what looked like a vegetable pie. 'There's more thunder on the way. I can feel it in my teeth.'

Iris said nothing but exchanged glances with Mary, who regarded Archie and his teeth in the same way as she regarded Sally's superstitions.

'Well, sit down, sit down. I made plenty of pie this evening, thinking you might be along. What's Sally up to?'

'She's on watch now,' Mary said, taking her seat.

'Well, when you go back tonight, do tell her and any others that they're very welcome to spend the night here.' She doled out pie onto plates with a shake of the head. 'I don't know what the Wrens are thinking, leaving young lasses like you to walk the cliff paths alone after dark.'

'We're used to it for the most part,' Iris said, 'but on days like today we're very grateful to be able to come here.'

'You're always welcome.' Elspeth glanced at the photographs of her sons. 'It does us the world of good to have young folk around.'

After a short while, Archie mopped up the last of the sauce with a piece of bannock then pushed back his chair. 'I'd better be off. The tide'll be on its way in by now, and I want to check the creels while there's a lull in the storm.' He glanced at the clock. 'Rob said he'd help. I thought he'd be here by now.'

Iris's heart gave a lurch at the mention of Rob. 'He was out in *Kelpie* earlier, but I think he should be ashore by now.'

'Perhaps he meant to meet me at the geo. I'll go and see.' He pulled on thick boots, waterproofs and after kissing Elspeth's cheek, he left. When he opened the door, they could all hear that the wind had dropped. The rain had eased to a soft drizzle. The clouds seemed lighter.

'Maybe it will have stopped altogether by the time Mary and I have to leave,' Iris said.

Archie shook his head. 'My teeth still ache. There's worse to come, you mark my words.' With that optimistic assessment, he strode off down the track that led to the geo.

He hadn't been gone more than a quarter of an hour, and Iris and Mary were stacking the last of the plates they were drying back upon the dresser, when they heard the sound of brisk footsteps outside.

'That's never Archie back already,' Mary said.

'It doesn't sound like Archie.' Elspeth replied, drying her hands on her apron.

There was a knock on the door, and Elspeth opened it to reveal Rob waiting outside.

'I'm not too late, am I?' he asked. 'I couldn't get here any earlier.'

Iris, heart thudding, stepped into the shadows beyond the dresser. While she might have been thinking about him all day, she didn't feel ready to speak to him.

'Archie's already left,' Elspeth replied. 'He thought you might be meeting him at the boat. Come in and wait – I expect he's on his way back. You must be half starved if you've been out on the water all day.'

Rob took a step over the threshold, pulling off his sou'wester. Then his gaze fell on Iris. She felt it like a jolt to the chest.

'Ah, how long has Archie been gone?' He addressed Elspeth, although his gaze drifted to Iris again as soon as the words left his mouth. Iris, torn between the urge to hide and the desire to fling herself into Rob's arms and beg his forgiveness, stood rooted to the spot. She couldn't work out if she wanted him to stay or go.

Elspeth glanced at the clock. 'Maybe fifteen minutes.'

'You know, I think I'll go and see if I can catch him up. He might be waiting for me.' Rob put his sou'wester back on and, after a brief nod at Elspeth and Mary, he bolted in the direction of the geo.

Iris, who just a few seconds earlier had been convinced she wanted him to leave, felt a lurch of disappointment.

'Aye,' said Elspeth, catching Iris's eye. 'No prizes for guessing who he wanted to avoid.' Iris, her face burning, was about to ask how she knew when Elspeth added,

'Where do you think Rob came last night when he needed someone to talk to?'

'Oh.' On the one hand, she was embarrassed to learn Elspeth and Rob must have been discussing her; on the other, she was relieved to know he'd had someone as kind as Elspeth to turn to.

Mary, who had been drying cutlery, dropped a handful of teaspoons into the drawer with a clatter that made Iris jump. 'Maybe you can talk some sense into her, then, Elspeth. I've tried and failed.'

'They both need their heads examining if you ask me.' But Elspeth's eyes twinkled, belying her words. 'I'll make us some Ovaltine. Then you, young Iris, can tell me your side of the story.'

Iris found she did want to know what Elspeth thought. She also wanted to know what Rob had said, although Elspeth proved annoyingly tight-lipped on the subject even after Iris had poured out the whole story, confessing her fears that she would always associate Rob with her guilt over her father.

'There are some things only you can know,' Elspeth said at last. 'You already know what you want, deep down. You just have to give yourself the time and space to listen to what your heart is telling you. No one can tell you what that is.'

'Do you think Rob would want me back?' Iris gazed into her mug, as though trying to read the answer in the powdery dregs of her drink.

'I can't speak for Rob.' Then Elspeth leaned across the table and patted Iris's hand. 'Just give him a chance if he tries to speak to you.'

That was when it hit Iris that, despite her fears, she wanted to try again. She didn't need time to listen to her heart. She already knew what it had been trying to tell her for some time now, only she had allowed her snobbish beliefs to deafen her. It was only now that she stood to lose the thing most precious to her – Rob's love – that she finally understood. She could only hope that Rob would give her a second chance.

Chapter Twenty-Five

Rob couldn't get away from Curlew Croft fast enough. Had Iris's presence been a misguided attempt by Elspeth to get them talking? But no – Rob cast that suspicion aside almost as soon as it occurred to him. Elspeth didn't resort to such trickery. Besides, she wouldn't have invited Mary as well. It was just an awkward coincidence.

He quickened his pace, bending his head against the rain. It had eased earlier but now the clouds seemed to have replenished their stores and hurled down rain with fresh vigour. Not the ideal weather for rowing out to Archie's creels. Still, the wind had dropped and the water was less choppy than earlier, so it would be best to go now in case conditions got worse later in the week.

When he got to the top of the geo, he peered down to see Archie stooped over the boat. Cupping his hands around his mouth, he hailed him. Archie straightened and waved. Rob jogged down the zig-zagging path to meet him.

'Sorry I'm late,' he said once he was down by the water. He helped Archie haul the *Mallimak* – Archie's yole – onto the water then scrambled in. 'Do you think it will stay calm long enough?'

'I hope so.' Archie picked up an oar and pushed them away from the shore. 'It's going to blow up again later, so we'd best keep an eye on the weather.'

Rob picked up his oar. 'Let's work fast, then. Anyway, I need to get back to Stromness in time for the liberty boat.' At least he had spent the day sweeping these waters for mines, so could be confident there were no mines waiting to go off. Not that Archie's wooden boat would trigger a magnetic mine. Still, he didn't fancy being in the water when there was lightning around. Could a lightning strike trigger mines? He didn't have a clue, but didn't want to find out the hard way.

As they made their way around the headland, Rob spared a thought for Iris. Tonight was her night watch, he knew. With Archie's prediction of the storm returning, he hoped she would be all right. A signal station on an exposed headland wasn't the best location for someone who had a fear of storms.

Rowing hard, they reached Archie's creels in good time, and Rob pushed his worries for Iris aside while he helped Archie pull them in and check their catch, throwing back anything too small.

'Not a bad haul,' Archie said later, once the last basket had been emptied and returned. 'There will be partan bree for dinner tomorrow, and some crabs spare to sell, too.'

Rob's mouth watered at the thought of the delicious crab broth, and he wondered if he might get leave the next evening and share the meal.

The trouble was, their catch had been so plentiful, it had taken longer than usual to sort it. When Rob reached for his oar, he noticed the wind had picked up and the water was becoming choppy again. Although the sun had not yet set, more black clouds had rolled in, casting them into twilight.

'This doesn't look good,' Archie said, frowning up at the sky. 'My teeth are tingling like mad.'

He had hardly finished speaking when a sudden gust rocked the boat, and spray whipped into their faces.

'We won't make it back to Kye Geo in this,' Archie said, raising his voice to be heard over the wind. 'I'll make for an inlet over there.' He pointed to a spot on the opposite side of the headland from Curlew Croft. 'There's no path up from there, so we'll have to sit out the storm until it's safe to go back on the water.'

Rob heaved on his oar. He knew the place Archie meant. It had a shallow beach, so they could at least get the *Mallimak* out of the water and use it as a rudimentary shelter. It wasn't far from the signal station, although with no path up the cliffs, it might as well be a hundred miles away. 'I'm going to get hauled over the coals for missing the liberty boat. Good thing we got all the creels in this evening, because it'll be ages before I'm allowed out to help you again.'

Thankfully, the inlet was sheltered from the wind, and they had no trouble pulling the *Mallimak* onto the narrow strip of pebbles beneath the cliff. There was a flat rock in the lee of the cliffs that offered a seat protected from the rain, so they hunkered down on it. Rob craned his neck to look at the cliff top. Iris would be returning to the signal station soon. From this angle, he couldn't see it, but it was a comfort to know they weren't far from help should it be needed.

A flicker of lightning lit the twilight.

'If I had teeth like yours,' Rob remarked to Archie, 'I would forget about starting a boat yard after the war. I could make a fortune as a weather forecaster.'

It was going to be an uncomfortable night.

–

Iris kept her hopes about Rob to herself as the evening wore on. Now she knew what she wanted to do, there was no point in discussing it further. Instead, once the three women had finished their drinks, she helped Elspeth hem a skirt she had been making.

'You know, I can't thank you enough for that coat you made me,' Elspeth said, admiring the stitches in the finished hem. 'All my friends wanted to know if I'd been to Edinburgh without telling them, they were convinced I must have bought it from one of the finest shops.'

'At least that's something I can do apart from signalling. Talking of which' – Iris looked at the clock – 'I suppose we ought to head back soon.' There was still an hour before she and Mary were due back on watch, but she guessed Elspeth would want to go to bed soon.

No sooner had the words left her mouth than a distant boom of thunder echoed around the walls. *Please, no. Not again.*

'Looks like I should pay attention to Archie's teeth after all,' Mary said. Then she frowned. 'Shouldn't he be back by now?'

'He'll be along soon,' Elspeth replied. 'I dare say he's left his boat in a cove closer to Stromness so Rob can get there on time to catch the liberty boat. That's what he usually does on the evenings Rob helps him out, and it'll take him longer to walk back from there.'

If Iris hadn't already known she wanted to see Rob, the sinking disappointment would have told her all she needed to know about her feelings for him. Still, maybe it was for the best. She didn't want to have the conversation she desperately craved in front of Elspeth and Mary.

She rose. 'I suppose we should head back. Thank you so much for your hospitality and advice, Elspeth.'

'I don't think I've given you much advice.'

'Oh, you have. You've really helped.' She jumped as another roll of thunder sounded. 'Still, I think we ought to get to the signal station before this storm gets any worse.'

Once bundled up in their waterproofs, they bid Elspeth goodbye and hastened up the track. Lightning flashed, and the gap between each jagged streak across the clouds and the claps of thunder decreased every time. This close to midsummer, the sun wouldn't have set. However, the storm clouds had cast them into a gloom that felt closer to midwinter.

'I hope Rob and Archie are safely out of this,' Iris said.

A searing blue-white light dazzled her eyes, accompanied almost immediately by a crack of thunder that sounded as though the sky were being ripped asunder. The ground shook, and Iris blinked to clear the stripes of colour drifting behind her eyelids. To her shame, she discovered she was clutching Mary's arm in a death-grip. 'Sorry.'

'Don't be.' Mary sounded shaken. 'I'd have grabbed you if you hadn't got there first.'

Another simultaneous crack of thunder and lightning shook the cliff top. Iris heard someone whimper and was embarrassed to realise it was her. She broke into a run, Mary beside her.

'That was way too close,' Mary gasped.

Iris was too terrified to speak. Ignoring her burning lungs and the stitch in her side, she sprinted for the signal station, her shoulder blades itching as though expecting to feel the lancing pain of a lightning strike at any moment. It felt as though the headland was crowned by lightning. She reached the door feeling as though her knees were on the verge of giving out and clutched the handle. She fell inside, gasping, Mary only inches behind.

The interior was in darkness. They were greeted with a cry of surprise, then Iris heard Sally's voice. 'Oh, it's you. Thank God.'

Iris was still too scared to utter any words. Mary, however, seemed to have recovered from her fright. She started to strip off her soaked waterproofs and said, 'What's wrong? Why aren't the lights on?'

'Everything just went out. I think lightning must have hit the generator.'

Iris, recovering somewhat, fumbled in her pocket and pulled out her torch. She switched it on and pulled off the layers of tissue paper used to comply with blackout regulations. 'Don't need this in here.' She shone the torch around, the beam shaking from her trembling hand, until she found Sally standing at the foot of the ladder. She could just see the white face of her oppo peering down through the hatch above. 'That's better. The signal lamps are battery powered, so we'll be all right. You two might as well leave early. Elspeth says you can bed down at Curlew Croft if you don't fancy going back to Stromness in this.'

Her words were punctuated by another crack of thunder, and Iris jumped again, sketching an erratic squiggle on the wall behind Sally with the torch beam.

'You don't understand. Everything's out.' Sally's eyes were wide circles. 'The phone line too.'

'You mean we're cut off?' Mary stepped forward into the light. She muttered a curse when Sally nodded.

Iris, while she wouldn't dream of using such coarse language herself, couldn't help but agree. With the telephone out of service, they couldn't pass on any messages between ships and headquarters. If there was an emergency at sea, they would be unable to telephone for help. Likewise, they would be unable to receive special orders about ships crossing the indicator loop. The knowledge helped her shake off her fear. 'I seem to remember Joe Pallant saying something about us having a motorcycle messenger posted here if the phone lines went down.'

'Yes, you're right,' Mary said. 'If two of us head down to Stromness we can send a request for a messenger.'

'We can go,' Iris said, looking at Mary. She wasn't going to send someone else out into a storm after what had happened to Sally. 'There's time for us to get there and back before our watch officially starts.'

But Sally disagreed. 'Then you'll start your watch soaking wet, and we' – she glanced at her oppo – 'will get wet going back anyway. It makes more sense if we go.'

'I hate to admit it, but she's right,' Mary said.

Iris couldn't argue with the reasoning but she watched Sally go with a heavy heart. Then she climbed up to the signal room where she and Mary gazed out to sea. Thankfully, Iris couldn't see any vessels on the water. The sea was no longer the calm millpond it had been that afternoon, but tall waves pounded the cliffs, sending spindrift floating high into the air, level with the signal room windows. Although the sun was hidden, it lit the base of the clouds with a red glow. At any other time, Iris would have thought it beautiful; now it filled her with foreboding.

Time stretched out with no sign of their messenger. Iris was just starting to worry that Sally had met with an accident when they heard the throaty roar of a motorcycle engine. Looking down the track, Iris could just make out a motorcycle through the gloom. Leaving Mary to keep watch, she slid down the ladder and opened the door in time to see a dispatch rider swinging out of the saddle and propping the bike on its stand. Although the figure was booted and swathed in waterproofs, from the slender figure Iris guessed it was a woman.

'Blimey, it's a bit breezy, innit?' The woman staggered as a gust of wind struck. 'Sorry I'm late. Had a spot of bother on my way out of Stromness.'

'Why, what happened?' Iris caught the rider's arm to steady her and help her inside. Then she slammed the door against the wind.

'That's better.' The woman slumped into a chair and kicked off her wellingtons with a sigh. 'I'm Agnes Finch, by the way, but you can call me Aggie.'

'I'm Iris, and Mary is up in the signal room. What kind of bother?'

Aggie peeled off her hat, revealing a mop of frizzy red hair and a bloodstained dressing on her temple.

'Oh no! How did you do that? Are you even fit to ride your bike?'

'Some idiot doctor was driving out on a call and turned right just as I was overtaking him.'

'Good grief, you should be in hospital, not here.' Iris hesitated. 'The doctor... it wasn't Stewart Irvine, was it?'

'That's the one. Neither of us were going that fast at the time, so it's not too bad. The doc patched me up and said I'd be fine.'

Iris held her tongue, but she wished she could be as confident as Aggie in Stewart's diagnosis. After his lack of concern when Sally had been injured, not to mention his misdiagnosis of Aldo, she had rather lost faith in his assurances.

'If you ask me,' Aggie continued, 'he'd been at the sherry. Still, I'm sure he knows his business.' She yawned. 'Riding in this weather don't half take it out of you.'

Iris pointed at the bunk room door. 'There are bunks through there. Why don't you have a lie-down? We'll give you a shout if necessary, but hopefully we won't need you.'

'Thanks. You're a gem. Oh. Nearly forgot. Message from base. You're to watch for the destroyer *Platypus* with two tankers. They've been delayed with engine trouble but should arrive at around 0400.' Agnes handed her a sheet of paper with the message she had just relayed, together with directions to send them to the anchorage off Lyness.

Agnes headed off to find a bunk, and Iris climbed back up to the signal room. She prayed they wouldn't need to send any urgent messages, because she didn't like the idea of sending a rider with a head injury.

—

Rob, hunched against the wind, found his gaze directed towards the cliff top more often as the night dragged on. He tried not to think about the punishment he would get for failing to return to the *Kelpie*. With each flash of lightning, he could see the towering cliffs surrounding the cove, blocking his way out. He might be able to climb up by daylight, but he wouldn't risk it in the dark. Anyway, he must have missed the liberty boat by now, so he might as well wait until it was safe to leave.

He glanced up at the cliff top again, this time his thoughts on Iris rather than the missed boat. How was she coping in the storm? He hated to think of her in that exposed signal station while the lightning seemed to be directing all its bolts at the headland.

Then he stiffened. Through the almost continual rumble of thunder, he thought he could hear a different noise. The regular thrum of an engine. Knowing there was a small flotilla of ships due to arrive, at first he assumed the noise indicated their arrival. But as the noise grew nearer, he realised it was up in the air rather than on the waters. Probably an aircraft from one of the RAF bases on the island, or possibly the Naval Air Arm. Poor sod, whoever was forced to fly on a night like this.

A flicker of light caught his eye. Not a flash of lightning but a signal light. 'Funny, I thought we wouldn't be able to see the signal station from here, but I think I can see someone flashing Morse.'

'You can't.' Archie's voice was definite. 'I got beached here a couple of years ago and tried to signal up to the station, but couldn't get a line of sight from anywhere.'

The first prickle of foreboding crawled down the back of Rob's neck. He could still hear the aero engines; from the sound, the unknown aircraft was circling nearby. Odd behaviour for a returning friendly plane.

Another flicker of light came from the cliff. Rob lowered his voice. Not that he thought anyone up there would be able to hear him over the thunder and wind, but he was gripped by a sudden conviction that something was very wrong. 'I think there's someone on the cliffs, signalling the plane.' He squinted into the rain, trying to make out the signal. If it was Morse, it was using a code he didn't understand, because it didn't make any sense in English.

A splash out to sea made him jump. He jerked his head around and strained his eyes to peer into the gloom, but he could see nothing. He was beginning to think he had imagined it when he heard another splash.

'Did you hear that?'

'Aye,' Archie replied, also looking in the same direction. 'I cannae see a thing, though.'

'Nor me. It has to be linked to that signal light.' Rob wanted to pummel the rocks with his fists. He had never felt so helpless. Something ominous was happening, a threat, he was sure. Worst of all, it seemed to be centred around the headland upon which Iris was based.

He happened to be looking in the right direction at just the right time. A flash of lightning illuminated an object drifting towards the water. He blinked water from his eyes. It took a moment to work out what he had seen. A parachute! But if men were parachuting from the plane, they were landing on water. Had they got the wrong location?

Then the truth hit him. Mines. It was an enemy plane, dropping mines. Over the route that had just been swept. The route a flotilla would pass through in just a few hours. Now the signaller up on the cliff made sense. Whoever it was had observed the minesweepers that day and was signalling the location to the enemy aircraft. The plane must have been caught unawares by the storm; possibly the system of communication with the traitor wasn't sophisticated enough to change their plans at the last minute. He had been right: there was a traitor in Orkney.

He sprang to his feet. 'Those are mines. I have to get a signal to Kyeness before our ships come past.'

'How?'

'Up the cliff. I'll get as high as I can until I can get a line of sight to the signal station.' Rob had already pulled his torch from his pocket. Now he removed the shielding as he spoke.

'I'll come with you.'

'No way. I'm not explaining to Elspeth how I let you go scrambling on the cliffs.'

'You can't expect me to do nothing.'

Rob thought fast. 'Look, I've no idea if my plan will work. If the sea drops enough for you to leave the cove, go to Stromness for help.'

'Aye. I can do that.'

Rob drew a deep breath and approached the cliffs.

Chapter Twenty-Six

She could do this. Iris forced herself to join Mary by the signal room window despite the lightning dancing in the clouds.

Mary glanced at her. 'You don't have to be up here. Why not grab a couple of hours' sleep?'

Iris shook her head. 'I'd never be able to sleep in this. And it's time I got used to storms.'

Sally's accident had been a wake-up call to Iris, and she wasn't prepared for anyone else to be hurt simply because she was too scared to go out in a storm.

'You've picked a cracker of a storm to get used to.' Mary put a steadying hand on Iris's shoulder as another crack of thunder shook the room. 'I haven't been in many storms like this.'

'Then if I can cope with this, I can cope with anything.' Iris picked up the binoculars and scanned the sea for any sign of a signal. It was too dark now to see any vessels on the water, although the lightning gave brief illumination.

'I would be happier if the phones were working,' Mary said, also gazing out over the water.

'I know. I was getting used to Orkney's solitude – even quite liking it – but not when we're cut off like this. I hope Stewart's right for a change, and the messenger's injuries aren't too bad.'

'Coming round to my way of thinking about Stewart, then?'

'I rather think I am. He wasn't at all apologetic for misdiagnosing that POW. And he wasn't an awful lot of help when Sally was hurt, either.'

'Just goes to show, a posh education isn't everything.'

'I'm beginning to see that.' Yet again, Iris was reminded of her lack of any skill she could use to support herself after the war.

They continued to keep watch in silence for a while. At one point Iris thought she heard aero engines, but it was hard to tell through the storm. In case it was a plane off course, she flashed the Morse for Kyeness, to give the pilot his bearings if he was lost. It was something they had been required to do on occasion when there was a missing plane. Iris felt the loss of the telephone keenly at that point, for it was the sort of thing they would usually get orders about over the phone. She briefly considered sending Aggie for instructions then dismissed the idea. She couldn't ask her to go out in this storm when she wasn't certain she had heard an aircraft.

Then all thoughts of the plane disappeared from her mind when she saw a flash of light coming from a most unusual angle.

She grabbed Mary's arm and pointed. 'What's that over there? It looks like a signal but it seems to be coming from the cliffs.' She raised her binoculars as she spoke and trained them on the location just in time to see two long flashes. 'There it is again. Grab the notepad. That was an M.'

The light wavered, making it hard to make out the words. Sometimes she was forced to interrupt and flash a signal to repeat. 'I don't think it's a trained signaller,' she told Mary. 'He's quite slow. Wait. There's more.' She read out each letter and felt like icy water had been poured down her back when they finally managed to get the full message in the right order. 'Mines!' she gasped. 'That's the plane I thought I heard.' She flashed back a signal to show she had received and understood. Then came another series of words. She read them out as they came. 'R-O-B-A-R-C-H-I-E. Oh my gosh – Rob and Archie.' The message finished: 'Stuck on cliffs.'

'Oh my gosh,' she said again. Her mind seemed to be paralysed with shock. 'What do we do? What do we do?' She drew several deep breaths. 'Okay, first we have to send Agnes to report about the mines.' Then she remembered about the destroyer with a thrill of alarm. 'And *Platypus* is due. It's heading straight for the mines.'

'Here.' Mary tore the paper she had written the message on from the pad and thrust it into Iris's hand. 'Send Agnes with this message. I'll go out on the balcony and signal a warning on the ten-inch lamp in case *Platypus* can spot it.'

Iris nodded and slithered down the ladder, feeling a gust of wind tear through the building when Mary opened the French windows. Her thoughts were torn three ways – with the need to get the message to base, the sickening dread that *Platypus* might sail straight into the newly placed minefield, and Rob who was trapped out on the cliffs. But when she burst into the cabin, a new worry emerged. Aggie groaned when Iris shook her shoulder then pushed herself into a sitting position on the bunk. She managed to stand but staggered like a drunk. She sank back down and buried her face in her hands. 'Feel sick,' she gasped.

Iris dashed out of the bunk room, tripping over a chair in the darkness. She managed to grab the table to stop herself from falling then groped her way around the wall and through the galley door. Her out-thrust hands closed around the basin in the sink. Then she remembered the torch in her pocket and pulled it out and used the dim light to guide her back to Aggie without falling over any more obstacles.

Aggie grabbed the basin and was violently sick. Perspiration dewed her bruised face, and although it was hard to make out colour in the torchlight, Iris thought she looked horribly pale. She was painfully reminded of Sally after her accident.

'Stay there,' Iris told her. 'You can't go out in this state.'

Her stomach in knots, she climbed back up into the signal room. Bracing herself, flinching as another flash of lightning split the sky, she joined Mary by the lamp. 'Any sign of *Platypus*?' she asked.

'Not yet. She's not due for another couple of hours but I daren't stop in case she's early. Has Aggie left?'

'She's not well enough. One of us has to go.'

'I'll go.' Mary stepped back from the lamp.

But Iris shook her head, feeling sick. 'No. I will.' After what had happened to Sally, she wasn't staying safe inside while another friend went into danger.

Mary grabbed her arm. 'Don't be an idiot. I know you feel bad about Sally's accident, but what if you panic in the storm?'

'Trust me. I don't want to go out in this either, but it has to be me. Have you ever ridden a motorcycle?'

'No, but I'll give it a go.'

'Now you're being the idiot. I have, so it makes sense for me to go.' Seeing Mary was about to argue, Iris said, 'I have to go. You can't ride a motorbike for the first time in a storm.' She put all the conviction she could manage in her voice, and finished, 'I have to go, and I have to leave right now. There's no time for you to learn.'

'I hate the thought of you being out there all alone, but very well.' Mary released Iris's arm. 'Just promise me you'll be careful.'

'Don't worry about me. Just make sure you get that signal through to *Platypus*.' Then she remembered the other part of Rob's message. 'And for God's sake, watch out for whoever was signalling that plane.'

There was no more time to waste.

—

With trembling hands, Iris pulled on her waterproofs. Then she paused, one hand on the door handle as she summoned up the courage to go out in the storm. The crew of *Platypus*; Rob and Archie; Aggie – all depended on her to get help. There was also a traitor in Orkney, maybe still on the cliffs, and she needed to get the authorities out searching for him before he could cause any more harm. She blew out a breath. She could do this.

She opened the door; wind and rain slapped her face, snatching away her breath. An ear-splitting blast of thunder nearly made her retreat inside and slam the door; it was only by reciting all those who depended on her that she found the strength to fight her way into the wind and get to the bike. Sending a prayer of thanks that her father had taught her to ride a motorcycle, she released the stand and kicked the starter. Nothing happened. She tried again. Still no luck. 'Come on. Don't let me down now,' she muttered, then flung her whole weight on the starter.

The engine roared into life. Releasing a shaky breath, she eased open the throttle and the bike bounced across the rough ground and onto the track.

Iris clung on for dear life, her teeth rattling as the bike jolted down the track. It was a good thing she knew the route well from her frequent walks to Curlew Croft, for the shielded lamp cast only a dim circle of light a short distance ahead. As she gained in confidence she increased the speed. No matter that she was terrified of losing control; too many people depended upon her getting the message through.

As she passed Curlew Croft, she threw it a longing glance. She could stop and wake Elspeth, send her with ropes to help Archie and Rob. But then she remembered Rob's warning about someone signalling the plane from the cliffs. Rob and Archie would be wet and uncomfortable, but they would have to wait. It was too dangerous for Elspeth to go out alone. She tore her gaze from the house and steered the bike onto the track leading to Stromness. Lightning clawed the sky accompanied by an almost simultaneous crack of thunder. Iris gave a low moan. She had never felt so alone. When she had been a child and afraid of a storm, she would scurry into her father's arms, and he would hold her, shelter her until the storm died away. Now she was struck afresh with the yawning chasm of her loss and the knowledge that she would never again know that security.

Every nerve screamed at the next blinding flash. She couldn't go on. It was madness. She eased back on the throttle, brought the bike to a halt and struggled to draw breath with chest muscles that seemed to have frozen solid. As soon as she could move she would turn the bike around and seek shelter with Elspeth. She had done her best, but her terrified mind couldn't force her to go on. The storm would probably die down before *Platypus* arrived. There would be time to get the message through once this mind-numbing lightning stopped.

She shifted, preparing to turn the bike, when she became aware of the strangest sensation. She could only describe it as a warmth, as though she were enfolded in strong, comforting arms. Then she could swear she heard a voice, speaking straight to her heart. *Courage, my rainbow. You're safe. You can do this.*

A great calm swept over her, and her taut muscles eased. She recovered her ability to draw breath and she could think clearly again. Were Sally here, she would surely say that her father was here, keeping watch over her. While Iris couldn't fully explain what had happened, she could only guess that her earlier memory of her father had enabled her to push aside her fear. Now she could think straight, she knew she couldn't abandon *Platypus* to her fate. Most of all, she couldn't abandon Rob. He had climbed a dangerous cliff in the dark to send a warning. She wouldn't let his risk be in vain, and she wouldn't leave him in an inhospitable, wind-swept cove for any longer than necessary.

She opened the throttle and, abandoning all caution, sped down the track, blinking stinging rain from her eyes. The storm still raged but she no longer feared it. The memory of her father's comforting arms seemed to hold her fears at bay, and thoughts of Rob drove her on. What a fool she had been to avoid Rob because she would never see him without remembering her father. That would be a blessing. She didn't want to forget her father, and now she found she could think of him without the crippling sense of guilt. Had Charles met Rob, he would have liked and admired him. It was time Iris trusted her own judgement and stopped allowing herself to be swayed by her mother's prejudices.

Leaning over the handlebars, she urged the motorcycle to its maximum speed. When the first houses of Stromness came into view, she drew a sobbing breath of relief. Now all she had to do was work out where to go.

The police station. Yes, that would be best. This might be a military concern, but there wasn't a naval base in Stromness, and the police would be able to telephone the relevant authorities. They would also be able to send out rescuers to Rob and Archie, search the cliffs for the mystery signaller and send an ambulance to collect Aggie. A bubble of hysterical laughter welled up in her chest. That was a lot to happen in one night.

The police station in North End Road was in darkness when she pulled up alongside. She didn't let that deter her, though. She hammered on the door until it was finally opened by a middle-aged man hastily pulling on his jacket.

Iris tumbled inside and poured out her tale. Everything became a bit of a blur after that. She had to repeat herself several times before she could be understood, but once the constable grasped the urgency, he lunged for the telephone and got through first to the navy, then she heard him calling for an ambulance, organising rescuers for Rob and Archie and arranging a cliff-top search. She breathed a prayer of thanks that the phone lines in Stromness were clearly still intact. Someone thrust a steaming mug into her hands, and she gratefully gulped down hot, sweet tea that must contain someone's entire week's worth of sugar rations. As the tea warmed her, she allowed herself to relax, knowing she had done all she could.

'I expect you'll want to take yourself to the Wrennery and wrap up warm,' the constable said once he had finally replaced the telephone receiver.

But Iris knew what she had to do. After draining the last of the tea, she put down the mug and rose. 'No. I'm still on watch. I need to get back.'

'A young lass like you? Surely you can let someone else take over.'

Iris raised her chin and put the full force of her authority as a Wren into the stare she fixed on the man. 'No. This is what I'm trained for. It's my duty.'

Chapter Twenty-Seven

Mary greeted Iris with a cry of relief. 'Thank God. I was so worried.' She had been in the middle of flashing another signal on the balcony and buffed her wet hands with a groan.

'It's all in hand now,' Iris told her. 'The navy are going to contact *Platypus* on W/T so we don't need to keep flashing a signal.' Although wireless telegraphy was usually avoided due to the risk of signal interception, it was the quickest way of getting a message through in an emergency.

'About bloody time. My hands are about to drop off. What about Aggie?'

'They're sending an ambulance.'

They returned inside and shut the doors. While Mary peeled off her waterproofs, Iris hunched over the stove and warmed her hands as she described what had happened. The only thing she held back was the strange sensation she'd felt of her father's presence when she'd been about to give up. Knowing Mary, she would scoff at the notion that her father had been watching over her. She wasn't altogether sure what to make of it herself.

By the time she finished, the ambulance arrived for Aggie. No sooner had that departed than a truck arrived up the track and parked beside the signal station. A group of men got out and took ropes to the cliff's edge where

Rob and Archie were. Others began a systematic search of the headland by torchlight.

She turned to Mary. 'Do you mind if I go and see how Rob's getting on?'

'Course not. The sooner the two of you talk, the better.'

Iris didn't even pause to put on her waterproofs. She hurtled out of the hut and along the cliffs until she reached the place where two men were hauling on a rope, shouting instructions. She hovered beside them in a fever of nerves, then Rob's pale face rose over the cliff's edge. A moment later, the men had dragged him to safety. They then flung the ropes back for Archie.

Rob looked exhausted. He wandered away from the cliff's edge then bent double, his hands braced on his knees, drawing deep breaths.

Iris approached, suddenly afraid of what he might say. She had rejected him in the cruellest manner. What right did she have to even expect Rob to listen to her, let alone take her back?

Then Rob glanced up and saw her. He straightened and took a step towards her. 'Iris?'

She couldn't contain herself. With a sob, she lunged towards him and hugged him close. 'Oh, Rob, I was so worried.'

For a horrible moment she thought he might push her away. Then his arms wrapped around her, pulling her even closer. '*You* were worried? There was an enemy agent up here. I was terrified he would hurt you.'

'*Was?* Did they catch him?'

Rob shook his head, spraying more drops of rain into Iris's face. 'They're still looking. But now the police are here, he'll be trying to get away. He's not a threat any more.'

'Do you know who it is?'

'I didn't see him. Just the light. They'll find him, though. Don't worry.'

The storm was waning, but the rain came down harder than ever. Although Iris knew she should take Rob inside to dry off, she couldn't bear to let him go. All along the headland came the sound of splashing feet and voices calling, directing the search. She couldn't spare much thought for the fugitive, though. Not now she was back in Rob's arms. She didn't care about the rain pouring down the back of her neck, nor that the headland thronged with searchers. All she knew was that Rob was safe, and she needed to put things right between them before it was too late.

'Can you forgive me?' she asked. 'I'm so sorry. I should never have broken up with you. I don't know what was wrong with me.' The words tumbled out. She feared they didn't make much sense but she had to release the burden from her heart. 'I hardly knew what I was doing. I had some mad notion of never being able to see you without blaming myself for my father's death, but I know that was foolish now. I can't bear the thought of being without you.'

'You're not foolish. I'm the idiot.' Then Rob was kissing her, his chilled lips upon hers, water dripping from their faces. A bubble of pure joy expanded in Iris's chest until she thought she might explode from happiness.

When they were forced to break the kiss to draw breath, Iris still couldn't bear to let him go. Wrapping her arms around his neck, she gave a breathless chuckle. 'Of all the things that have happened tonight, this is by far the most unexpected.'

When she leaned in for another kiss, Rob drew back, frowning.

'What's the matter?' she asked with a sick twist of dread. Had he changed his mind?

'I need to apologise.'

'*You?* You didn't do anything wrong, it was all me.'

'No, listen. I was an idiot of the highest order, trying to propose when you had just lost your father. I had some fool idea of showing I could look after you.'

'I don't need looking after.'

And in a flash as brilliant as lightning, she knew that was true. Aunt Sybil was right. When she had needed to dig deep and solve a problem, she had managed it, fighting her terror of storms in the process. If she could do that, she knew she had the determination to succeed at anything she put her mind to.

'No,' said Rob, brushing back the soaking hair that clung to her forehead. 'I can see that. You're quite the heroine, roaring off on a motorbike through the storm.'

Iris leaned into the caress. 'How did you know that?'

Rob pointed at the men who were at that moment hauling Archie to safety. 'They told me a crazy signaller Wren on a motorcycle had woken the whole of Stromness and hammered down the police station door. I knew you must have cast off your upper-class inhibitions at last. Anyway, let me finish.' He drew a deep breath. 'I should have known my timing was off. When you broke up with me, I should have gone after you, told you I'd be there for you, no matter what.'

'I didn't exactly give you a chance.'

'But I should have fought harder for you. To tell you the truth, I let my parents' relationship colour my view of our relationship.'

'How?'

She was about to suggest they go into the dry, seeing the two men who had rescued Archie accompanying him towards Curlew Croft. But then the ambulance for Aggie rolled up, and Iris knew there wouldn't be a chance of a private conversation once they went inside. Aware that she needed to relieve Mary soon, she grasped at this opportunity to mend her relationship with Rob before it slipped away.

'My mother grew up in a wealthy family,' Rob said. 'They fell on hard times – I don't know the details because my mother doesn't like to speak of it, but I think my grandfather made some unwise investments and lost his entire fortune. But my mother never forgot the luxuries of her early childhood and always considered herself a cut above my father's family. Oh, I don't doubt my mother loved my father at first, but she could never forgive him for not aspiring to make more of himself.' Rob bowed his head. In the distance came a boom of thunder, the dying throes of the storm. Iris hardly registered the sound. All her attention was focused on Rob. She could see all too clearly how her own snobbery and upper-class attitudes must have put Rob on his guard. 'My mother's eaten up with bitterness now, and envious of anyone with more,' he continued. 'What love they once had has long since died, and my parents are trapped in a miserable marriage.'

'How awful. It can't have been easy growing up in that atmosphere.' An icy hand seemed to squeeze Iris's insides. 'You… are you saying we're doomed to follow the same path?'

'No.' Rob pulled Iris close, resting his damp forehead upon hers. 'I'm saying I was so caught up in my fears, I didn't see that you are utterly different from my mother. Yes, you arrived here with some undeniably posh notions…'

Iris couldn't resist a grin. 'Like inspecting all the glasses at the Christmas party in case they might give me some hideous disease?'

Rob chuckled. 'Something like that. But I was blind to how you were prepared to learn. Look at your friendships with Mary and Sally. You don't look down on them.'

'I wouldn't dare. Mary would eat me alive.'

'But you're not my mother. If you were like her, you would have waited out your time in Orkney, keeping yourself to yourself, until you got a transfer away south. Instead, you've thrown yourself into island life, helping out with the knitting drive, making clothes for people, befriending Elspeth and Archie. You have a good heart, through and through, and that's why I love you.'

Unable to resist, Iris raised herself on tiptoe to brush her lips against his. When she pulled back, she tried to speak and found her voice hoarse with emotion. 'I love you too. I was such a fool to try pushing you away. Thank you for believing in me enough to try again.'

'I'll always believe in you. You'll always have my heart.'

When Rob kissed her again, Iris forgot the rain, the wind and the fading thunderstorm. All she knew was the blissful certainty that Rob loved her, and she would never be foolish enough to drive him away again.

'Steady on, you two. You're embarrassing the men.'

Iris jumped and stumbled back from Rob, her face burning. She found herself face to face with one of the policemen. In the dim light, she made out the features of the constable from the police station. She gasped an apology, unable to look him in the eye.

Rob, however, seemed unruffled. 'You wouldn't want us to catch cold, would you?'

Iris was too happy to be annoyed with him. Even so, she decided it was high time she changed the subject before she died from embarrassment. 'Any sign of the spy?'

'You mean the man sending the signal?' The constable shook his head. 'We heard a large splash a while back. In my opinion, he took a tumble into the water and drowned. Good riddance, if you ask me.'

'But you don't know?' It was starting to sink in that she had been out alone in the night when an enemy agent was on the prowl. She couldn't bear to think he might still be on the loose.

'Can't be sure of anything on a night like tonight. Don't worry, lass. We'll keep looking.'

But Iris wasn't comforted. 'I hope you find him.' The signal station wasn't particularly secure, and until they knew for sure, she didn't relish the prospect of being alone there at night with only one other Wren for company.

'Well, I'd better get on. You two should go and dry off in the signal station.'

It was only then that she remembered Mary, who would be all alone and waiting for news. 'Come on,' she said to Rob. 'We can dry out by the stove.'

Rob must have divined her misgivings, because once they had caught Mary up with the news and were hunched in front of the stove, a gentle steam rising from their soaked clothes, he said, 'I'm sure if the police don't find the spy, it means he fell into the sea. I don't see how he could have got away without anyone seeing.'

'I hope you're right.' But she couldn't help thinking of all the times she had been up on the cliffs alone. Had she been near the spy without realising?

For some reason, Stewart popped into her head. They had, after all, seen him up on the cliffs several times. 'Oh my goodness,' she said. 'What about Stewart?'

Rob scowled. 'What about him?'

'We're always bumping into him up on the cliffs. You don't think he had anything to do with all this, do you?' Then another thought struck. 'And what about Aggie's accident?' She had already told Rob about how the dispatch rider's collision with Stewart's car had left the signal station cut off from communications. 'What if it wasn't an accident? What if it was deliberate?'

At this, Mary, who was stationed by the windows, cut in. 'Now you're getting carried away. I'm not exactly Stewart's number one fan, but there's no way he could have known she was on the way to Kyeness. It's just a coincidence.'

It was on the tip of Iris's tongue to say he had hung around Kyeness enough times to know about the telephone connection, and that if he severed the lines, they would be cut off. If he'd been responsible, he would have known to look out for any dispatch rider heading in the direction of Kyeness. Maybe it wasn't coincidence.

Then she caught herself. What was she thinking? Just because she had reason to dislike Stewart, it didn't make him a traitor, and it was a dangerous accusation to make. She gave a shaky laugh. 'You're right, Mary. There are plenty of perfectly innocent reasons for taking a stroll along the cliffs. I'm letting my imagination get the better of me.' She should trust the authorities to do their job and not hurl groundless accusations that could cost an innocent man his life. She moved closer to Rob and leaned against him, the worry and exhaustion of the past few hours catching up with her. 'I hate how the war makes us suspicious of the people we should be able to depend on.'

Rob wrapped an arm around her shoulder, and she swallowed, overcome with a wave of gratitude that she had him back. Whatever trials might come her way, she knew that in him, Mary and Sally she had three people she could always trust.

–

The following evening, Iris walked into the common room and waved at Mary and Sally when she saw them already seated by the fireplace.

Sally dropped her knitting and patted the seat next to her. 'Well – what did she say?'

That morning, Iris had been summoned to see the WRNS officer overseeing the visual signaller Wrens in Stromness. Iris had gone to her office dreading a dressing-down. Now she grinned at her friends. 'She wasn't impressed by my taking the motorbike.'

Mary stabbed a knitting needle into the ball of yarn and flung her knitting into her lap. 'Typical. You risk your neck delivering a vital message, and you get hauled over the coals.'

Iris held out her hands in a pacifying gesture. 'But then she acknowledged it was the best thing to do in the circumstances and commended me instead.'

'That's more like it,' Sally said.

'You deserve more than a commendation,' Mary said.

Iris didn't mention it, but Second Officer Hilton had gone as far as saying that Iris might even receive a medal.

She held her tongue, knowing that it might not happen. However, the knowledge that she had impressed her superiors to that extent had filled her with a glow of achievement. Even so, that was nothing compared to Mary's indignation on her behalf. After the rocky start to their friendship, Iris cherished Mary's loyalty far more than any medal.

'What else did she say?' Sally asked. 'Did she say anything about the man who had been signalling to the enemy plane?'

'Or how Aggie's getting on?' Mary added.

Iris dropped into the seat Sally had indicated. 'Aggie's fine. She's got a nasty concussion but she's doing well.'

'Yet another black mark against Stewart's name.'

'It might interest you to know that after people heard about what happened to Aggie, other people on the island have come forward to complain about him. He's been suspended pending an enquiry.'

'Good.' Sally's tone held deep satisfaction. 'A pity they didn't come forward sooner.' She put a hand to her St Christopher medallion. 'I've never forgotten what Aldo said about him completely ignoring the awful pain he was in.'

Iris nodded. She was looking forward to describing this latest development in the next letter to her mother. Almost as much as she looked forward to telling her that she was back with Rob. She doubted she'd get a reply, but she didn't give up hope her mother would eventually accept Iris's choices in life. Although perhaps she should tone down her glee at Stewart's disgrace if she was to have a hope of eventually winning Letitia around.

'Bad news about whoever was signalling that enemy aircraft, though,' she said with a grimace. 'The police couldn't find a trace of him. They're sticking with the assumption that he was drowned.' She kept her misgivings to herself, although she was sure Mary and Sally would be equally unhappy about the possibility that he could still be at large.

'Pity. I'd have liked to know who it was.' Mary scowled. 'Don't forget the rumours that someone on the island guided the U-boat that sunk the *Royal Oak*. If the signaller had been caught, we might have found out the truth.'

'I know. I'm sorry.' Iris felt bad that Mary might never know the truth behind the sinking of the *Royal Oak*. 'Anyway I haven't told you the best news yet.' She was going to enjoy this.

'What?' Sally sat up straight.

'Hilton said she knew I'd wanted a posting on the south coast. Said there was a place for me in Portsmouth if I wanted.'

'Oh.' Sally's shoulders sagged. She picked up her knitting and wound the wool around her index finger without apparently noticing.

'I'm pleased for you.' Mary made a valiant attempt at a smile that failed to reach her eyes. 'Promise you'll write to us, won't you?'

'I won't have to.' Iris relented when Mary's smile faded altogether. 'Because I'm not going, you clot. Why would I want to leave the best posting in Britain, with the best friends in the world?'

Sally pulled Iris into an enthusiastic hug with a whoop of delight, tangling them both in blue yarn. 'You truly mean that?'

'Course I do.'

'But you won't get to go to any of the posh functions you would down south.'

Iris extricated herself from a loop of yarn. 'I'm not interested in any posh dos if it means I don't get to be with you.'

'Or Rob,' Mary said, eyes twinkling.

'Or Rob.' Iris could feel her face stretching in a soppy grin. She had found herself smiling all day, hugging the knowledge of Rob's love to her heart.

'I'm glad you're staying. The place wouldn't be the same without you.' Mary, her eyes unnaturally bright, gave Iris a hug which, while not as enthusiastic as Sally's, expressed equal joy. Iris found her own eyes misting at having such true friends.

'I said all along that you and Rob were destined to be together, didn't I?' Sally said.

'You did and I should have listened to you. It would have saved me a whole lot of heartache.'

And as she chatted with her friends and looked forward to a future in Orkney with Rob, she felt the same sense of love and calm that she had the previous night. With it came the deep knowledge that whatever trials the war might throw at her, she would stay strong with the help of Rob and her friends.

Author's Note

I was tempted to dedicate this book to my internet service provider because Shropshire, while lovely, isn't the most convenient place to be during a national lockdown when researching a book set in Orkney. Without the internet, this book really couldn't have been written. Even with it, there was still vital information I was unable to find. This meant that while I had originally intended to use only real locations, I was forced to make up some places. In particular, Kyeness is completely fictional, as is the signal station where Iris and her friends were based. I can only apologise to the inhabitants of West Mainland for callously stretching the coastline near Stromness and adding a new headland and hill. The anti-submarine indicator loop, however, did exist, although it would have been monitored with the help of signallers based in a different location.

Acknowledgements

This book was mostly written during lockdown, and so I'd like to thank all the friends who inspired and motivated me when I was finding it a struggle to write. Especial thanks go to my Apricot Plots buddies for the regular Zoom chats that kept me sane(ish), everyone in the Author Support Network for being the best cheerleaders, and the WHS girls who should all be heroines in books of their own.

A huge thank you to my editor, Emily Bedford, and to the whole team at Canelo and also to my wonderful agent, Lina Langlee. You're a joy to work with.

Finally, thank you to the readers, reviewers and bloggers who have taken the time to review and let me know how much you've enjoyed my books. Your encouragement has kept me writing!